RIVER BASIN ADMINISTRATION
and the DELAWARE

RIVER BASIN
ADMINSTRATION
and the
DELAWARE

Roscoe C. Martin
Guthrie S. Birkhead
Jesse Burkhead
Frank J. Munger

SYRACUSE UNIVERSITY PRESS

Preface

IN THE spring of 1957 Delaware River Basin Research, Inc. (now the Water Research Foundation for the Delaware River Basin), in harmony with a grant made by the Ford Foundation for the purpose, entered into a contract with the Syracuse University Research Institute for a study of a "governmental organization for development of the water resources of the Delaware River." The research contract was fulfilled with the submission to the Water Research Foundation, on September 1, 1959, of a report titled *The Problem of Water-Resources Administration, with Special Reference to the Delaware River Basin.* This book represents a thorough revision of that report. Its authors were those responsible for executing the terms of the contract in behalf of the Research Institute.

The research techniques employed in the study involved first a review of the general literature relating to water-resources management and to river basin (and other regional) administration; second, the accumulation and analysis of documentary material; third, field trips to many of the major river basin development projects and a widespread interviewing program which took staff members into most parts of the country; fourth, employment of a number of individual consultants on special problems; and fifth, a series of research subcontracts, the chief of which were executed with the Philadelphia Bureau of Municipal Research-Pennsylvania Economy League, Alderson and Associates (a management consultant firm of Philadelphia), and the United States Bureau of the Census. The staff of the BMR-PEL in particular contributed substantially to the project, both by preparing memoranda on various topics and by advising on the organizational and financial aspects of Delaware development.

Research assistants, employed for varying lengths of time, included Professor Douglas Price, of the faculty of Columbia University; Messrs.

Bruce Andrews, Donald G. Baker, Robert M. Gidez, Donato Pugliese, and William M. Shear; and Mrs. Lillian Mohr. Mrs. Vilma Brumberger and Mrs. Jeanne Pilger were the principal typists. The maps were made by Eileen W. James. To all these the authors acknowledge their indebtedness.

The government study was conceived originally as a companion piece to the Comprehensive Survey of the Delaware River Basin undertaken under the direction of the United States Corps of Engineers. Relationships with the staffs engaged in the Survey have been uniformly cordial; in particular, the authors wish to recognize the cooperation of Mr. Russell Morgan, technical director of the Survey for the Corps. Among those who read and commented on parts (in some instances, considerable parts) of the manuscript during its preparation were Messrs. Irving K. Fox and John V. Krutilla, of the staff of Resources for the Future; Professor Arthur Maass, of the faculty of Harvard University; and Professor David Haber, of the faculty of the Rutgers University School of Law. To these the authors tender their cordial thanks.

Worthy of separate mention are those who read and criticized the completed draft of the manuscript. These include Gordon R. Clapp, President of the Development and Resources Corporation; James W. Fesler, Professor of Political Science, Yale University; Charles M. Haar, Professor of Law, Harvard University; and Frederick C. Mosher, Professor of Political Science at the University of California. To name these individuals is not to impute to them any responsibility for the study, but only to recognize and thank them for the critical judgment which they brought to bear on the manuscript.

In addition to the foregoing, a large number of persons who made contributions to the study cannot be named here. The authors join, then, in a blanket tender of appreciation of the assistance freely given by literally scores of public officials, professional colleagues, and private citizens. At the same time, it would not be appropriate to omit mention of the warm relations which have existed throughout between the research group on the one hand and the Delaware River Basin Advisory Committee and the Water Research Foundation for the Delaware River Basin on the other. More particularly, the authors wish to acknowledge with cordial thanks the counsel and assistance made available by Mr. Walter M. Phillips, Executive Secretary of the Delaware River Advisory Committee, and his staff associates, Messrs. Blair Bower and W. Brinton Whitall, and by Mr. James

Kerney, Jr., Executive Vice-President of the Water Research Foundation.

The authors are grateful for the cooperation of the publishers and authors who gave permission to quote from their works, as noted in the text.

The officers and directors of the Water Research Foundation desire us to acknowledge their debt and express their thanks to the Ford Foundation, whose generous support made possible the research which eventuated in this book.

Syracuse   Roscoe C. Martin
Spring, 1960   *Director of the Study*

Contents

Part I: Setting

Part II: Organizing for River Basin Administration

Part III: Financial Considerations

ix

Part IV: American Experience in River Basin Administration

Part V: Conclusion

Illustrations

Tables

Part I: Setting

CHAPTER 1

Introduction

THERE was a time, in the early days of the country, when the individual householder could and did supply his own water needs. Further, he could perform for himself many of the services subsequently associated with water use, notable among them waste disposal. With the growth of population and the rise of urban communities, responsibility for these rudimentary water functions shifted from the householder to a public body, in the first instance the village or city closest at hand. From these first beginnings has grown an extremely complex arrangement for the administration of water-resource activities. A considerable part of the administrative system remains in private hands, principally those of industry; but a larger (and an increasing) share falls to government. Local government was paramount in water management so long as the problem was mainly one of supply, and by tradition it remains so. As the issues have become more complicated, however, other governments have asserted their interests: the states to regulate and facilitate, the federal government to facilitate but also to participate through direct action. The trend is toward more and more public involvement in water-resource activities through a larger and larger number of administrative agencies. Yet a central issue, indeed the central issue, remains that of adequacy of management of the generous water resources available over most of the country.

The problem will be readily recognized as that of organizing government for the development and administration of water resources. This work treats of an important aspect of the problem, namely that of areal (geographical) adaptation to water-resource needs. Concluding that an overwhelming majority of all existing governments are unequal to the tasks of water-resource administration on any save a limited, local basis, it finds in the river basin an area on which the

3

management of a broad water-related program may appropriately be centered. The significance of drainage basins has long been recognized, but not their implications for public action. This study examines river basin administration and the functions of water-resource management, and analyzes their import for the organization of government.

This is an examination, then, of the concept of river basin administration, of American experience in that field, of the problems encountered and the lessons learned. The central problem is national in scope and significance. It is one appropriate for consideration by all major governments, but especially by the government of the United States; for it is worthy of the time and attention of the representatives of all the people. The focus here is on river basin administration as a national problem.

The exploration in breadth of the country's experience is complemented, however, by an examination in depth of the significance of the concept of river basin administration for a particular area. The area chosen for intensive study is the Delaware River Valley, which by familiar criteria is a small basin. The Delaware is one-sixth as long as the Rio Grande and carries perhaps one-fifteenth as much water as the Columbia. Its drainage area (12,765 square miles) is less than one-fortieth the size of that of the Missouri. It lies in the states of Pennsylvania, New Jersey, New York, and Delaware, in the approximate proportions of 50 per cent, 23 per cent, 19 per cent, and 8 per cent respectively. The Basin's population is about 6,000,000. Its outstanding features are density of population and industrial concentration. As will develop from the study, the Valley of the Delaware in many respects is unique among American river basins. In a larger sense, however, the water-resource problems encountered there are comparable with those found elsewhere. The Delaware has many lessons to learn from experience in other basins—and many lessons to teach as well. Its story serves as a case study running throughout this volume.

If testimony should be taken at various places in the Delaware region, it would become clear that the water problem differs in kind and intensity from one spot to another. To the residents of metropolitan New York, there are not many things more important than an adequate supply of good water. The maintenance of such a supply has sent the City to the Delaware River of recent years for what shortly will be a good half of its water requirements. To Margaretville, on the East Branch of the Delaware high in the Catskills, water means trout fishing and tourism, and its people are wary of any action that might change the character of their mountain stream. To Easton, the problem of too much water is a recurrent one; a basic concern there is to control the river and so to avoid its excesses. Trenton has a primary interest in the maintenance of low flow at a reasonable minimum, lest its industries languish for want of water. To Philadelphia, the main problem is one of water quality; enough water flows past that city to serve its needs, but in the past it has sometimes been water of unsatisfactory quality and could become so again. Wilmington's interest in water arises principally from the fact that its present source of supply threatens soon to become inadequate in the face of its rapidly growing needs, though its concern for quality control is scarcely less insistent.

The point particularized for the Delaware is no less applicable to other rivers. To some the Colorado symbolizes power, to others irrigation, to others municipal and industrial water, to others still a temperamental stream to be feared in time of flood. The Columbia means variously energy for cities and industry, the threat of flood, and a vital link in the important commercial fisheries industry. The Tennessee represents power, excess of water, navigation, or recreation, depending upon the bias of the viewer. Water thus presents different faces to different places and people, and moreover the face it presents varies over time—indeed it varies with the seasons.

The central water problems of the Delaware River Basin do not differ greatly in kind from those found elsewhere. They revolve around the familiar concepts of quantity and quality. In terms of quantity, there is frequently either too much water or too little at any particular place and any given time. In August of 1955 the Valley of the Delaware was visited by the worst flood in its recorded history. There was more water than could possibly be disposed of with the facilities at hand, and the surplus cost a hundred human lives and destroyed many millions of dollars worth of property. Two years later, at about the same time of year, too little water came down the Delaware, with the result that the River failed to achieve the minimum flow promised for the Trenton reach, and the Attorney General of New Jersey charged that New York City was not living up to the Supreme Court decree with respect to releases from its Catskill Mountains reservoirs. The problem of water quantity involves both spatial and temporal considerations: spatial in the sense that there is frequently too much or too little water at a particular place, temporal in the sense that there is frequently too much or too little water at a particular time. If excess water could be stored against the time of shortage, and if then it could be moved from the places where it is not needed to the places where it is, the problem of water quantity could be solved—assuming, as it is fair to assume for all but a few river basins, that there is enough water in the aggregate to meet reasonable needs.

The problem of water quality is one primarily (though not exclusively) involving pollution and its control. Pollution may arise from natural causes, in the sense for example that erosion may result in choking a stream—though even here the hand of man often is not without responsibility. More widespread, more damaging, and more dangerous sources of pollution are wholly manmade: they consist primarily of municipal and industrial wastes. The Delaware and its tributaries know well all forms of pollution; and if substantial abatement of the pollution nuisance is to be discerned, there is still no occasion for complacency.

The proposition that some water problems, particularly on interstate streams, are not susceptible of solution by local action alone under modern conditions of urban/industrial life requires no demonstration. New York City was not permitted to take water from the Delaware Basin at its pleasure, but instead was forced to seek acquiescence by other interested parties (principally New Jersey and Pennsylvania) through negotiations covering almost two decades. Its quandary was resolved, temporarily at least, by a Supreme Court ruling. Easton will not solve the problem of excess water, nor Trenton that of minimum flow, nor Philadelphia that of pollution, nor Wilmington that of supply, through individual action; for the manifold problems encountered by each in "going it alone" would transcend both its legal powers and its economic resources. The successful treatment of the water problem, in many of its larger aspects, clearly requires a broader view than can be brought to it by local communities through individual and independent action.

This study develops the position that the most appropriate organization for the administration of the Delaware's water resources in their larger setting is a Basin-wide agency with jurisdiction over water and water-related activities.[1] The new agency will not supersede the traditional units of government, but on the contrary will build on and strengthen existing national, state, and local agencies and programs. Its chief responsibility will be to introduce an overview of Basin water problems, to plan a comprehensive water program, and by comple-

---

[1] "Basin-wide agency" as used here does not mean an agency with jurisdiction defined precisely or uniformly in terms of the hydrologic basin of the Delaware. On the contrary, a regional agency for water of necessity will have variable jurisdiction, since some of its activities will not extend to the limits of the basin while others may reach well beyond.

mentary action to assist in effectuating the Basin plan. Its principal influence on existing governments may be expected to result from persuasion and example, and from the introduction of positive thinking through assertion of leadership.

The existing panoply of government is fatally lacking, both in organization and in program scope, in capacity to deal with regional water problems. Clearly this need not be so. The challenge is to identify new and changing public needs and to devise measures that will enable government to meet them. It is the purpose of this study by making a systematic examination of the problems of river basin administration to provide background for effective action in the important and increasingly complex field of water-resource management.

CHAPTER 2

The Delaware River and Its Environs

IT is a truism that government in an important sense reflects the temper and structure of the society it serves. It follows then that an organization for the administration of the water resources of a river basin must be planned with proper regard for the region's distinguishing features. Among these may be listed physical characteristics, social and economic structure, institutional organization, and political pattern. In terms appropriate to the Delaware, these features may be analyzed variously from the points of view of the River itself, the Basin, the Service Area, and the states with an immediate concern for the River.[1] Map 1 affords a general orientation to the Delaware River and its environs.

THE RIVER

Under authority of federal statute the demarcation of the boundary line dividing the high seas from rivers, harbors, and inland waters is assigned to the Commandant of the United States Coast Guard.[2] Pursuant to this authorization the Coast Guard Commandant in 1956 delineated the Delaware, its Bay, River, and tributaries to consist of those waters confined within "a line drawn from Cape May East Jetty Light to Cape May Inlet Lighted Bell Buoy 2CM; thence to Overfalls Lightship; thence to the northernmost extremity of Cape Henlopen."[3] It is here the Delaware begins.

To describe the waters above this line, it will be convenient to draw upon the table of channel mileages prepared by the Corps of Engineers

[1] The interest of the country as a whole is reserved for separate treatment in Chapter 3.
[2] 28 United States Statutes at Large 672 (1895).
[3] 33 Code of Federal Regulations 82.25.

Map 1

THE DELAWARE RIVER
AND ITS ENVIRONS

After A Map by Arthur F. Loeben and
Kenneth L. Pyle

- ·—·—· State Boundary
- ──── River Basin Boundary
- ─ ─ ─ Service Area Boundary
- ■ Metropolitan Area

and published in the preliminary *Data Book,* preparation of which was
one of the first steps taken in the research for the 1956-1960 Survey.[4] A
column of figures running over some 18 pages, it provides mileage dis-
tances from the entrance of the Bay to each major point in the River
and so reduces the entire River to a measurable dimension, a total
distance of 330.7 miles from the Bay entrance to the junction of the
East and West branches of the Delaware at Hancock, New York. An
inspection of this column of figures is a mathematical equivalent of a
boat ride up the Delaware to its source.

Immediately above the entrance to the Delaware, between Capes
May and Henlopen, Delaware Bay begins to bell out, widening particularly on the New Jersey side. On the Delaware shore, hidden behind
Cape Henlopen, is the Harbor of Refuge, protected by an 8,000 foot
breakwater completed by the Corps of Engineers in 1951 and with a
15-foot-deep dredged channel to Lewes, a major fishing port on Delaware Bay. At mileage 11.17 the first important tributary enters the Bay,
the Mispillion River with a drainage area of 126 square miles, all in
Delaware. At mileage 19.43 the first major tributary on the New Jersey
side, the Maurice River, joins the Bay. This river, with a drainage of
388 square miles, is the fifth largest tributary of the Delaware River.

The upstream end of the Bay, where Delaware Bay becomes Delaware River, comes at 48.23, a point arbitrarily defined by the legislatures
of New Jersey and Delaware as the line extending between a monument at Liston Point, Delaware, to a monument on the south side of
the entrance to Hope Creek, New Jersey. Below this point the Bay
runs generally in a northwest-southeast direction, its marshy shores—
refuges of migratory fowl and other wildlife—cut through by numerous
tributaries, many with shallow channels dredged out by the Corps of
Engineers to service small fishing ports: on the Delaware side the
Leipsic River, the Little River, the Broadkill River, the Mispillion
River, the Murderkill River, the Smyrna River, and the St. Jones; on
the New Jersey shore the Cohansey River, the Maurice River, Dennis
Creek, and Goshen Creek. The greater part of the dredging projects
are now old and the channels little used. The few more recent projects
have largely been at ports used by party fishing boats, an indication
of the deterioration of the oyster industry in the Bay which, however, is
still described as a multi-million dollar business.

At mileage 58.60 is the entrance to the Chesapeake and Delaware

[4] This survey of Delaware Basin water resources is being carried out by federal
and state agencies under Corps of Engineers direction. It will be referred to in this
study as "the Survey."

Canal, a protected channel between Chesapeake Bay and Delaware River now being widened and deepened by the Corps of Engineers. On both sides of the canal entrance an industrial area is growing rapidly along the Delaware waterfront; the most impressive development here is the Tidewater Oil Company refinery, said to be the largest in the world. Aiding and abetting the industrialization of the State of Delaware is the Delaware Memorial Bridge, which has provided a trucking connection for local industry as well as a new route for passenger traffic from Washington, D. C. to New York City. The river flows under it at mileage 67.70.

Three miles above the bridge the Delaware's fourth largest tributary, the Christina River, enters the River. The Christina's drainage basin of 568 square miles includes the drainage of the better known Brandywine. At the juncture of the two streams is the city of Wilmington, the second largest city in the Delaware Valley. Beginning just below Wilmington the Delaware River swings off to the east, making almost a 90 degree turn. Actually, the axis of the Delaware River as a whole comes very close to being due north and south, but like a sailing ship tacking into the wind, the River flows southward irregularly, alternating now southeast, now southwest.

This stretch of the River extending from Wilmington past Philadelphia and on to the head of the estuary at Trenton is the most heavily industrialized section of the River and one of the most highly industrialized regions in the world. Concomitantly, it is also the area of heaviest water demand. At its northern end is the Fairless Works of U.S. Steel, the largest integrated steel plant ever built at one time; but numerous other industries contribute traffic which makes the Delaware River estuary the largest fresh water port in the country. Although there are channel improvements on some of the smaller rivers—the Cooper River, Big Timber Creek, Woodbury Creek, Mantua Creek, Raccoon Creek, the Salem River, and Alloway Creek—the most important improvement of man upon nature in this section of the River has been the dredging of the main channel to permit the entry of deep-draft vessels into the estuary. Earlier, this channel was 40 feet deep as far as Philadelphia and 25 feet deep beyond; after the building of the Fairless Works the controversial decision was taken to deepen the channel to 40 feet all the way to the upstream end of Newbold Island, with a 35-foot channel to the Trenton Marine Terminal. The Corps of Engineers is now engaged in this work.

At mileage 78.74, the River passes the Pennsylvania-Delaware line and, from being a boundary between Delaware and New Jersey, becomes the division between New Jersey and Pennsylvania. Some 15 miles upstream, in the Philadelphia-Camden area, the Delaware is joined by its largest tributary, the Schuylkill River. Its watershed of 1,909 square miles, one-sixth of the total Delaware drainage area, includes the cities of Norristown, Pottstown, Reading, and Pottsville among others. The Schuylkill's sources lie high in the mountainous anthracite country of southeastern Pennsylvania, a circumstance responsible for one of the River's most serious problems, the deposit of coal dust (culm) in the river bed.

Just below Trenton, the main stream of the Delaware makes another 90 degree turn, swinging sharply off to the northwest. At 131.80 is the Trenton Marine Terminal, but the head of navigation is set a short distance above Trenton by rapids as the Delaware falls briskly within a few miles. This is the beginning of the recreational as opposed to the industrial Delaware. It is also the historic Delaware, for the famous crossing by General Washington occurred in this stretch. A series of small streams join the River: Assunpink Creek, Jacobs Creek, Alexauken Creek, Wickecheoke Creek, Lockatong Creek, the Musconetcong River, and Pohatcong Creek on the New Jersey side and Tohickon Creek, Tinicum Creek, and Durham Creek on the Pennsylvania side. Excellent fishing is found in most of these streams.

The Delaware Valley changes abruptly at mileage 183.3, as the second largest tributary, the Lehigh, joins the River. At the mouth of the Lehigh River is Easton, Pennsylvania; with Phillipsburg, across the Delaware from Easton on the New Jersey shore, and Bethlehem and Allentown, a few miles up the Lehigh, Easton is a part of a major industrial complex. These cities are subject to flooding at times as the Lehigh, unlike the Schuylkill and the lower Delaware, is capable of producing severe flood crests. In both 1942 and 1955 serious damage was done in this area and a flood-control project on the Lehigh, consisting of Bear Creek dam plus local protective works at the cities, is now under construction.

Above Easton is the most famous and beautiful section of the River. The Delaware has swung around again and in this section runs generally north and south. In this reach is found the most spectacular natural feature of the Basin, the Delaware Water Gap, where the River breaks through the Kittatinny Mountains. Like the section of the river below Easton, this resort country was hard hit in the 1955 hurricane floods. The worst single disaster wrought by the flood was the destruction of Camp Davis, a few miles above East Stroudsburg, by the rampaging Brodhead Creek.

North of the Delaware Water Gap the River makes still another turn as it parallels the Kittatinny Mountains to the north before breaking through the ridge. The Delaware has swung over toward the east until by the time it reaches Port Jervis (New York) its direction is almost east-west, at right angles to the main axis. The most frequently discussed proposals for mainstem reservoirs on the Delaware involve sites at Tocks Island and Wallpack Bend, both in this reach. Either dam would back water up to Port Jervis, at mileage 254.7, just above the Tristate Rock that marks the intersection of the boundaries of the States of New York and New Jersey and the Commonwealth of Pennsylvania.

To the north of Port Jervis the River Valley turns abruptly back to the west. Here the River serves as the boundary between New York and Pennsylvania. Its tributaries fall rapidly and their swift current carries both the promise of hydroelectric power and the threat of flood damage. Both the Mongaup River, flowing down from New York, and Wallenpaupack Creek, a tributary of the Lackawaxen River on the Pennsylvania side, have been developed for electric power, the former by the Rockland Light and Power Company and the latter by Pennsylvania Power and Light. Moreover, Lake Wallenpaupack is almost as important for recreation as for power. Serious damage was done on the Lackawaxen—whose drainage area of 601 square miles makes it the third largest tributary of the Delaware—in the flood of 1942. A flood project, consisting of Prompton and Dyberry Reservoirs, was subsequently authorized and constructed.

The official length of the Delaware is 330.7 miles, the measurement reported for the junction of the East and West Branches of the River at Hancock, New York. Between that point and the headwaters of the River in the Catskills, both branches possess further control works; Pepacton Reservoir on the East Branch and Cannonsville Reservoir (under construction) on the West Branch, together with Neversink Reservoir, will make up the system that supplies New York City with water from the Delaware. In addition to their water supply uses, Pepacton is and Cannonsville will be operated to store water for release in times of drought for low-flow augmentation downstream.

THE RIVER VALLEY

So far the discussion has been of the Delaware River, the running water itself. Planning its use requires that consideration be given to the valley of the River and to the people who live in it, their characteristics and their interests. A part of this, of course, has been implicit in the description of the River above. One of the principal characteristics of the population of the Delaware Valley has been suggested there, namely, its uneven spread over the area. Some reaches of the River are heavily industrialized and urbanized: the estuary from Wilmington to Trenton, the valley of the Schuylkill, and the area around the mouth of the Lehigh; other sections are only sparsely populated save, in some parts, in the vacation season.

A more complete picture of these population characteristics is provided by Maps 2 and 3. These maps show the distribution of population and some detail concerning economic activity for the counties contained within the River Basin. There are in all 25 counties included wholly or in substantial part [5] within the Delaware Valley, while varying but minor parts of 13 others fall within its bounds. Of these Pennsylvania provides the largest share, contributing 13 of the 25 counties lying largely within the Basin.

The first map makes possible a ready, twofold classification of the valley. One part, the Upper Valley, consists of areas with low population densities. Six of the counties in this region have population densities below 100 persons per square mile, indicating predominantly rural occupancy; these are Delaware and Sullivan Counties in New York, Sussex in New Jersey, and Wayne, Pike, and Monroe in Pennsylvania. The pieces of other counties located in the Upper Valley likewise have only small populations; though parts of Lackawanna (Scranton) and Broome (Binghamton) Counties are included, they lie outside the major urban concentrations. Port Jervis, a city of less than 10,000 population,[6] is the largest city of the Upper Valley. By contrast only one county in the Lower Valley, Kent in Delaware (at the foot of the map), has a density below 100 per square mile.

The generalization can be made, then, that the Lower Valley is more densely populated and more highly urbanized than the Upper Valley, a situation both natural and typical of American river basins. A further distinction can be made, however, among the urban areas of the Lower Valley. The most striking concentration of population is, of course, the almost continuous urban strip that extends along the western shore of the Delaware estuary from Wilmington through Philadelphia to the city of Trenton.

[5] In this case "substantial part" means that 50 per cent or more of the county's land area falls within the Valley, except for Schuylkill County, Pennsylvania, which has been included although only 48.5 per cent of its area qualifies.

[6] 9,372 by the 1950 Census.

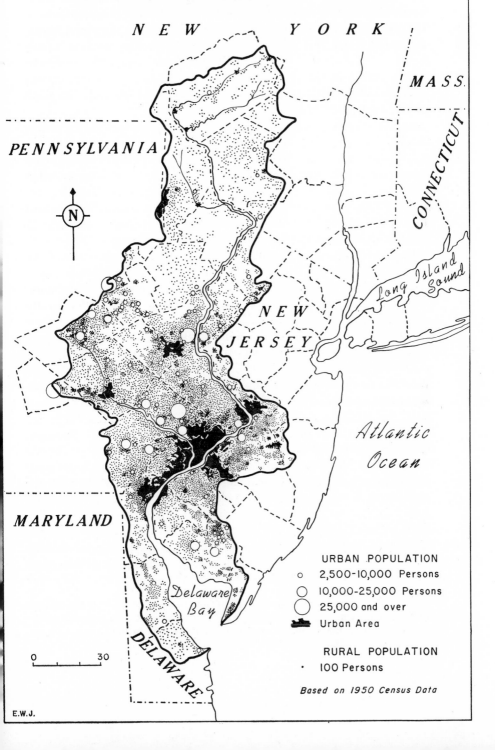

Map 2

POPULATION DISTRIBUTION
IN THE DELAWARE BASIN

NEW YORK

MASS.

PENNSYLVANIA

CONNECTICUT

Long Island Sound

NEW JERSEY

Atlantic Ocean

MARYLAND

Delaware Bay

DELAWARE

0   30

URBAN POPULATION
○ 2,500-10,000 Persons
◯ 10,000-25,000 Persons
◯ 25,000 and over
⚓ Urban Area

RURAL POPULATION
· 100 Persons

Based on 1950 Census Data

E.W.J.

The east bank's most significant concentration of population below Trenton centers in the industrial city of Camden.

To the north and west of this urbanized ribbon is a second densely populated area. The largest cities found here are Reading (Berks County), Allentown (Lehigh), Bethlehem and Easton (Northampton) and, crossing to the New Jersey side of the Delaware, Phillipsburg (Warren). Although arranged in an irregular line and with some discontinuities, they collectively form a second urban strip, roughly parallel to that from Wilmington to Trenton and crossing the boundaries from the Upper Schuylkill Valley to the Middle and Lower Lehigh.

The economic base for the differences in population densities between the Upper and Lower Valleys is suggested by Map 3, which indicates the shares of employment occupied by manufacturing and mining within the counties of the Valley.[7] The map is further useful in that counties with low industrial employment, as revealed there, generally have high agricultural employment. The results are not surprising: the Lower Valley is an area of manufacturing activity; the upper Delaware has a substantial interest in agriculture, although the recreation industry is also of great importance. Map 3 does serve to reinforce the distinction drawn above between two sub-units of the Lower Valley; the more diversified economies of the counties in the Trenton-Philadelphia-Wilmington metropolitan strip show smaller proportions of the labor force engaged in manufacturing than the parallel strip of industrial counties, Warren-Northampton-Lehigh-Berks. The map also identifies a third sub-unit within the Lower Valley in the cluster of mining and manufacturing counties (Schuylkill, Carbon, and Luzerne) found at the headwaters of the Schuylkill River.

Some distinctions can also be made among the counties categorized simply as agricultural. Actually these counties are quite diversified. Measuring agricultural activity by the cash income received from the sale of farm products,[8] Delaware and Wayne counties, plus Sussex and Warren in New Jersey, would be classified as dairy counties, for over half of the farm income comes from the sale of dairy products. In Sullivan and Pike, on the other hand, the eastern half of the uppermost

[7] On this map counties are classified according to the characteristics of the whole county population in the absence of employment figures for that part of the county within the Valley area. Some distortions undoubtedly result. Thus it is probable that the heavy manufacturing employment indicated for Broome county (New York), while accurate for the county as a whole, is not descriptive of the outlying sections of the county actually found in the Delaware watershed.

[8] Figures from the Census of Agriculture are reported in the *County and City Data Book* (Washington: Bureau of Census, 1956).

Map 3
EMPLOYMENT
IN MANUFACTURING AND MINING
IN THE DELAWARE BASIN

B	BERGEN
C	CAMDEN
CA	CARBON
D	DELAWARE
E	ESSEX
G	GLOUCESTER
HU	HUNTERDON
L	LEHIGH
M	MERCER
MO	MONTGOMERY
N	NASSAU
NO	NORTHAMPTON
P	PHILADELPHIA
PA	PASSAIC
R	ROCKLAND
S	SOMERSET
U	UNION
W	WARREN
WE	WESTCHESTER

NEW YORK   MASSACHUSETTS

GREENE

BROOME   DELAWARE

ULSTER   DUTCHESS

PENNSYLVANIA   WAYNE
SULLIVAN

LACKAWANNA   ORANGE   PUTNAM
PIKE   CONN.

LUZERNE   WE

MONROE   SUSSEX   PA   R

CA   W   MORRIS   N
SCHUYLKILL   NO   E   New York City
L   HU   U
LEBANON   BERKS   BUCKS   S   MIDDLESEX

CHESTER   MO   MONMOUTH

P   OCEAN

CECIL   D   C   NEW
JERSEY
NEW   G   BURLINGTON
CASTLE   SALEM   ATLANTIC

CUMBERLAND   CAPE MAY

KENT

N

SUSSEX   Atlantic
DELAWARE   Ocean
MARYLAND

40-55% in Manufacturing

30-39% in Manufacturing

20-29% in Manufacturing

6-19% in Manufacturing

20% or more in both
Mining and Manufacturing

0   30
MILES

E.W.J.

Valley, the principal cash product is poultry and eggs. In the southern-most farm counties, Gloucester, Salem, and Cumberland in South Jersey, Chester in Pennsylvania, and Kent in Delaware, the sale of crops produces more income than either cows or poultry. These are truck farming areas, though poultry is of some importance in Salem and Cumberland and dairying in Salem and Chester.

Any definition of regions is in part a matter of convenience since, by varying the criteria used, either broad inclusive areas or a multiplicity of smaller units can be set up. In one sense—its definition by water flow—the entire Delaware Valley makes up one region. By using additional tests, the Basin can be subdivided into smaller units. The most important of these is the division into a sparsely populated Upper Valley and an urbanized, industrialized Lower Valley: the Delaware Water Gap might conveniently serve as a dividing point. Within these two areas the maps permit further subdivisions. The Upper Valley might be divided east and west; the western portion, the most agricultural section of the whole Basin, is dairy country; in the eastern section chickens and tourists take a bigger place. The Lower Valley might be divided into at least four parts: an anthracite coal mining and manufacturing area in the Upper Schuylkill Valley; an industrial strip extending from Reading through Allentown to Phillipsburg; a continuous metropolitan area linking Trenton, Philadelphia, and Wilmington; and a rural and agricultural area at the southern tip of the Valley, including particularly Kent and Sussex Counties in the State of Delaware and Cape May County and adjacent areas in Southern New Jersey.

There are two dangers involved in a detailed examination of these maps, however. The first is that of equating space with population size or importance. It would be incorrect to assume that because the areas on the map show a relatively even division between the sparsely populated counties of the Upper Valley and the metropolitan counties of the Lower Valley, the two are equal in numerical strength. The entire Upper Basin has about one-eighth the population of the Philadelphia Metropolitan area *alone* (using the terms as defined for the Corps Survey and as indicated in Map 4). This fact must continually be kept in mind when drawing conclusions from spatial representations. The second danger concerns the extent to which the Delaware Valley forms a unit to itself, capable of analysis as an entity. It involves in part the relationship of the Delaware River to its Service Area as distinguished from its Valley, and is best considered in that context.

The Service Area

If the maps of the Delaware Valley included herein were presented without explanation or comment, not many would be able to identify their subject. This is another way of saying that few persons living in the Delaware Valley are conscious of that fact. The Delaware Valley can be defined as an area by its hydrology; few people, however, sense much regional attachment to it. Even those who use the phrase "Delaware Valley, U.S.A." or "Delaware Valley Council" have traditionaly included within their range of interest only a part of the totality that is physiographically the Valley of the Delaware River.

There are good reasons for this. One lies in the fact that water, and the watershed of his residence, does not play an important enough role in the life of the average Easterner to impress itself upon him as a description of his place in the world. Water is essential, of course; life would be impossible without it, and in a general way most people know this. But in the humid East the ordinary citizen assumes its presence and, unworried over where his next drink is coming from, never says to himself: "I live in the Wissahickon Sub-Basin of the Schuylkill River Watershed of the Delaware Basin; now, what am I going to do about it?" There are too many other associations of greater immediate importance to him by which he locates himself—his municipal government, his community, his county, his state, his bus route, his neighborhood, perhaps his parish, and a dozen others.

And in this the Easterner is right. For the second major reason why the Delaware Valley as such has never given rise to a regional consciousness is that in the urban East water is used where it is convenient without much regard to the watershed from which it is taken. The Supreme Court has now authorized the city of New York to withdraw from the Delaware 800 million gallons of water per day (mgd) for use in the Hudson Valley, and further has authorized the state of New Jersey to withdraw 100 mgd through the Delaware and Raritan Canal for use in the Raritan Basin. It seems inevitable that Delaware water will eventually be drunk in the Valley of the Passaic as well. (The difficulty involved in identifying New Jersey communities in this way itself serves to illustrate the point made.) Nor is there any reason to think inter-basin transfers will take place in only one direction. At the time the Tidewater Oil Company built its great Delaware refinery, it considered the purchase of water for industrial use from behind Conewingo Dam on the Susquehanna River; and the City of Chester, Pennsylvania, actually brings in to the Delaware Basin 30 mgd from the Susquehanna. There is no reason to doubt that transfers of water from one basin to another will increase substantially in the future. Along the crowded eastern seaboard, patterns imposed by man often disregard natural boundaries. The narrow watersheds, which parallel each other closely, and the relatively level terrain facilitate rather than hinder inter-basin transfers. In these circumstances hydrologic unity is not the overriding consideration it may be in other regions.

In reality the Delaware Valley is not a region that does or can stand alone for any purpose save drainage. Effective use of the Delaware's water must consider the entire area served or likely some day to be served by that water. This is the meaning of the term "Delaware River Service Area" as used in the Corps Survey. It is intended to describe not the basin drained by the Delaware River but the area with an active interest in the way the Delaware is developed. It will be a progressively larger area as time goes on.

Any delimitation of such a service area must be arbitrary, for it requires, among other things, a look into the future to determine eventual uses of Delaware water. Map 4 indicates the area defined as the Delaware River Service Area for the purpose of the Survey. For statistical purposes it was further divided into eight sub-regions, six of which are represented on the map. The first six were designated in the Survey as the Upper Basin,[9] the Bethlehem-Allentown-Reading Area, the Philadelphia Metropolitan Area, the Trenton Metropolitan Area, the Wilmington Metropolitan Area, and the Southern Basin and Coastal Plain. The Survey distinguished further between a New York City Metropolitan Area and a Supplement to the New York City Metropolitan Area, the latter consisting of Monmouth County in New Jersey; Orange, Dutchess, and Putnam Counties in New York; and Fairfield in Connecticut.[10]

The significance of this map lies not in the sub-regions, however, but in the unity of the whole area. For the purpose of managing the water resources of the Delaware this entire area has a common concern, though the extent of the interest varies from one area to another. The

[9] The term is here used in a sense different from that employed before since the Survey's Upper Basin includes both the Upper Basin previously discussed and the anthracite region in the headwaters of the Schuylkill.

[10] The two can be separated from one another on the map in that the New York City Supplement consists of those counties shown as within the New York Metropolitan Area sub-region, but not shaded as within the census classification of a standard metropolitan area. (In the case of Fairfield County where the application of census criteria for New England governments differ, the county—in the Supplemental Area—is partly shaded.)

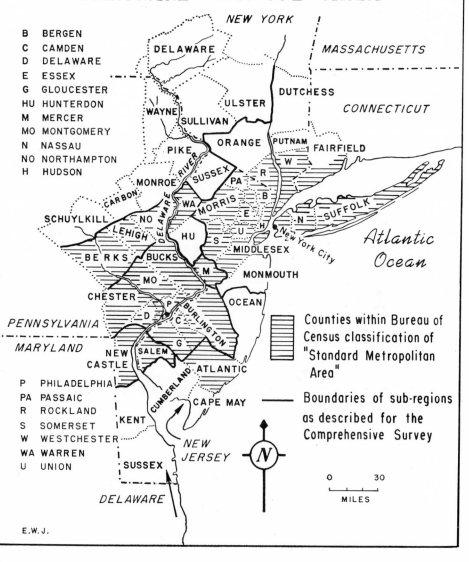

Map 4
METROPOLITANISM
AND THE
DELAWARE SERVICE AREA

B   BERGEN
C   CAMDEN
D   DELAWARE
E   ESSEX
G   GLOUCESTER
HU   HUNTERDON
M   MERCER
MO   MONTGOMERY
N   NASSAU
NO   NORTHAMPTON
H   HUDSON

P   PHILADELPHIA
PA   PASSAIC
R   ROCKLAND
S   SOMERSET
W   WESTCHESTER
WA   WARREN
U   UNION

NEW YORK

MASSACHUSETTS

DELAWARE

DUTCHESS

CONNECTICUT

WAYNE

ULSTER

SULLIVAN

ORANGE

PUTNAM

FAIRFIELD

PIKE

W

MONROE

SUSSEX

PA

R

S.

SUFFOLK

CARBON

WA

MORRIS

B

E

N

SCHUYLKILL

LEHIGH

NO

DELAWARE RIVER

HU

U

H

New York City

Atlantic
Ocean

BERKS

BUCKS

S

MIDDLESEX

MO

M

MONMOUTH

CHESTER

OCEAN

D

P

BURLINGTON

PENNSYLVANIA

C

MARYLAND

G

NEW
CASTLE

SALEM

ATLANTIC

CUMBERLAND

CAPE MAY

KENT

NEW
JERSEY

N

SUSSEX

DELAWARE

Counties within Bureau of
Census classification of
"Standard Metropolitan
Area"

Boundaries of sub-regions
as described for the
Comprehensive Survey

0   30
MILES

E.W.J.

common interests extend far beyond this to other inter-connections among the separate communities, in industry, in culture, in transportation, and in other fields. On the map those counties are shaded that are classified by the Bureau of the Census as attached to a standard metropolitan area. Starting originally from separate central cities, these metropolitan areas have now spread out until they touch one another and form a common metropolitan strip extending up and down the Atlantic Coast from New York City through Jersey City, Newark, Trenton, Camden, and Philadelphia to Wilmington—and, indeed, beyond the boundaries of the map at both ends to become one with what has been described as the megalopolitan region of the East Coast.

It is the metropolitanism of this area that gives the Delaware Service Area its special character. In recent years increasing attention has been given to the problems of metropolitan growth, an attention forced by the pressure of events. Urban areas have always faced the difficulties inevitable when a large population densely inhabits a small territory and lives in close interdependence. As population has spread beyond the boundaries of the central city, however, these problems have been further complicated by the multiple jurisdictions of local government, each with only a part of the urban population and a part of its financial resources but with all of its governmental problems. In the area serviced by the Delaware the problem emerged in even more acute form when the metropolitan areas themselves grew together and so intermingled their problems. Today the same towns provide commuters to both New York City and Philadelphia and the lines bounding the Wilmington, Philadelphia, Trenton, and New York City metropolitan areas are necessarily arbitrary. A typical metropolitan problem elsewhere is to provide a water supply for the various governmental units that rule parts of the total metropolitan area; the atypical problem of the Delaware is to resolve the intermingled water supply problems of no less than four virtually contiguous metropolitan areas. The trend in metropolitan growth and spread throughout the country suggests that the Delaware's problem may one day soon become typical of other regions as well.

The Delaware Basin, defined hydrologically, constitutes an arbitrarily determined slice out of this continuity. In terms of population, it is not even a major part of the Service Area. Seventy per cent of the estimated 1955 population of the Service Area was located within the New York City Metropolitan Area and its Supplement. In descending size the shares of the total Service Area population found in the other subregions were: Philadelphia Metropolitan Area, 19 per cent; Bethlehem-

Allentown-Reading, 4 per cent; Upper Basin, 3 per cent; Southern Basin and Coastal Area, 2 per cent; Wilmington Metropolitan Area, 1 per cent, and Trenton Metropolitan Area, 1 per cent.

The economic concept of effective utilization suggests that the water resources of the Delaware River be used to optimum advantage over this entire area, that maximum value increments of water be obtained at minimum cost. Geographic use of water and a jealous regard for a prior water-use right by those who live within the river's basin will necessarily be uneconomic use under the circumstances of metropolitan population growth. The account would not be complete, however, unless acknowledgment were made that not everyone would accept the proposition that planning for the use of the Delaware's waters should take into account *equally* the interests of every part of the Service Area. The idea that those who live within a river valley have a special right to the use of its waters, a right superior to that of outsiders, is both venerable and vigorous. And since, within the context of the Delaware, it is the Philadelphia Metropolitan Area that is within the Valley and the New York City Metropolitan Area that is outside it, the question of priority has become entangled in the conflicts between those two metropolitan areas and between their respective states. (New Jersey, as the state within both metropolitan areas, has traditionally played the role of broker, and on such occasions as the Second Delaware Diversion Case has tipped the balance between New York and Pennsylvania with the position it has taken.) [11]

Today it seems highly unrealistic to believe that New York City can be driven out of the Delaware, the water returned to its "rightful owners," and the City told to drink its own water from the Hudson. For better or for worse, New York City has come to the Delaware to stay. The arguments in the future will probably turn on questions of relative rather than absolute rights: on whether the expanding New York City metropolitan area has a right to equal treatment in the development of the Delaware, or only to "fair" treatment; on whether the communities of the Delaware Valley would have a right to redress if the preëmption of Delaware waters as a supply source by New York City should compel them to develop more expensive alternative sources; on how the City operates its water supply reservoirs on the Delaware; etc.

In any event it seems clear that some consideration must be given to the Delaware River Service Area as a whole in planning the develop-

[11] The history of the Delaware's development, including reference to the two Supreme Court cases, is discussed below in Chapter 15.

ment of the Delaware River. Three characteristics of the Service Area are worthy of particular note.

1. The Delaware River Service Area is a wealthy region. Average annual personal income in the area in 1955 was estimated at more than $2,300 per capita, one-fourth higher than the United States average. In the wealthiest sub-region, the Wilmington Metropolitan Area, average personal income was in excess of $2,800. At the same time there are substantial variations among the sub-regions of the Service Area; two sub-regions, the Upper Basin and the Southern Basin and Coastal Area, were actually below the national average.

The average per capita personal income for 1955 in the United States was $1,846; the average for the Delaware River Service Area was $2,323. By sub-regions, per capita personal income figures for 1955 were:

New York City Metropolitan Area	$2,468
New York City Supplement	$2,088
Bethlehem-Allentown-Reading	$1,935
Trenton Metropolitan Area	$2,296
Philadelphia Metropolitan Area	$2,134
Wilmington Metropolitan Area	$2,830
Upper Basin	$1,456
Southern Basin and Coastal Area	$1,652

2. The economy of the Service Area is growing less rapidly than the national economy. In the first quarter of the twentieth century the economy of this area grew more rapidly than that of the rest of the nation. From 1929 to 1955, however, the rate of yearly increase in personal income was just over 2 per cent in the Service Area, while in the nation as a whole it was 3 per cent. This is not equally true in all sections of the Service Area: Trenton, Wilmington, and the Southern Basin and Coastal areas showed average to better-than-average growth rates in personal income over this period. Generally, however, the economy of the Service Area is more mature and so is growing less rapidly than the national economy.

3. Shifts are occurring in the sub-regions of the Service Area as a result of differential growth. From 1930 to 1955 employment in the New York City and Philadelphia metropolitan areas increased a little more than one-fifth as against one-fourth in the nation as a whole. Before 1939 the Bethlehem-Allentown-Reading area grew rapidly, but has lagged since. Nearly one-third of the manufacturing employees in this sub-region, centered on Allentown, are in the textile and apparel

industry, which has experienced slow growth. The Upper Basin has also been hard hit. Farm income in the Valley increased more rapidly than average income during the period 1929-1955, but this growth was not sufficient in the Upper Basin to offset the steady deterioration of the anthracite coal industry.

At the same time that growth in some areas has slowed down, that in others has bettered the national average. The New York City Supplement has grown rapidly and promises to continue to grow as population spills over from the metropolitan area proper to the outlying ring of peripheral counties. The Trenton and Wilmington metropolitan areas and the Southern Basin and Coastal Area have also enjoyed above-average growth and the trend there is expected to continue. There is no reason to anticipate any revolutionary readjustment of the balance among the sub-regions in size—the New York and Philadelphia metropolitan areas will remain the two largest components of the area into the far-distant future—but differential growth rates are bound to cause shifts in the balance among the regions. At the same time simultaneous growth in all the sub-regions is likely, by filling in the breaks in the metropolitan areas, to minimize the impact of regional differentiation.

THE DELAWARE STATES

Just as the Delaware River is located within a Delaware Valley, and the Delaware Valley within a Delaware River Service Area, so in turn the Delaware River Service Area is a part of a larger grouping, the several states that exercise jurisdiction over parts of the Service Area. Actually, the Service Area sprawls across four state boundaries, covering all of two states and parts of three others.

These five states differ substantially, however, in their degree of concern with the Delaware. One hundred per cent of the populations of Delaware and New Jersey are defined as within the Service Area, but smaller shares of the total populations of the other three states are considered to be within the area. By states, the percentages of state population in the Delaware Service Area in 1955 were:[12]

Connecticut	25%
New York	68
New Jersey	100
Pennsylvania	39
Delaware	100

[12] Though a very small part of Cecil County, Maryland, is within the Delaware Valley, it was not included within the Service Area as defined for the Survey.

These percentages have considerable significance for an appraisal of the likely contribution to be made by the states toward the development of the Delaware River. A citizen of New York resident in an upstate community outside the Delaware Service Area, or a western Pennsylvanian, or an inhabitant of northeastern Connecticut is not likely to see the necessity for action to protect the water resources of the Delaware. The presence of a substantial population within the state unconcerned with the problems of the Delaware is likely to serve as a potent brake upon state activity. Even within the states defined as entirely within the Delaware Service Area the problem of citizen detachment appears. Although South Jersey and southern Delaware have been classified as parts of the Service Area, their concern with its problems is much more limited than that evident in the metropolitan areas of northeastern New Jersey or New Castle County, Delaware, where an expanding urban population requires that serious consideration be given to problems of water supply. One limit, therefore, on state action in the Delaware is the presence of large segments within several of the states unconcerned with the Basin's water problems.

Another limit is imposed by the sheer incapacity of the states to act. The state governments have not been notable for their effectiveness as a general rule. Handicapped by outmoded constitutions, ineffectual administrative organization and procedure, and inexperienced and part-time legislatures, the states have failed to confirm their positions through positive action and so in many fields have lost the initiative to the federal government by default.

These general criticisms are not equally applicable to all the Delaware Basin states. New Jersey possesses an up-to-date constitution, while that of New York compares favorably with most others. Similarly, the governors in those two states have enough power and sufficiently cohesive executive organizations to be able to provide the policy and administrative leadership that is too often sorely lacking. The same cannot be said of Pennsylvania and Delaware, which would not rank high in any general assessment of state governments. Administrative efficiency is undermined in both by poor organization and excessive regard to patronage considerations in appointments. Attention is currently being given to administrative reorganization in the water-resource field in Delaware and to general constitutional revision in Pennsylvania.

The caliber of governors in all four states suggests, however, that the attractiveness of the office is high and/or that the voters are fairly discerning. In part this phenomenon results also from the fact that all of these are currently two-party states where the political parties are forced by necessity to offer qualified candidates.[13] Both the point and some of the problems that result are suggested by the fact that at the time of the creation of the Delaware River Basin Advisory Committee each of the four governors faced a legislature of contrary party complexion in at least one house. In New York, New Jersey, and Pennsylvania, this partisan conflict was the typical product of legislative malapportionment which, by giving non-metropolitan[14] districts representation disproportionate to population, assures Republican control of the legislatures even when statewide elections produce Democratic governors. In Delaware, which politically is a border state, it resulted again from legislative malapportionment and consequent disproportionate representation for rural Kent and Sussex Counties. Delaware's situation provides an incidental demonstration that rural over-representation is not a monopoly of northeastern Republicans, for there that phenomenon normally produces a Democratic legislature.

Nor is such a partisan division an accident of circumstances; it is a regular occurrence in the politics of the mid-Atlantic states. In his study of American state politics, V. O. Key found that from 1931 to 1952 the governorship and legislature (at least one house) were in opposite party hands in New York 12 years of the 22. Similar party divisions were found in Delaware for 10 of the 22 years, in New Jersey for 9 of 22, and in Pennsylvania for 4 of the 22.[15] Only in Pennsylvania was the same party regularly in control of both executive and legislative branches and this was primarily a product of Republican dominance throughout the period; with the resurgence of the Democratic Party in Pennsylvania in the 1950's it seems probable that Pennsylvania's pattern increasingly will resemble that of the other three states.

The fact of party division would be interesting to politicians alone if partisanship were irrelevant to the making of public policy. It is

[13] Cf. Joseph A. Schlesinger, "A Two-Dimensional Scheme for Classifying the States According to Degree of Inter-Party Competition," *American Political Science Review,* XLIX (December, 1955), pp. 1120-1128; and Austin Ranney and Willmoore Kendall, "The American Party Systems," *American Political Science Review,* XLVIII (June, 1954), pp. 477-485.

[14] This awkward term is not a fully accurate one for describing the over-representation typically provided the out-state urban areas in New York, New Jersey, and Pennsylvania, but is more suitable than the word "rural" when used to describe legislatures in which less than a twentieth of the members are farmers.

[15] V. O. Key, *American State Politics: An Introduction* (New York: Alfred A. Knopf, 1956), p. 55.

not irrelevant, however, but on the contrary is an important influence in deciding what the state's legislative product will be. The mid-Atlantic states are notable for the high degree of partisanship manifested in the legislative process. Though many issues are settled in the legislature without acrimony, those questions which are controversial ordinarily become involved in party disputes. Thus party issues include not only such traditional matters of party concern as patronage, election law changes, and legislative apportionment, but also broad issues of social and economic policy, labor-management relations, and the like.[16] On these issues the importance of the legislative apportionment lies in the fact that it tips the balance in the legislature toward what is generally considered the conservative position.

In the past natural resource development has not typically been an issue of partisan conflict in these states except as it has related to the generation of electric power, which at times has been a matter of party controversy. The political situation suggests that no long-range program of resource development can be expected to be viable without substantial support within both political parties.

SUMMARY

The Delaware River can be viewed from the perspective of its Valley, its Service Area, the states in which the service area is located, and the nation of which all are part. In fact consideration needs to be given to each viewpoint. Concerning the River and its various settings, these points can be made in summary:

1. The Delaware River with its system of tributaries serves many functions today. Its waters are employed for navigation, water supply, waste disposal, recreation, and power, among other purposes, uses which demand both quality and flood control.

2. Like the River, the Delaware Valley is not all of a piece. Subregions can be identified within it, of which the most distinctive are the sparsely populated Upper Valley dominated by agriculture and recreation, and an industrialized and urbanized Lower Valley which contains the great bulk of the Valley's population.

3. Water from the River, however, is not used exclusively within the Delaware Basin. Delaware water is presently used outside the valley, and such uses will not only continue but increase. Diversion outside the

[16] Malcolm E. Jewell, "Party Voting in American State Legislatures," *American Political Science Review*, XLIX (September, 1955), pp. 773-791; William J. Keefe, "Parties, Partisanship, and Public Policy in the Pennsylvania Legislature," *American Political Science Review*, XLVIII (June, 1954), pp. 450-464.

Basin is but one of several factors, albeit a central one, which require that consideration be given to the more inclusive Delaware River Service Area.

4. The Delaware River Service Area is characterized by a wealthy population and a mature economy; the economic concern of the area is to maintain a parity of growth with other sections rather than to accomplish rapid development.

5. The states which overlie the Delaware River Service Area have differing degrees of concern with its problems. Some fall entirely within the Service Area; others, where only a portion of the state population (sometimes a minority portion) has a stake in the Delaware, cannot be expected to take an equal interest in its problems.

CHAPTER 3

The Parties at Interest

In the number of people served by its waters and the economic importance of their activities, the Delaware ranks first among American rivers. Residents of two of the largest metropolitan areas in the country, those centering on New York City and Philadelphia, drink water from the Delaware. Within the Delaware Service Area live 21,500,000 people, one-eighth of the entire population of the United States, who provide one-seventh of the total employed working force in the country and receive one-sixth of the aggregate personal income. The River provides water-borne transportation for a major slice of the megalopolitan urbanized area of the Atlantic seaboard. Further, it serves as a source of cooling water and a means of waste disposal for an important segment of the nation's industry. Although the Mississippi River system as a whole services a greater population, only one of its component valleys, the Ohio, is comparable to the Delaware in economic activity. The Incodel tag, "The Mighty Delaware: A Midget in Size—A Giant in Service," [1] is truly suggestive of the unique character of the Delaware River.

The most important feature affecting the future of the Delaware is not the hydrology of the River nor the undeveloped natural resources of its Valley, but rather its people and the demands they make upon it. What the people of the Delaware Basin want to use the River for is the most important determinant of water-resource activities there. And the program to be pursued, it goes without saying, will determine the administrative arrangements to be proposed for the Valley.

[1] Interstate Commission on the Delaware River Basin (Incodel), *Annual Report,* 1958 (Philadelphia).

THE PUBLIC(S)

Unfortunately, it is not a simple task to discover the wishes of the public with respect to the utilization of the River's water. In part this difficulty stems from the size of the population involved and the problems entailed in sampling public opinion. In part it arises from the amorphous character of the area; for the Delaware River Service Area is not a fixed concept over time but an expanding one, used to describe at a particular moment the territory that finds it convenient and suitable to use Delaware water. To illustrate the fluid nature of the concept, the Service Area even now is on the point of expansion to include a population in northeastern New Jersey that has not previously been served by water from the Delaware.

The greatest difficulty, however, arises from the fact that there is rarely, if ever, unanimity of opinion within the public on any point. After a catastrophic flood or a disastrous drought there may be widespread agreement—among the minority who take an interest in public affairs, at least—that something must be done about flood control or water supply. But under ordinary circumstances, one identifiable group will be interested in development of the River for its own purposes; a second group, without necessarily opposing the first, will have quite different aims in mind; a third will have a different goal; and so forth. For this reason analysts of public opinion often find it convenient to talk not of the opinions of the *public*, but of those of the several separate *publics* into which the population—or its articulate segment—can be divided.

A general indication of the kinds of separable interests that exist so far as development of the Delaware is concerned can be seen in Table 1, which summarizes the results of a questionnaire circulated to several hundred citizens' associations in the Delaware River Service Area in the early days of this study. The table is based upon 156 answered questionnaires (the other organizations either did not reply or returned incomplete answers). Each organization was asked to indicate the areas of action it was interested in. Most frequently cited was fish and wildlife protection, concern with which was reported by 78, exactly half of the associations tabulated. In second place was flood control, cited by 72 organizations, 46 per cent of the sample. Following in decreasing order of importance were small watershed development, pollution control, water-based recreation, industrial water supply, municipal water supply, irrigation, port development, navigation, and hydroelectric power generation.

TABLE 1

*Indicated Program Interests in Water-Resource Development
of 156 Citizens' Associations in the
Delaware River Service Area, 1958*

Program	Organizations Expressing Interest	
	Number	Per Cent
Fish and wildlife protection	78	50
Flood control	72	46
Small watershed development	67	43
Pollution control	66	42
Water-based recreation	61	39
Industrial water supply	54	35
Municipal water supply	53	34
Irrigation	37	24
Port development	36	23
Navigation	28	18
Hydroelectric power	7	4
Other (volunteered responses)	11	7

It would be risky to draw any conclusions from the table as to the relative strength of the demands for action in the functional areas. It is, of course, obvious that the responses obtained are dependent both upon the organizations to which questionnaires were sent and upon those which replied. An attempt was made to solicit all of the larger groups concerned with water-resource development—the table includes, for example, the Delaware Valley Council, the Atlantic Deeper Waterways Association, the Greater Philadelphia Chamber of Commerce, the Greater Philadelphia Movement, the Lehigh Valley Flood Control Council, the New Jersey Farm Bureau, the Delaware State Chamber of Commerce, the Pennsylvania Federation of Sportsmen's Clubs, the New Jersey Taxpayers Association, the Joint Executive Committee for the Improvement and Development of the Philadelphia Port Area, and the Greater Trenton Council—but undoubtedly there were omissions which were further accentuated by the failure of some groups to respond. Nor were the associations of equal strength: many of the votes for fish and wildlife protection, for example, come from relatively small sportsmen's clubs. A safer way of interpreting the table would be to conclude that interests in fish and wildlife (to continue the example) are among the most common causes for the formation of citizens groups with a concern for water-resource development.

What the table does show, however, is that specialization of interest exists with respect to water, with organizations grouped around each major resource function. While many associations are concerned with more than one kind of water development, they tend to form into separate publics interested in different segments of the whole water problem. This specialization of interest and activity became even more apparent when the organizations were asked about the matters concerning which they have actually taken action. The questionnaire called for an indication of action taken regarding seven specific proposals: (1) the 40-foot Delaware channel, a navigation improvement; (2) Round Valley, a water supply reservoir for New Jersey; (3) Tocks Island Reservoir, considered by the Corps of Engineers as part of its plan and proposed for immediate construction by Incodel for flood control, stream flow regulation, and future water supply; (4) the Schuylkill Restoration Project, a pollution control program; (5) Bear Creek Reservoir, a Lehigh River flood control project; (6) the Incodel plan of 1951, a basin-wide plan for water supply and stream flow regulation; and (7) Public Law 566 and its implementation, concerned with small watershed development. The answers of various groups are tabulated in Table 2, based upon a smaller sample of 72 organizations reached in the first round of questionnaires.[2]

Several conclusions are apparent from the table. The first is that considerably fewer organizations have "done something" about water-resource development on the Delaware than indicated an interest in the problem: over half the organizations reporting, 40 in all, have taken no action on any of the seven issues. A second inference derivable from the table is that an organization's range in water interests is less broad when it comes to positive action than when a general expression of interest is involved; for although the number of organizations taking action on each of the seven proposals indicates that some took steps on more than one subject, it is obvious that the typical organization took action on no more than one or two topics. A third conclusion has to do with the relationship between the various kinds of organizations and the interest shown in resource development. The business organizations were typically interested in the navigation project (the 40-foot channel) and the Round Valley water supply plan; farm organizations

[2] This sample of 72 organizations includes most of the larger groups of the kind separately enumerated above. The second round of questionnaires reached principally small organizations such as sportsmen's clubs.

TABLE 2

Action Taken by 72 Citizens' Associations in the Delaware River Service Area on Seven Issues of Water Policy

| | | | | | Kinds of Organizations Taking Action | | | | | |
| Issue | All Organizations (72) | | Business (24) | | Recreation-Wildlife-Conservation (20) | | Civic (21) | | Farm-Professional-Miscellaneous (7) | |
	No.	Per Cent	No.	Per Cent	No.	Per Cent	No.	Per Cent	No.	Per Cent
Forty-Foot Channel	14	19	9	38	1	5	4	19	0	0
Round Valley	7	10	4	17	2	10	1	5	0	0
Tocks Island	3	4	0	0	2	10	1	5	0	0
Schuylkill Restoration	11	15	3	13	7	35	1	5	0	0
Bear Creek Reservoir	5	7	1	4	4	20	0	0	0	0
Incodel Plan	12	17	4	17	6	30	2	10	0	0
P.L. 566	16	22	3	13	10	50	1	5	2	29
None of These	40	55	12	50	7	35	16	76	5	71

were most concerned with watershed development under P.L. 566;[3] so were the recreation-wildlife-conservation groups, but these latter were also interested in the cleanup of Schuylkill pollution and the Incodel plan.

The clustering of certain types of organizations about issues of a particular kind is shown even more clearly when the treatment of the data is reversed to indicate the organizations interested in each proposal. To illustrate, action of one type or another on the 40-foot channel was reported by the Atlantic Deeper Waterways Association, the Delaware State Chamber of Commerce, the Delaware Valley Council, the Foreign Traders Association of Philadelphia, the Chamber of Commerce of Greater Philadelphia, the Greater Burlington Chamber of Commerce, the Greater Philadelphia Movement, the Greater Trenton Chamber of Commerce, the Manufacturers Association of Delaware County, the Joint Executive Committee for the Improvement and Development of the Philadelphia Port Area, the New Jersey State Chamber of Commerce, the Philadelphia Port Bureau, the Southern New Jersey Development Council, and the Vessel Owners and Captains Association. Clearly these organizations possess common characteristics.

On the other hand five organizations, not one of which had taken action on the 40-foot channel, reported action concerning the Bear Creek flood control reservoir: the Delaware Valley Protective Association, the Easton Area Chamber of Commerce, the Lehigh Valley Flood Control Council, the Izaak Walton League (Philadelphia chapter), and the Pennsylvania State Fish and Game Protective Association.[4] Still other organizations indicated primary interest in Round Valley, others still in the Schuylkill River Restoration, and so on.

[3] The farm-professional-miscellaneous category of organizations is the smallest shown in the table. This includes 3 farm and 2 professional groups, along with 2 of a miscellaneous character. The small number results from the low level of response from organizations in these categories. Of 12 professional organizations solicited, only 2 answered; 13 farm groups were contacted, only 3 responded. This small response, the lowest of any group, presumably reflects the low level of interest, which is manifested also in the fact that 5 of the 7 organizations responding had taken action on none of the 7 proposals. Similarly, 5 labor organizations were solicited, but none answered.

[4] The answers from the questionnaires suggest that the fish and wildlife implications of Bear Creek reservoir as well as its flood control features produced organization action. From the second round of answers it would be possible to add the Lehigh County Fish and Game Protective Association, the Mauch Chunk Rod and Gun Club, the Perkiomen Valley Sportsmen's Association, the Wilkes-Barre Rotary Club, and the Wind Gap Rod and Gun Club.

The point is a fairly obvious one, but its significance is substantial. Around each possible use of water, that is, for each potential water program area, associations of persons particularly interested in water-resource development for that goal tend to be formed. Their separate influence on individual proposals or programs often is great and sometimes is determining, while collectively they may exercise considerable pressure toward inducing or inhibiting government action on a broader front. Their tendency is to seek to have governmental responsibility for water-resource development for their particular purpose vested in a separate agency to which they have special access and in which they have confidence.

FEDERAL AGENCIES AND PROGRAMS

For each of the demands for governmental action in the water-resources field, made for the Delaware Valley or elsewhere, a federal program can be identified, though the extent of federal responsibility varies from one program to another. And the tendency has been, as indicated, to establish a specific agency with particular authority for each major activity. A reciprocal relationship has then developed between those who sought the service in the first instance and the public agency established to provide the service, or, as it is often put, between the government bureau and its clientele. In most instances the clientele is formally organized through a nationwide association or associations, each with local offshoots, in the Delaware Valley as elsewhere. These can be readily identified for each of the major interests expressed in Delaware development, as listed in Table 1.

Flood Control

Federally-provided flood protection has traditionally been the special province of the Corps of Engineers of the United States Army, at least insofar as flood control dams, channel improvements, and protective works are concerned. Beginning with its work on the Mississippi River in the construction of the great levee systems, the Corps has expanded into other areas of water management largely by the process of addition, building upon the base afforded by flood protection. The parallel private association in this instance is the National Rivers and Harbors Congress, which provides both general support for the appropriation of funds for the civil functions of the Corps of Engineers and, through its endorsement of individual projects, specific support as well.[5] A typical association of this kind on the local level is the Lehigh Valley Flood Control Council, formed to seek congressional authorization for and appropriation to (the two processes are distinct and require separate legislative acts) Bear Creek Reservoir and associated projects on the Lehigh River.[6]

Since the construction of flood control works is not the only answer to flooding, the Corps of Engineers is not the only federal agency concerned with flood protection. Flood warning systems can serve at least to minimize danger and damage; they are the responsibility of the United States Weather Bureau (Department of Commerce) and the Geological Survey (Department of the Interior). Federal concern with emergency aid after a disastrous flood is expressed through the Corps, but also at times through the Office of Civil and Defense Mobilization and the U.S. Coast Guard (Treasury Department).

Watershed Development

Federal programs in the area of flood protection and erosion control by watershed treatment, which date from the 1930's, were expanded by Public Law 566 in 1954. The "small watershed" program is administered through the Soil Conservation Service of the United States Department of Agriculture. The SCS operates through farmer-organized soil conservation districts which, with their national organization, the National Association of Soil Conservation Districts, constitute a powerful ally of the Service in its perennial struggles with other agencies in Agriculture and with opponents of its proposed budgets in Congress.[7] Such private organizations as the American Farm Bureau Federation and the National Grange also are interested in small watersheds and their development.

P.L. 566 calls for something somewhat different from long-established soil conservation practices, as the benefits involved include also flood control and at times water supply and recreation. Such programs are

[5] See Arthur Maass, *Muddy Waters: The Army Engineers and the Nation's Rivers* (Cambridge, Mass.: Harvard University Press, 1951), pp. 45-50.

[6] The Lehigh Valley Flood Control Council, it might be added, has defined its interests more broadly than many similar organizations, giving attention to flood warning, small watershed development, reforestation, etc.

[7] See Charles M. Hardin, *The Politics of Agriculture: Soil Conservation and the Struggle for Power in Rural America* (Glencoe, Ill.: The Free Press, 1952).

broader than traditional soil-saving practices and have typically been espoused by so-called watershed associations.[8] One of the most vigorous of these, the Brandywine Valley Association, is located within the Delaware Valley. Another active organization of the kind in the Delaware Basin is the Neshaminy Valley Watershed Association. There are others as well. The national organization that brings these together is the American Watershed Council. Within the Delaware Valley the watershed associations appear stronger than the soil conservation districts, though nationally the latter are more typical.

The small watershed program is concerned with flood control among other purposes. The Forest Service (in Agriculture along with the SCS) has related interests. Though the respective jurisdictions of Agriculture and the Corps of Engineers in this field have been defined by the size of the problem involved and the magnitude of the works, the possibilities for conflict are obvious. Such conflict may take the form of competition for funds from Congress, with disputes as to which approach is more meritorious.[9] It is possible that direct conflict may arise as to which agency is to build a particular structure, though disputes of this kind are not yet common. An uneasy truce prevails at present between the two agencies.

Pollution Control and Water Supply

Both these problems, though to varying extents, are the province of the same federal agency, the Public Health Service within the Department of Health, Education, and Welfare. PHS responsibility is more complete in the pollution field, where the federal government has gone farther. A substantial and steadily growing program provides grants-in-aid to municipalities and states, and the Public Health Service also possesses an enforcement power which it has not fully employed to this time. The close connection between the search for good water and the control of epidemic disease, an aspect of the general struggle

[8] Address of Clayton M. Hoff, "Small Watershed Development Programs," in Incodel *Proceedings, 1958 Annual Conference.* See also "A Watershed Workshop," Incodel, *Proceedings, 1957 Annual Conference.*

[9] The polemic literature on the subject is substantial. See, for example, Elmer T. Peterson, *Big Dam Foolishness: The Problem of Modern Flood Control and Water Storage* (New York: Devin-Adair Co., 1954). A balanced appraisal of the merits of the controversy will be found in Luna B. Leopold and Thomas Maddock, Jr., *The Flood Control Controversy: Big Dams, Little Dams, and Land Management* (New York: The Ronald Press Company, 1954).

for public water supplies in the United States,[10] has caused this task to be lodged with the Public Health Service.

Federal programs in the field of water supply, just now emerging, were first recognized in a general way in Title III of the Omnibus River and Harbors and Flood Control Act of 1958. For study purposes, federal water supply responsibility is assigned to the Public Health Service; but to the extent that federal action calls for the provision of storage for water supply in reservoirs, such action involves the Corps of Engineers since it is the chief federal construction agency in the East. Indeed under earlier specific and individual authorizations, the Corps has already built reservoirs on the Ohio River and elsewhere in which storage is sold for municipal water supply, along with others in which storage space is used for low-flow augmentation under circumstances where this amounts to industrial water supply.

Recreation

As noted in Table 1 the interest in water most often mentioned was that of fish and wildlife protection. Interest in water-based recreation was also widely reported. Federal programs in both areas are administered primarily by two divisions of the Department of the Interior, the National Park Service and the Fish and Wildlife Service. Both in the federal organizational structure and in national interest associations, a distinction has been drawn between the two types of programs pursued by these agencies; both count as recreational activity, but each appeals to a different clientele. Indeed the picture is even more complicated. At least three separate groups of recreationists can be identified with different and at times conflicting interests: (1) those who are interested in natural areas that provide scenic drives, picnic groves, and camping sites; (2) hunters and fishermen; and (3) the "packrats" who wish to preserve the wilderness in its natural state to the maximum extent possible. There are national organizations devoted to each interest. Among those with branches in the Delaware Valley are the Izaak Walton League, the National Wildlife Federation, and Ducks Unlimited, all interested in fish and wildlife; and the American Recreation Society, the National Audubon Society, the National Recreation Association, and the National Council of State Garden Clubs.

[10] Cf. Nelson M. Blake, *Water for the Cities: A History of the Urban Water Supply Problem in the United States* (Syracuse: Syracuse University Press, 1956).

Port Development and Navigation

These two interests can conveniently be treated together, because they are closely related and because the programs in both fields are administered by the Corps of Engineers. Activities of the Corps in this area are in fact much older than its flood control work. Nationally the same association, the Rivers and Harbors Congress, works with the Corps in both flood control and navigation fields, but on the local level the interests are distinct and specialized citizens groups have grown up around each. The Lehigh Valley Flood Control Council has already been referred to; a parallel organization which emphasizes navigation is the Atlantic Deeper Waterways Association, dedicated to the construction and maintenance of a protected intracoastal waterway the length of the Atlantic Seaboard. In providing navigation aids and enforcing federal navigation law, the United States Coast Guard exercises some responsibility in this field and possesses a citizens' offshoot in the Coast Guard Auxiliary. Navigation should not be understood to include only commercial users; increasingly the intracoastal waterway and other Corps-maintained channels have been used by smaller craft for recreational purposes, and these groups also have their national associations. They in turn find powerful political allies in such associated organizations as the National Association of Engine and Boat Manufacturers, equally interested in the expansion of pleasure boating in the United States.

Irrigation

Though not frequently mentioned, use of water for irrigation in the Delaware Basin is steadily growing. In the western states irrigated lands dominate the agricultural picture, and the National Reclamation Association, parallel to the Bureau of Reclamation within the Department of the Interior, has powerful influence over western water resource development. Reclamation law does not, however, apply to the states of the Delaware, and the Bureau of Reclamation exercises no authority there. Such federal programs as are relevant to irrigation of farm lands in the Delaware Valley are carried on through the regular units of the Department of Agriculture and, indirectly, through the land-grant agricultural colleges. One indication of the still limited importance of the subject is the lack of an organization or organizations to represent eastern irrigators; their interest is so far expressed only through the traditional farm associations, the National Grange, etc.

Hydroelectric Power

The generation of electric power from falling water, like irrigation, is of greater importance in the western states than in the Delaware Basin. Like irrigation also, responsibility for administration of the federal power programs is lodged with the Department of the Interior, and in considerable part with the Bureau of Reclamation within Interior. Unlike irrigation, however, the federal power program does extend also to the east and the Secretary of the Interior has general jurisdiction over the sale of electric power from all federal dams, whether constructed by his own department or not. The beneficiaries of such federal power sales, municipally-owned utilities, rural electric cooperatives, and other public bodies (the preferred customers under existing legislation), are in turn organized into two principal national organizations, the National Rural Electric Cooperatives Association and the American Public Power Association, both with members in the Delaware Valley.

Although power marketing is assigned by law to the Department of the Interior, the Federal Power Commission also exercises substantial responsibilities with respect to hydroelectric power generation. The FPC conducts investigations of potential power sites and joins in federal planning of water resources with regard to hydroelectric possibilities. Private water power developments on navigable streams or on government lands require licenses from the Commission. In addition the FPC regulates wholesale rates on power sold in interstate commerce. The Commission is an independent agency, but the same interest groups that concern themselves with the Department of the Interior's power marketing procedures take an active interest in the work of the FPC.

The Problem of Integration of Federal Programs

To this point, twelve federal agencies have been enumerated with major responsibilities in the field of water-resource management. These are scattered among six departments—Defense, Interior, Agriculture, Health-Education-Welfare, Commerce, and Treasury—plus two independent agencies, the Federal Power Commission and the Office of Civil and Defense Mobilization. Even this is not a complete listing: some eleven additional agencies participated in the Survey of the Corps of Engineers. A number of these were data-gathering agencies: the Agricultural Research Service of the Department of Agriculture and the Office of Business Economics, the Bureau of the Census, and the Coast and Geodetic Survey of the Department of Commerce. The Geological Survey (Interior), already referred to, is again relevant here. Included also for their substantive interest are the Bureau of Mines (Interior), the Offices of Area Development and of the Under Secretary for Transportation plus the Bureau of Roads (Commerce), the Departments of Navy and Labor, and the Atomic Energy Commission.

For the purposes of the Corps Survey these various agencies were all coordinated through a temporary inter-agency committee, the Delaware Basin Survey Coordinating Committee, under the sponsorship and general direction of the Corps of Engineers. There is ground to question the efficacy of this effort at coordination, and in any event it represents a special arrangement for a particular purpose. So far as the ongoing activities of these agencies in the Delaware Valley are concerned, there is little attempt at coordination of efforts or programs. Moreover, there is no authority short of the President and Congress with jurisdiction broad enough to cover all federal agencies and so to take effective action with regard to the national administrative structure. While this is not the place to develop the theme, nevertheless it may be noted that the integration of federal water-resource activities in the Delaware Valley is less a problem in field staff relations than in relations among the parent agencies in Washington. The resolution of the problem of Balkanism in the field awaits the rationalization of organizations and programs at the top. The place to attack this problem is not in the Delaware Valley but in the national capital.

STATE AND LOCAL AGENCIES AND PROGRAMS

The pattern at the federal level is duplicated, in essence, at the level of state action. Again the responsibilities for the various programs are fragmented among a large number of agencies and for many of the same reasons. Partly the causes lie in the logic of organization—the conviction, for example, that water pollution is more closely related to health than to other water-resource functions, or that watershed treatment is more closely allied to other agricultural activities than to water programs generally; but partly also they reflect the divisive impact of the multiplicity of interest groups in the field of water. Those keenly interested in the promotion of fishing are reassured if that function is placed in the hands of an autonomous agency over which they can exercise dominant influence, the friends of the forest preserve would like their ward lodged in a separate place, and so on for each of the major interests in the water field. The final result is a labyrinth of agencies which, in abbreviated form, takes on the following character.[11]

Flood Control

The only state to pursue its own active flood control program, Pennsylvania lodges it in the Department of Forests and Waters along with stream gauging and flood forecasting. New Jersey and New York assign flood protection studies to the Division of Water Policy and Supply (within the Department of Conservation and Economic Development) and the New York State Flood Control Commission respectively. New York goes furthest in dividing flood control responsibilities; in addition to the Flood Control Commission, the operation of flood control works in the State's charge is assigned to the Department of Public Works and the supervision of drainage districts to the Water Power and Control Commission, attached to the Conservation Department. The latter limited type of flood control, local drainage, is the only responsibility assumed by Delaware, which places it with an independent Board of Ditch Commissioners.

Watershed Development

Watershed treatment is generally regarded by the states as more closely related to soil conservation than to water-resource management and so is delegated to agricultural agencies: the State Soil Conservation Commission in Delaware, the Department of Agriculture in Pennsylvania, and the State Soil Conservation Committee in New York (associated with the State College of Agriculture). Only New Jersey has brought watershed development into the orbit of an over-all conservation agency. There the State Soil Conservation Committee is a part of the Department of Conservation and Economic Development.

Pollution Control

Without exception, pollution control (and the approval of public water supplies) is administered by the health departments in the four

[11] The material on Pennsylvania, New Jersey, and Delaware in this section is based upon studies made by the Fels Institute of Local and State Government at the University of Pennsylvania; that on New York is taken from Roscoe C. Martin, *Water for New York: A Study in State Administration of Water Resources* (Syracuse: Syracuse University Press, 1960).

states, with policies set by the Sanitary Water Board of the Pennsylvania Department of Health, the Division of Environmental Sanitation in the New Jersey Department of Health, and the Water Pollution Control Board in New York's Department of Health. Though Delaware assigns pollution control to a Water Pollution Commission with inter-agency representation, the Commission operates through the State Board of Health as its "administrative agent."

Municipal and Industrial Water Supply

Although the state board or department of health uniformly examines and approves water for quality, additional administrative approval is required before use of new or extended water supply sources in three of the four states. Such applications are acted upon by the Water and Power Resources Board in Pennsylvania, an autonomous unit within the Department of Forests and Waters; the Water Power and Control Commission in New York, similarly situated within the Conservation Department; and the Water Policy and Supply Council of New Jersey's Department of Conservation and Economic Development.

In addition to this regulatory action, New Jersey and New York supply water in limited areas. The Department of Conservation and Economic Development at present operates the Delaware and Raritan Canal for water supply, both municipal and industrial, and will run the Raritan development when completed. An autonomous state commission, the North Jersey Water Supply Commission, operates the Wanaque Water Supply System. In New York low-flow augmentation is provided by the Black River Regulating District and the Hudson River Regulating District, now consolidated under a single board. Neither area, however, is within the Delaware Valley.

Recreation

The administration of both parks and forests is assigned to the conservation department or its equivalent in three of the four states: Forests and Waters in Pennsylvania, Conservation in New York, and Conservation and Economic Development in New Jersey. Delaware has separated the two functions and assigned them to separate independent agencies, the State Park Commission and the State Forestry Commission.

Fish and Wildlife

Pennsylvania has done something of the same with wildlife management which is divided between a state Fish Commission and a state Game Commission, both independent of the Department of Forests and Waters. Delaware unites the two in a single autonomous Board of Game and Fish Commissioners, though it maintains independently a Commission of Shell Fisheries. New Jersey assigns both functions to its Department of Conservation and Economic Development, and New York both to its Conservation Department.

Port Development

All four states have state-operated port development agencies, though only two affect the Delaware: the South Jersey Port Commission of New Jersey, which operates the Camden Marine Terminal; and the Delaware Waterfront Commission (which shares some of its authority with the State Highway Commission), charged with the maintenance of groins and jetties along the waterfront and of the Delaware Memorial Bridge, which however is administered through an autonomous Interstate Highway Division within the department. The principle of assigning port development to independent commissions is followed in the other two states; examples are found in Pennsylvania's State Park and Harbor Commission of Erie, New York's Albany Port District Commission, etc.

Navigation

State navigation activities generally are limited to licensing and regulation of pilots, registration of pleasure boats, and the like.[12] These duties are performed in Delaware by a State Board of Pilot Commissoners, in Pennsylvania by the Navigation Commission for the Delaware River (which is autonomous, though technically within the Department of Forests and Waters), in New Jersey by the Department of Conservation and Economic Development, and in New York by the Conservation Department.[13]

[12] The principal exception, the New York State Barge Canal, operated and maintained by New York State's Department of Public Works, lies outside the Delaware Basin.

[13] Complete coverage of state navigation activities would require mention of the Harbor Master for the Port of Lewes and the Lewes and Rehoboth Canal, who is

Irrigation

A clear indication of the fact that irrigation is not yet of critical importance in the Delaware Valley states, or at least has not yet forced administrative recognition of its claims, lies in the absence of any state agency or bureau charged particularly with its consideration. The New Jersey State Department of Agriculture is authorized to "investigate, ascertain, [and] disseminate" information regarding agriculture, including "irrigation and drainage of lands used for agricultural purposes," but the closest thing to a state irrigation agency was New York's Temporary State Commission on Irrigation, a study group now terminated. The irrigation problem in New York State, moreover, is not centrally related to the development of the Delaware, involving as it does areas which lie largely outside its Basin.

Hydroelectric Power

All four states, of course, have regulatory agencies charged with supervision of public utilities and control over their rates: the Delaware Public Service Commission, the Pennsylvania Public Utility Commission, the New Jersey Board of Public Utilities, and the New York Public Service Commission. To the extent that water supply service remains in the hands of private enterprise, their jurisdiction extends also to municipal and industrial water. In addition, in Pennsylvania, the Water and Power Resources Board passes on applications to charter, merge, or dispose of the properties of corporations supplying water or water power. In New York the Water Power and Control Commission licenses hydroelectric power developments and collects rentals where state waters are used (as at Niagara Falls). Only New York State is engaged in the generation of hydroelectric power. Through the Power Authority of the State of New York, that state produces and markets power from both the St. Lawrence and the Niagara developments.

Integration of State Programs

A number of additional agencies, variously concerned with parts of the total process of water-resource management, might be identified.

---

charged with the disposal of "abandoned boats" found either in the harbor or in the canal. The report of the Fels Institute notes: "It is said that since in actual practice boats are not abandoned, the duties of the Harbor Master are negligible." He serves without compensation.

The Marine Biology Laboratory of the University of Delaware carries on experimental work relevant to Delaware River estuary development. The Delaware Geological Commission and the Bureau of Topographic Survey in Pennsylvania's Department of Internal Affairs, among other agencies, are engaged in data collection programs connected with resource developments. The enumeration of agencies in Table 3 is sufficient to suggest the complexity of administrative organization within the states.[14] Two principal techniques have been used in the effort to coordinate these various programs and agencies into coherent *state* programs of water-resource development. One approach has been that of bringing the separate agencies and bureaus together under a single departmental head responsible to the governor. This process has been carried furthest in New Jersey, where the breadth of responsibilities assigned to the Department of Conservation and Economic Development might well be the envy of the advocate of a department of natural resources at the national level. The opposite extreme is found in the state of Delaware, where virtually every water-resource activity has been vested by law in a separate agency. Pennsylvania's Department of Forests and Waters and New York's Conservation Department stand somewhere between, though both span a range of functions broader than any single comparable department in the national government. While location within a single department is not a guarantee of integrated activity,[15] it at least enhances its probability.

The second means used to coordinate programs has been the ex officio commission, with inter-agency representation from the affected departments. This device is particularly widely used in Pennsylvania; the State Soil Conservation Commission within Agriculture consists of the Secretary of Agriculture, the Secretary of Forests and Waters, and four others; the Sanitary Water Board, technically within the Health Department, comprises the Secretary of Health, the Secretary of Forests

[14] State agencies confined to a geographic area not including any part of the Delaware Valley have been excluded from this tabulation, with the exception of the Power Authority of the State of New York. Generally, the administrative agency has been designated by its departmental name, except in the case of functions performed by a semi-autonomous component or by a division of the major conservation agency.

[15] See, for example, Hardin, *op. cit.* It may be suspected that the picture is not actually as bleak as indicated on the organization chart even in Delaware. Most of the commissions and departments in that state have small office staffs and it seems plausible that personal relationships afford much of the coordination not provided by statute. There is, of course, no assurance such a happy state of affairs actually exists.

TABLE 3

Principal Public Water-Resource Agencies in the Delaware Valley States
(1958)

Function	Delaware	New Jersey	New York	Pennsylvania
Flood Control (including drainage)	Board of Ditch Commissioners	Division of Water Policy and Supply*	State Flood Control Commission Department of Public Works Water Power and Control Commission*	Department of Forests and Waters*
Watershed Development	State Soil Conservation Commission	State Soil Conservation Committee*	State Soil Conservation Committee	State Soil Conservation Committee
Pollution Control	Water Pollution Commission	State Department of Health	Water Pollution Control Board	Sanitary Water Board
Water Supply		Water Policy and Supply Council*	Water Power and Control Commission*	Water and Power Resources Board*
Recreation	State Park Commission State Forestry Commission	Bureau of Forestry, Parks and Historic Sites*	Division of Parks* Division of Lands and Forests*	Department of Forests and Waters* Brandywine Battlefield Park Commission

	Delaware	New Jersey	New York	Pennsylvania
Fish and Wildlife	Board of Game and Fish Commissioners Delaware Commission of Shell Fisheries	Division of Fish and Game* Division of Shellfish*	Division of Fish and Game*	Pennsylvania Fish Commission Pennsylvania Game Commission
Port Development	Delaware Waterfront Commission State Highway Commission	South Jersey Port Commission		
Navigation	State Board of Pilot Commissioners	Bureau of Navigation* Board of New Jersey Pilotage Commissioners*	Conservation Department*	Navigation Commission for the Delaware River
Hydroelectric Power	Public Service Commission	Board of Public Utilities	Public Service Commission Power Authority of the State of New York Water Power and Control Commission*	Public Utility Commission Water and Power Resources Board*

* Agency is a part of principal state conservation department: Forests and Waters in Pennsylvania, Conservation in New York, Conservation and Economic Development in New Jersey.

and Waters, the Secretary of Mines, the Executive Director of the Fish Commission, and three others; the Water and Power Resources Board, administratively within Forests and Waters, consists of the Secretary of Forests and Waters, the Secretary of Health, a member of the Public Utility Commission, the Executive Director of the Fish Commission, and one other; and so on. This practice is widespread in New York also, and is used to a much more limited extent in Delaware.

Unfortunately, the two techniques conflict directly with one another. When the various programs are administered by autonomous ex officio commissions, over whose selection the departmental executive has little control, and when each commission is supported in turn by its special clientele of sportsmen's groups or whatever, the coordination of program achieved through departmentalization is largely illusory. This is what has actually happened in Pennsylvania and New York, where departmentalization has been combined with proliferation of inter-agency commissions and where, as a result, the head of the consolidated conservation department has little effective control over certain sub-units of his department, notwithstanding his strong formal position. Where coordination ensues under these circumstances it is largely the result of the personal effectiveness of the individual holding the office of commissioner or secretary, and is achieved despite the organizational structure rather than because of it. Only in New Jersey, where the relevant programs are brought together in a single department *and* placed under the effective control of the department head, do the institutions maximize the probability of coordinated programming.

Interstate Programs and Agencies

The tendency toward the fractionalization of administrative programs, documented at the federal and state levels, applies even more strongly at the level of interstate action. Rarely has an interstate commission been created with more than a single function to perform. In the Delaware Valley states the Palisades Interstate Commission has been concerned with recreation, the Delaware River Joint Toll Bridge Commission with the construction and operation of bridges, the Delaware River Port Authority with the same (in practice), the Atlantic States Marine Fisheries Commission with commercial fishing, and the Interstate Sanitation Commission with pollution control. The Interstate Commission on the Delaware River Basin, discussed elsewhere, from time to time has essayed a variety of functions but has pursued pollution abatement as its primary task. The Port of New York Authority initially embraced a similarly narrow definition of duties; and though it has moved beyond its original goals, it still tends to confine its activities to one area and to resist assignment of other responsibilities.

Local Programs and Agencies

None of the above enumerations of programs and agencies purports to be complete. There are an estimated 43 state departments and commissions and 14 interstate agencies engaged in one way or another in the management of the water resources of the Delaware, or in closely related activities. Mention must also be made of the local water enter-

TABLE 4

Traditional Governments in the Delaware Basin, by States
(1958)

	N. Y.	Pa.	N. J.	Del.	Total
States	1	1	1	1	4
Counties	8	17	14	3	42
Cities	1	9	11	3	24
Towns	45	—	4	—	49
Townships	—	318	130	—	448
Boroughs	—	212	67	—	279
Villages	18	—	—	31	49
Total	73	557	227	38	895

prises that make up a part of the total picture. The most convenient place to begin is with the traditional units of government, the counties, cities, towns, townships, boroughs, and villages into which the territory is divided. Table 4 records the number of each to be found in whole or part within the Delaware Valley. More difficult to secure is an enumeration of the governments actually carrying on water programs, and of the programs pursued through special districts. It is estimated that there are 252 water supply enterprises in the Valley. A few of these are privately owned, although the great majority are governmental in nature.

The water programs of municipalities operate, of course, only in a few limited fields. Water supply, sewage disposal, often water-related recreation, and (very rarely) electric power distribution comprise the list. Consequently, municipal governments do not face the same internal pressures toward fragmentation of program that affect governments engaged in a broader variety of water-related activities. Viewed more broadly, however, the assignment of statutory responsibility for these functions to the municipalities, while other programs are operative at the state and federal levels, has the effect of discouraging the coordination of effort among the agencies dealing with water. One of the most serious problems of this kind has been the difficulty in relating water supply storage to such other water activities as flood control, stream flow augmentation, promotion of recreation, and hydroelectric power generation. All these goals (and others as well) often are attainable through the same reservoir system but, assigned by law to different governmental levels, are rarely united in a comprehensive program of development.

Few formal organizations to express the conflicting claims of the proponents of varying water uses are found at the local level. At times, indeed, the government agency will itself become the spokesman for a particular interest group. The most notable example within the Delaware Service Area probably is the identification of the Board of Water Supply of New York City with the demand for a high-quality upland water supply for the city. The Board was created in 1905 as a result of activity by citizen groups that were interested in maintaining the policy of an ample, good, public water supply set at the time of the Croton Project.[16] Today the Board has become the conscience of the City so far as water supply is concerned; it needs no parallel private association to defend the cause of good water since its prestige and implicit power to rally powerful public support are sufficient to ensure respect for its program.

The Role of Private Enterprise

It is obvious without further exploration that many of the demands for government action in the water-resource field come from business and industry, and that many of the associations supporting or seeking state and federal programs represent commercial interests exclusively or in part. The business and industrial community provides the largest

[16] Notable among them were the Manufacturers Association of Brooklyn, the Merchants Association of New York, the Chamber of Commerce of the State of New York, the City Club, and the New York Board of Fire Underwriters. See Blake, *op. cit.*, p. 280.

component of the population concerned with the Delaware River and its development and appears to exercise the most influence in decisions concerning it. It would be a serious mistake, however, to think of this influence in the sometimes popular image of a monolithic business group working together toward common goals and forcing its demands upon the public. Business groups can be found within each of the (often conflicting) several publics concerned with water-resource management.

Private enterprise has a further significance in the water field: private business not only originates demands for water uses, but may also serve as the means to carry on and provide the services demanded. If recreation is needed, the state or nation may provide it; so also might a business firm. If electric power is required, a government might generate it; more frequently, the power will be produced by a private utility. Numerous private enterprises are engaged in segments of the total task of water-resource development in the Delaware Valley and still more in the Service Area; but if it is difficult to enumerate accurately the government programs in water resources, it is manifestly impossible to name a specific number for the private enterprises performing parts of the task of water development. It is, however, possible to suggest the types of businesses that take action in this area.

An indirect clue to such identification may be found in the records of hearings before congressional committees and officers of the Corps of Engineers, the proceedings of the annual conference of Incodel, the meetings of the Delaware Survey Coordinating Committee, and the like. Attendance lists record those present at these gatherings. Presumably only those individuals with some interest in the subject of water are likely to attend, hence an indication of the business enterprises represented may serve to suggest the industries most concerned with water.

1. The first category of these is perhaps the most obvious, the private water companies. Generally municipal enterprise has replaced private business in the supply of water to the cities. There still remain, however, such undertakings as the Philadelphia Suburban Water Company, the Elizabethtown Water Company, and General Waterworks, all represented at recent meetings of this kind. Actually, since 90 per cent of the water used in the Valley is withdrawn by self-supplying industrial users, this part of the total water picture is more important than might be imagined; by rights all those corporations withdrawing their own water might be included in this category of private enterprise.

2. A second category of firms, the electric utilities, are involved in

water-resource development in two ways. First, since they use enormous amounts of water for cooling purposes, they are among the largest of the industrial self-suppliers of water. They are involved in a second way through the potentiality of hydroelectric power generation. A few utility companies have already established hydro installations, others have given the matter consideration, all are concerned at the possibility of government generation of power. It is hardly surprising to find such firms as Pennsylvania Power and Light, Philadelphia Electric, and New Jersey Power and Light represented at Incodel conferences, Coordinating Committee meetings, and hearings.

3. Water is used extensively as a means of disposing of wastes, and many industries are concerned with water for this reason. Negatively put, these are the firms that contaminate the water; positively put, they require the use of water for economical disposal of wastes. Such firms as du Pont and the New Jersey Zinc Company have engaged in systematic model tests of the results of waste discharges in the Delaware estuary.[17] Many other industries have similar concerns.

4. A fourth variety of private water enterprise is found in the engineering and contracting firms. Few federal agencies do their own construction work; most depend on private construction companies. Rarely do the states in the Delaware Valley carry out their own engineering work. Such firms as Tippetts, Abbett, McCarthy, and Stratton, Engineers; Albright and Friel; and Malcolm Pirnie, Engineers, are often involved deeply and directly in Delaware development.

5. The legal firms regularly represented at the various water conferences likewise are concerned with Delaware development. Their interests in the first instance are those of their clients. It is also true, however, that they carry on a part of the task of water-resource management through the function of legal representation. They possess a collective interest in minimizing the intrusion of public regulation into the arena of private litigation.

6. Curiously, a sixth major type of water-related business appears more rarely at conferences and hearings concerning the Delaware—the recreation industry. In part the demand for water-related recreation forces action by government; the greater part of the task of providing the public with recreational opportunities, however, still rests in commercial hands. Those engaged in selling recreation to the public have a clear-cut interest in the water that is an indispensable part of many

[17] James H. Allen, "Delaware River Basin Water Pollution Abatement Program," Incodel, *Proceedings, 1958 Annual Conference.*

attractive forms of recreation, but they have been tardy in expressing that interest.

The parties at interest in the management of water resources may be said, then, to be three-fold: (1) the individuals and the groups seeking the satisfaction of wants through performance of functions that require the management of water; (2) the governmental agencies that operate programs to satisfy a part of these demands; and (3) the private enterprises that operate programs to satisfy a part of these demands. In the interactions of these three forces are found the pressures that produce water-resource policy.

A NOTE ON THE PUBLIC INTEREST

It seems unsatisfactory, however, to stop at that point. Three kinds of forces bear upon one another, and in their interaction the issue of public policy is decided. Although this may be an accurate summary of the reality of the policy-making process, it does not assist the un-committed individual—or administrator—in deciding where he will throw his weight. And though the concept can never be defined with precision or to anyone's complete satisfaction, some standard of public interest is required to apply to the compromise of these conflicting pressures.[18]

In the field of water resources a fairly clear, if unspecific, standard describes the public interest, that of comprehensive development or multi-purpose use. Each individual and group is interested in maximizing the satisfaction of his own desires; the interest of the public as a whole lies in recognizing desirable additional objectives, in ensuring that the less important segmental interest does not triumph over the more significant whole.

Governmentally, this requires as a beginning the coordination and integration of the separate agencies and programs based upon specific demands. It is for this reason that it is important that some mechanism exist for reconciling the interests of the various publics to a common development program within this definition of the public interest. Coordination at the state level, however, cannot possibly meet all of the problems of this kind encountered on an interstate stream. Even assuming that each of the four states in the Delaware Valley possessed the

[18] Cf. Frank J. Sorauf, "The Public Interest Reconsidered," *Journal of Politics,* XIX (November, 1957), pp. 616-639; Glendon A. Schubert, " 'The Public Interest' in Administrative Decision-Making," *American Political Science Review,* LI (June, 1957), pp. 346-368.

administrative structures to resolve their own conflicting internal demands into a coordinated state program, the fact would remain that no state would mirror the complexities of conflicting interests in the use of the whole river. The likelihood is that an upstream state will have interests distinctly at variance with those of the states below. Some New York State farmlands suffer from the construction of storage reservoirs; New York City needs drinking water; anglers are concerned over the protection of trout streams. These may be considered conflicts, but even if they were resolved into a common state program for the Delaware based upon economic use of its waters, that program would not provide for the needs of downstream states for water supply, stream flow augmentation, flood control, etc. New York may desire to divert water for use in New York City; the countervailing interest will be found nowhere in that state, but resides in other states that have, in turn, only a secondhand awareness of New York City's needs.

It would be a mistake, of course, to suppose that the active conflicting interests, each expressed through its own associations and organizations, are incapable of showing awareness of other interests. A suggestive demonstration of the interlocking interests of the organizations responding to the first round of questionnaires will be found in Chart 1. One of the questions inquired with what other organizations the respondent association cooperated. Linking these organizations, and linking also those organizations which either shared common officers or, in the case of some federations, were members of other associations, this interesting pattern emerged.

The size of an organization as shown on the chart reflects its importance as a link in this network—defined as the number of times it was mentioned—rather than any implied political or other strength. This graphic representation is far from a definitive report on each organization; undoubtedly other links exist among these groups and in some cases one may be a member of another without the fact appearing here. Entire reliance was placed upon the questionnaires in constructing the pattern, hence those organizations that did not themselves reply but are recorded only from the answers of other groups are peculiarly subject to under-reporting.[19] Nonetheless, the chart is sufficient to demonstrate both the specializations of interest found among the groups

---

[19] In this as in all attempts to analyze power relations among groups, the most difficult problem is the attribution of influence to groups not ordinarily concerned with water problems, but capable of exercising great influence when they do feel an interest. The Pennsylvania Manufacturers Association, a very small circle on the chart but extremely influential within its state, is an obvious illustration.

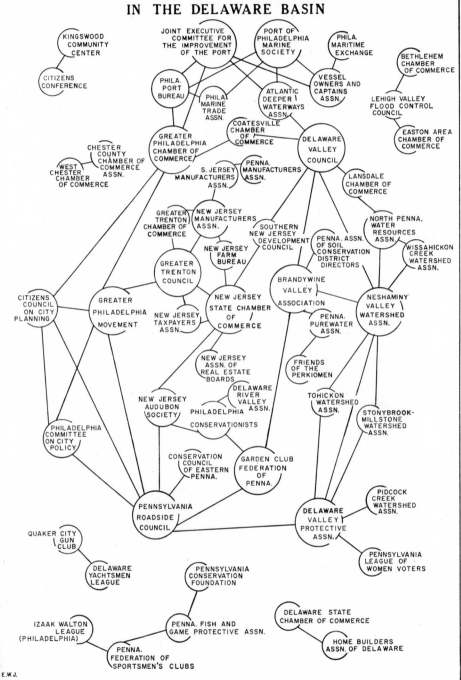

Chart 1

INTER-RELATIONSHIPS OF ORGANIZATIONS
IN THE DELAWARE BASIN

E.W.J.

and the existence of linkages among them. It is apparent that certain clusters of related organizations exist, cooperating one with another. A group of port and navigation organizations at the top surrounds the Joint Executive Committee for the Port of Philadelphia and the Port of Philadelphia Marine Society. A second category, watershed associations and related groups, cluster around the Brandywine Valley Association and the Neshaminy Valley Watershed Association. A third group of recreation-oriented associations gathers around the Garden Club Federation of Pennsylvania and the Pennsylvania Roadside Council. A fourth cluster, consisting largely of New Jersey business and industrial groups, centers upon the Greater Trenton Council and the New Jersey State Chamber of Commerce.

These groups are distinct from one another, but are linked together by what might be thought of as broker organizations with a foot in each of several camps. Some of the most important of these are business groups from the Philadelphia area: the Greater Philadelphia Movement maintains ties with New Jersey groups as well as with certain Philadelphia associations; the Greater Philadelphia Chamber of Commerce is connected also to the navigation groups; the Delaware Valley Council provides a link between the watershed associations, the New Jersey and Philadelphia business groups, and the interests centering on the port.

In all, 56 of the 85 organizations that replied to the questionnaire appear in one way or another on the chart. Three major groupings exist without links to the central network: a group of fish and wildlife associations in the lower left hand corner, two Delaware organizations in the lower right, and three groups, all concerned with flood control on the Lehigh, in the upper right. It seems probable that a fuller report of the links among these groups, and responses from some of those missing, would fill in these gaps. There is one striking omission, however, that would still be obvious. The chart indicates the interlocking of interests among the Pennsylvania and New Jersey groups and, by inference, those in Delaware as well, but there are no indications of cooperation with groups in New York City and New York State. The ties among the organizations suggest what might be called a natural base for concern for the comprehensive development of the Delaware; the lack of ties to New York City interests indicates the important gap in the network.[20]

[20] In part the explanation of the omission of New York State groups lies in a general lack of concern with the problems of the Delaware, reflected among other ways in a failure to return questionnaires concerning its development. It would be

It is from this point of view that the position of the Interstate Commission on the Delaware River Basin becomes of considerable importance to the Delaware. Incodel consists of five members from each of the four states in the Valley: one member of the state senate, one from the lower house of the state legislature, one representing the governor, one from an administrative or planning agency, and one chosen at large by the Commission as a whole. This structure provides a forum for communication among the states on matters concerning the Delaware.

Perhaps more important than the formal machinery for cooperation is the informal occasion provided by Incodel's annual meetings. Representatives of government agencies, interest groups, and private water enterprises concerned with the Delaware have an opportunity to meet there and exchange views. At the 1957 and 1958 meetings together, 13 federal agencies were represented, including all of those most important in the Delaware's development. Also present at one or both meetings were spokesmen of three interstate agencies; four states (seven agencies from Delaware, nine from New Jersey, seven from Pennsylvania, and six from New York); the New York Board of Water Supply, the Philadelphia Water Department, and numerous other local governments; and a number of private associations and enterprises.

A weakness of Incodel has resulted from the fact that this occasional exchange of views among the affected interests has not been tied to a positive action program, except in the field of pollution control. A somewhat more active role in the last two years has been played by the Coordinating Committee for the Survey. Meeting more frequently, it has provided a fuller opportunity for cooperation—and for appreciation of other points of view—among the governmental agencies involved. Representatives of non-governmental interests also attend its meetings on occasion, though they do not formally take an active part in the discussions. Since the Committee is not a permanent organization, however, it cannot continue indefinitely to serve as a forum for the discussion of conflicting interests in the Valley.

The situation may be summarized thus: (1) around each of the functions for which the Delaware River may be used, a separate public has tended to emerge; (2) each interest group has tended to project itself, at both state and federal levels, into a separate governmental agency with as much autonomy as the clientele group can command for

a mistake to visualize a second chart showing a group of New York interest groups linked together among themselves and united in a hostile front against the groups shown in Chart 1.

it; (3) both in the federal government and in the Valley states (with the possible exception of New Jersey) machinery is lacking for the effective reconciliation of these individual interests and activities either through coordinated action or through adoption of a comprehensive program; (4) although Basin-wide informal links interconnect many of the associations and agencies, no permanent action-oriented organization exists capable of harmonizing or coordinating the various parties at interest in the development of the water resources of the Delaware River Valley.

CHAPTER 4

The Functions of Water Resources Administration

THE thesis of the following pages is the proposition that form, in some important measure, follows function. That is, the form a public enterprise takes will be determined in part by the activities it handles. This is not at all to say function dictates *one best* structure. The work to be done nonetheless sets rather strict limits within which there are alternatives. The choice among alternatives in turn is based upon considerations of legal, fiscal, and political possibilities. These factors are dealt with at length elsewhere in this study; in the present discussion of functions, they will be mentioned only when they bear directly upon the subject under examination.

WATER AS A BASIS FOR ORGANIZATION

There are conceptual difficulties to be dealt with in beginning a discussion of organizing for the administration of water resources. For water moves freely over the surface of the earth without reference to political boundaries, and thus does not fit into traditional patterns of thought about government or into established ways of public action. A useful basis for organizing nevertheless may be found in the various parts of the process of water-resources administration. Some of these parts or activities are being performed by existing governmental agencies at all levels of the federal system and by private organizations; others are not being performed either in the Delaware Basin or elsewhere in the country. It has been customary to analyze water functions in terms of the various purposes of development—navigation, flood control, water supply, quality control, fish and wildlife, etc. Later in this study the purposes are acknowledged to be of prime importance. This chapter is organized, however, in terms of the parts of the process, in order better to illustrate their organizational implications.

Following is a list of the segments of the water administration process that might be performed in the Delaware Basin—a "model" of activities:

1. Research and data collection in general and for each specific part of the process
2. Planning
3. Representation and information
4. Designing and building major structures
5. Operating and maintaining major structures
6. Designing, building, and operating other structures
7. Other operating programs:
   a. Adjusting to floods
   b. Withdrawals and diversions
   c. Quality control
   d. Marketing and distributing hydroelectric power
   e. Designing, building, and operating recreation facilities
   f. Fish and wildlife
   g. Watershed management

For each activity there are certain innate attributes which bear upon administrative and organizational requirements; for example, the physical processes involved in the activity, the geographic area wherein it may be performed most easily and efficiently, the clientele affected, and the fiscal outlay required. Furthermore, we may better understand activities now performed by examining history, constitutional and statutory arrangements for administration, and current placement of responsibility in and out of the Basin. Finally, the extent and nature of popular needs and expectations about them also are relevant. These, however, receive primary stress elsewhere in this study.

To be sure, all of these characteristics may change as time goes on. When the dollar fluctuates, costs of dams and canals are modified; new technologies appear, and the amounts of water used by the many parts of society vary in response. So the nature of an activity will in turn be influenced. This process of inevitable change must be kept in sight throughout the entire business of choosing and proposing an organization for Delaware water management.

It will be useful to think of these activities as extending over a long period of time. Certain of them might be assigned to specific agencies as a first step in activating a water program for the Delaware. Others, however, might remain quiescent for years until specific demands for their performance are identified.

To choose functions for any organization, then, is in some measure to choose its goals and to select also the values to be employed in seeking those goals. The functions influence heavily the structure to be established, the kinds of personnel to be employed, the sources of funds, and the kind and extent of public attention to be focused on the organization.

The heart of this chapter is the description of these water functions. Emphasis is placed upon (1) characteristics most relevant to the allocation of functions to specific agencies; (2) the sharing of functions among different levels of the federal system; and (3) the particularly close association among certain functions and the consequent need for their performance by the same agency.

RESEARCH AND DATA COLLECTION

The role of research in water resources administration is that of providing a solid foundation of facts on which plans may be based and action programs built. Scientific and technological advances derive from the continuation of such research even after action programs are established. This strong need for more and more and better and better knowledge about all aspects of water resources—ground water characteristics, surface water flows, census information concerning population growth and movement, and economic and social attributes—has been fully documented and argued by a succession of national study commissions. So has the pressing need for maps of all types. Two Hoover Commissions, the 1950 President's Water Resources Policy Commission, the 1952 President's Materials Policy Commission, the 1955 Presidential Advisory Committee on Water Resources Policy, and numerous other authoritative bodies have pointed out the importance of a continuous flow of fundamental data and basic and applied research results. They have also indicated many gaps in existing programs.

Existing data collection programs by national agencies generally are of a high caliber, but they are seldom of maximum use in a limited area, since they are usually organized on a national basis. These data from the Coast and Geodetic Survey, Geological Survey, Bureau of the Census, Weather Bureau, and other agencies include statistics and information in the fields of topography, geology, geodesy, soils, and hydrography among the many involved in water development programs. State agencies in each of the four Delaware Basin states co-operate in certain of these programs, and in addition have a few of their own. New York State, for example, recently has spent $600,000 annually on natural resources data collection and research.[1]

One still finds in the reports of the national data-gathering agencies and in those of the cooperating state organizations a recurring call for more information and expanded data collection programs. Intensive development of the water resources of a given basin will inevitably demand the stepping up of these research activities. They should be chiefly area- and problem-oriented; morever, they should be an integral part of all other operations. At numerous points in the Corps of Engineers' Survey of the Delaware Basin serious deficiencies of information have been brought to light, as, for example, with respect to ground water data. Adoption of a well-defined basin program also will require a secondary network for collecting more specific localized data than provided for by existing programs.

Beyond basic data collection, however, one can discern a serious gap in information about the changing uses of water and about the relation of water to other resources. In the highly complex, industrialized, and urbanized Delaware Basin, intelligent planning and execution of water resources projects must find their rationale in applied research on a wide variety of economic and social problems directly connected with water. In some cases this can be accomplished by simply augmenting or better coordinating the existing national and state programs, in others new research activities will be necessary. For example, in the field of industrial water technology and costs, no existing governmental agency has a program of sufficient dimensions to satisfy the needs of development in the Delaware. Nor is there any apparent method by which the existing diverse programs may be fitted together other than by giving that responsibility to a single organization.

PLANNING

Planning is a systematic way of raising policy issues for consideration by responsible officials and by the public. From another viewpoint, it is ". . . the process of preparing programs or courses of

[1] Guthrie S. Birkhead and Clark D. Ahlberg, *Science and State Government in New York* (Chapel Hill: University of North Carolina, Institute for Research in Social Science, 1956), p. 72.

action for accomplishing approved objectives."[2] With an adequate foundation of basic information, planning can become the central, guiding force behind basin development in helping to formulate its goals and provide substance to its programs.

It is commonplace to distinguish between the planning phase and the action (construction and operation) phase of basin development. Planning itself in most cases may be discussed in two parts. First, logic demands (and in practice there has often been) an initial plan that sketches out the main steps or projects. Second, planning must continue into the indefinite future as needs arise for details of the original plan to be filled in and effected, and as changing technological or social conditions require the revaluation or reinterpretation of the original plan. The authors of the California Water Plan speak of that pioneering document ". . . as a comprehensive pattern, with broad flexibility and susceptible of orderly and progressive development as needed. . . ." At the same time, they maintain that ". . . investigation and planning for further water resource development must be a continuing process."[3]

In the Delaware until recently each agency, federal, state, and local, has planned separately for its action programs.[4] Once there was hope that Incodel might provide a unifying force in planning activities in the Basin. An Incodel working committee undertook an over-all, long-range plan in the late 1930's but never finished it. The 1951 plan for the Basin was less than comprehensive, though moving in that direction; it won approval in three states but failed in the Pennsylvania Senate. In the four states of the Delaware there were in 1959 three state planning agencies. In none of the three cases, however, was staffing or financing at even a minimum level to give continuing attention to water-resource problems. If all were so equipped, attention would still be divided.

The present Corps Survey will afford an initial plan for the Delaware. What is demanded is a single headquarters where a full-time staff of trained professionals may exercise a continuing surveillance over water programs and problems. More specifically, such a unified planning office could perform the following tasks:[5]

[2] Coleman Woodbury, "Introduction," *Model State and Regional Planning Law* (New York: National Municipal League, 1954), p. 1.

[3] Department of Water Resources, State of California, *The California Water Plan*, Bulletin No. 3 (Sacramento, May 1957), p. 7.

[4] A major water program for the Delaware was contained in a Corps 308 report in 1934, but it was never adopted. H. Doc. 179, 73d Cong., 2d sess. See Chap. 15.

[5] Based in great part on Missouri Basin Survey Commission, *Missouri: Land and Water* (Washington, 1953), p. 227.

1. establish uniform policies, objectives, standards, and procedures on the basis of the Corps Survey and subsequent revisions;
2. review and appraise project plans;
3. schedule investigations in proper sequence;
4. recommend priorities for project development;
5. contribute to adequacy and continuity in planning; and
6. recommend ways to coordinate Basin plans with those in neighboring basins.

The end product of such a planning process for the Delaware Basin would be a continuously revised, dynamic program for all phases of water resources development, regardless of which governmental authority might perform the individual activities. This new planning office should have talented staff and sufficient funds to prepare basin-wide plans that are well-documented and convincing enough to be accepted by state and local authorities as a framework within which state and local planning could be effectuated. Their local, intra-basin plans could be shored up and filled in by the broad-based studies of a basin agency. Its experts could help them in a number of ways. Among its services could be examining industrial location and water use patterns in the Valley and providing information and technical assistance with special reference to water-using activities.

The new Delaware Basin agency should be empowered to plan generally for water and to implement its plans with respect to a few cardinal functions. It should not be empowered to disregard or override the operations of state or local authorities in fields appropriate to state and local action. It should be able to make the basin point of view plainly heard in state and local deliberations. The interchange of views at each step of local, state, and basin planning should be mandatory. And where any structure or program would have effect across state lines, basin plans should be controlling.

REPRESENTATION AND INFORMATION

If the place of water in modern civilization is as vital as it appears in 1959, the necessity for public advocacy of intelligent water use may be taken for granted. Many public and private groups by their nature are drawn into seeking support for their opinions about the use or misuse of water: manufacturers, utilities, shippers, conservationists of many hues, farm groups, municipalities, special districts, state and federal units. As the commodity grows dearer, their concerns and interests will increase.

Pressures, economic and otherwise, will grow stronger with the passing of time.

Inevitably and appropriately, these groups will be most concerned with their own special problems and their own particular needs. In the conflict and negotiation among them, however, the area-wide viewpoint about water may be subordinated or lost to view entirely. Some institution must be assigned responsibility for voicing the regional interest in balanced water use and the national interest in the region's development. The regional approach to water resource development must be provided with a spokesman before the Congress, state legislatures, private groups, and the general public. Through the continuous dissemination of accurate information to industry, officials, and the public, the major policy issues can be kept foremost. Education for conserving water may be fostered.

At the present time, bits and pieces of this job are performed by several agencies, public and private, among them the Delaware River Basin Advisory Committee. For some purposes, Incodel assumes this responsibility. The functions of information and representation are discharged haphazardly at best, however; clearly they can be performed most effectively if integrated into the process of continuous planning for basin-wide development.

A central agency with a modest public education budget could publish the most important of its research findings, issue annual reports, interpret its policies, organize conservation seminars, prepare articles for the press, express varied views as to emerging water problems, and the like. With little extra expenditure, basin agency representatives could testify before congressional and state legislative committees and confer with officials at all levels about common problems. Without such public representation, the process of planning for the Delaware would have little or no support. All public and private agencies perform these activities as a matter of course and of simple belief in their goals. A central agency must assume this responsibility for the Delaware Basin.

DESIGNING AND BUILDING MAJOR STRUCTURES

Designing the steel, concrete, and earthen structures on the main stem and tributaries of the River is a complicated business, demanding the utmost in engineering and related skills. Preliminary designs for some dams and reservoirs will probably be included in the Corps of Engineers' Survey report. Complete designs will be needed at once for the first structures to be built, while in succeeding years more designs must be devised for completing the control system.

When the system of structures is finished, each dam on the river will play an integral part in its operation. Storage to prevent floods in the lower reaches may be divided among several of the upstream dams. Water released from a dam will raise the reservoir level in the dam or dams below. They in turn must be so designed as to accommodate those flows and to help maintain proper levels in downstream channels or reservoirs for a variety of other purposes. In any given system, the purposes to be served are set forth in the original plans. As demands for new or altered water uses appear in the course of time, changes in the design or operation of structures must fit into the plan for the whole system and perhaps be compensated for by changes in other structures upstream or downstream. To illustrate, if a barrier dam is built one day in the lower estuary, operation of all dams must then be reconsidered. In view of the essential unity of the River and so of any system devised for its control, it is highly desirable if not mandatory that all major structures be designed and built by the same agency. The goal for the Delaware should be consolidation of design and construction functions in the same hands.

There are river control systems in which different agencies have built single dams and reservoirs—for example, on the Columbia River construction has been divided between the Bureau of Reclamation and the Corps of Engineers; and a local government, the Grant County Public Utility District No. 2 of the State of Washington, has recently been authorized to build a major unit. That situation in the Pacific Northwest, however, is to be attributed more to intra-regional politics and inter-agency accommodation than to considerations of engineering and administrative theory. The advantages deriving from a single agency's drawing up plans for and (as a minimum) supervising construction of all dams of a system goes without further demonstration.

The proposition that designing and building are best performed by the same hands is supported by the long experience of the Corps of Engineers and Bureau of Reclamation with both processes. Like the Bureau, the Corps turns to private contractors for highly specialized designs and for the actual building. The Corps has more know-how with regard to basin *systems* than any existing alternative builder in the East. This agency constructed the St. Lawrence dams for the New York Power Authority, and it is now designing a system of dams for the Delaware. There are functional reasons, therefore, why the Corps' building of the first of the new Delaware dams may be supported, although other factors may dictate a contrary decision.

Pennsylvania's Department of Forests and Waters has built some medium-size structures, as has New York (through the agency of two river regulating districts). These have not been multiple-purpose systems, for, indeed, no state has designed and built a comprehensive, multiple-purpose control system.[6] Furthermore, the inter-state flow of Delaware water is a characteristic that must be kept constantly in the forefront in planning this designing and constructing process.

OPERATING AND MAINTAINING MAJOR STRUCTURES

The very complex processes of designing and building a system of dams and reservoirs needs little description in this brief resumé, but the equally complex task of operating such a multiple-purpose system requires some clarification. It is apparent that the Survey by the Corps of Engineers will recommend the construction of a number of dams on the main stem and major tributaries of the Delaware. It is altogether likely that these dams will be dedicated to a variety of purposes. A few may be single-purpose in nature—devoted to flood control or water supply storage; several may combine those two uses, while still others may emphasize the generation of hydroelectric power. The underlying fact, however, is that as a system they will normally depend upon each other for proper operation even of those single purposes, since opening the gates at one will raise the pool level at another, and so forth in chain reaction downriver. Moreover the other, less-easily recognized purposes of dams and reservoirs also will be interdependent and will affect the major purposes. As a single illustration, experience in other basins has revealed that spawning fish or migrating wild fowl may find unlivable the coves and inlets along a reservoir shoreline; for changing retention or releases at one reservoir, as its purposes require, automatically means changes in levels there and at other reservoirs. The very term *system* connotes a need for unity in operation just as it does in designing and building.

"Where a group of projects has to be operated as a unit, it is necessary to have a river control group or comparable organization working in close collaboration with other government agencies. . . ."[7] There is a wealth of experience on the Missouri, the Columbia, and the Tennessee rivers to support this view. If the projects involved on the Dela-

---

[6] Texas has come closest with its Lower Colorado River Authority, but the hand of the federal government was prominent in that undertaking. The two dams shortly to be begun by New Jersey in the Raritan, like the other enterprises mentioned, will fall short of a multiple-purpose control system.

[7] Luna B. Leopold and Thomas Maddock, Jr., *op. cit.*, p. 107.

ware are to be truly multiple-purpose and if they are to add up to a river control system, both plans and directions for operation must emanate from a single source.

Here is the *core function* of a river control system. Here is the principal means of ensuring the multiple-purpose and comprehensive character of such a system's operation. This is precisely the task of the River Control Branch of the Tennessee Valley Authority, which annually maps out an integrated plan for operation of the system's dams and assumes continuing responsibility for executing that plan. A similar task is performed for the dams on the Missouri River main stem by the Reservoir Control Center in the Omaha office of the Corps of Engineers. A Coordinating Committee of other agencies participating in basin development advises the Reservoir Control Center about its operation and shares in the planning.

It is common engineering practice to develop operating plans before a single dam or a system of dams goes into service. Such plans must be based upon a detailed analysis over a long period of the annual, cyclical pattern of rainfall and runoff in the basin. Water feeds into the system from natural ground and surface routes, and there it is stored and released for all its uses. The amount of water likely to be present at different seasons during the year must be compared annually with the manifold demands for water to be met during that year. Here, again, on the supply side we encounter the pressing need for large amounts of carefully derived basin data. On the demand side, needs for water may be computed by the different federal, state, and local agencies, together with private industries and other water users, and reported to the central control group for the river.

The process of estimating and balancing water demand against water supply is one applicable to all rivers. Nowhere else, however, has the function been developed to the point described for the Tennessee and the Missouri. One variation on the practice employed there is the "water master." As commonly known in the West and Southwest, this official enforces a distribution of water previously determined by judicial or administrative processes. On the Delaware since 1954 a "river master" has enforced the provisions of a Supreme Court decree. In all cases the control agencies act within a framework set by higher authority—federal or state laws, federal or state courts, or interstate compacts.[8]

[8] The operation of a basin control system is examined in some detail in Chapter 16.

Now, it might be argued that a central agency could establish policies and even issue directives from day to day, while the actual operation of facilities could be left in the hands of differing authorities from reservoir to reservoir. Some such arrangement may eventuate as a compromise settlement on the Delaware; indeed some precedents pointing in this direction are at hand. For example, the Corps of Engineers is charged with the preparation of plans for operating the flood control increments of virtually all dams on navigable rivers in the country.[9] It will be noticed, however, that this scheme applies only to a *single* function. It is notable further that the Delaware's flood waters do not compound flood problems on other rivers downstream. If a new agency is established to manage the Delaware Basin system, there are no physical reasons for any other organization's having responsibility for any one part of that necessarily unitary task.

Plainly, what is required is a central office for managing the river control system. The office might be provided with a committee or other coordinating mechanism to represent the varied water-use purposes to be served in the basin. Such a central staff should (1) receive and collect all relevant hydrologic data; (2) analyze those data; (3) apply the findings to conditions on the river daily (or even hourly) and impound or release water at each structure to maintain the desired river levels and flows; and (4) supervise withdrawals and diversions. The decision-making function here involved is one which, in final analysis, must be exercised in a unified manner. It should not be shared. At that future time when the first multiple-purpose dam comes into operation, the need for discharge of this function will appear. The task will be further complicated and made more necessary as subsequent dams come into operation. At some indeterminate time, even the larger dams existing in 1959—Wallenpaupack, the Catskill dams—must be integrated into the system.

With respect to the river channel, two results may ensue from system operation: (1) flood or "high-flow control," and (2) "low-flow control" or augmentation. Flood control is a familiar idea, but the latter term may require explanation. "Control," indeed, may be too strong a

[9] The Tennessee River is expressly excepted by the Flood Control Act of 1944, which provides, however, that ". . . in case of danger from floods on the Lower Ohio and Mississippi Rivers, the Tennessee Valley Authority [shall] regulate the release of water from the Tennessee River into the Ohio River in accordance with such instructions as may be issued by the War Department" (Section 7). The line for control of releases by the Corps thus is drawn at the downstream side of the Tennessee River system.

word in a low-flow context, if it imparts the idea that there is a minimum level below which the flows of the river will never be allowed to fall. A period of several consecutive years of low precipitation may reduce the flows of even the most highly-controlled river to undesired and unplanned-for lows. "Augmentation" is a more accurate term. It has been achieved in almost every case where a system of dams has been constructed—the Missouri, Columbia, and Tennessee Rivers are examples. It is obvious that the immediate downstream portion below any dam from which releases can be controlled will be affected thereby, even though the resulting minimum may not be ideal. The effects of a complete system will be correspondingly greater.

Low-flow augmentation is not a purpose of basin development exactly paralleling the traditional purposes of navigation, flood control, hydroelectric power, and water supply. Regulation to provide minimum flows at certain points achieves some of these other purposes and affects them all. It can make water available for local use downstream, firm up channel depths, assist in diluting pollution, and retard estuarine salinity. Thus "low-flow augmentation" goes with flood control or "high-flow regulation," and is another way of depicting an end product of the operation of a system of dams.[10]

DESIGNING, BUILDING, AND OPERATING OTHER STRUCTURES

Construction and operation of a system of dams and reservoirs will necessitate many other capital facilities for a variety of purposes. Among these will be local flood control works, trunk lines and treatment plants for water supply, sewage disposal plants and perhaps trunk mains, power distribution facilities, incidental fish and wildlife projects such as hatcheries, dams on small watersheds, ground-water recharge operations, irrigation structures, and so forth. Most of them are parts of action programs by individual or cooperating governments. Singly their impact on the river may be little, but their total effects even today alter the regimen of main stem and tributaries. These smaller

[10] See the testimony of Congressman Robert E. Jones on this point, *Congressional Record*, 104 (House), p. 3248. See also the discussion of the meaning of low-flow control by Congressman William H. Natcher, *Congressional Record*, 104 (House), pp. 3455-6. There have been fears that low-flow control will be used as an unjustifiable substitute for sewage treatment works. U.S. Senate, 85th Cong., 1st sess., Committee on Public Works, "River and Harbor, Beach Erosion Control, and Flood-Control Projects, 1957," Report No. 168, 1957, p. 112. The Corps of Engineers is also on record as not considering low-flow control to be either a substitute for or an excuse for the omission of sewage treatment works.

structures may one day blanket the whole basin and handle virtually all water.

Governments and private firms of course perform these ancillary functions now in all four of the Delaware Valley states. In some instances, the structures are the results of grant-in-aid programs—for example, the grants for small watershed development[11] and for sewage plant construction.[12] The professional personnel employed by the wide variety of agencies which build and operate such structures are varied —hydraulic and other engineers, biologists, economists, and so on. Capital and operating funds are found in current revenues or loans of state and local governments or in the revenue-producing activities themselves. Summary evaluations of many of these subsidiary programs as they operate along the Delaware today appear at other points in this study.

Responsibility for building and administering virtually all of these structures might remain in present hands. The arguments for drawing them together in one agency are less persuasive than those relating to the major structures because of the number of agencies involved, the widely scattered locations, the variety of skills employed, the many sources of funds utilized, and the relatively smaller impact on water-in-the-channel. The same factors, however, indicate the logic of having a central planning agency to prescribe basin-wide objectives, scrutinize plans for other structures to see that they complement the main system, and set minimum standards for their design and operation. Such a central agency might provide expert advice, design facilities, provide grant-in-aid assistance, and even have authority to build and operate these smaller structures. Beyond any doubt, it should be able to control standards of sewage disposal (in the absence of tighter federal controls) and ground water recharging, because of the physical connection of these activities with the bulk of Basin water.

Where precise control by the central agency should end and state or local control take over is a vexing problem that cannot be disposed of by easy generalization here. Clichés about "big dams v. little dams" can offer no practical help to administrators worrying with the very real problems of managing the Basin's water. The fitting of these pieces into a major system of valley-wide controls will be done over a period of years by time-consuming but vital negotiations, conversations, and compromises between the many state and local agencies and private enter-

[11] P.L. 566, 1954, as amended.
[12] P.L. 660, 1956.

prises on the one hand and the new Basin agency on the other. In this process the leadership of the regional agency will prove invaluable.

OTHER OPERATING PROGRAMS

Note has been taken of the patchwork of state and local governments that overlie the Basin and the Service Area and that have ongoing programs in water management. Some of these programs are weak, some are vigorous. Weak or vigorous, new or old, however, they are in operation. Their legal patterns are set, and it will be difficult indeed to alter those patterns to clear the way for exercise of significant powers by any new Basin organization.

In the following paragraphs some problems arising from these groups of activities-in-being are reviewed briefly under the headings: adjusting to floods, control of withdrawals and diversions, quality control, marketing and distributing hydroelectric power, recreation, fish and wildlife, and watershed management. No two of these measure up the same way when compared with the criteria employed here. That is, their relationships to the central core of water administration vary.

The relation between flood adjustment measures and Basin water-management is manifest. In the case of control of withdrawals it is also apparent that the physical connection with water-in-the-channel is most intimate. The case of withdrawals from streams and reservoirs is, prima facie, one with the problems of central control, whether the uses involved be consumptive or not. For draw-downs on ground water, data are complete enough now to warrant affirmation of the same interdependence. As to quality control, the diffusion downstream of wastes from points of discharge has been recognized for years as a single problem for a whole river system. Here again, it is the dynamic quality of water, its ubiquity, its intermingling that must be emphasized.

The relation of recreation, fish and wildlife, and watershed management to water, however, is not always paramount. Each of these three activities is to some degree dependent upon water, may be adversely affected by water conditions, and in turn may affect both ground and surface water. Recreation is being organized more and more around lakes and streams and seashores. Finally, upstream soil and forest conservation programs have a basic connection with neighboring rivers, although their precise impact on volume of water, sediment load, and so forth, depends upon many variable factors.

The relationship, however, between any one of these groups of activities and water-in-the-channel is affected by the relationships—physical, administrative, cliental—with similar activities outside the drainage basin limits. Even control of withdrawals may be a function with roots outside a basin—as where underground waters fail to observe basin limits. The connections are perhaps easier to show where regulatory or service programs by state governments cut across watershed lines and succeed moderately well in attaining their goals—as in the case, for example, of anti-pollution and fish and wildlife management activities. These observations underline the generalization that basin boundaries at best are approximations.

Adjusting to Floods[13]

Floods are natural phenomena because flood plains are part of a river's domain. Today's flood damages are the results of man's trespassing on flood plains. The traditional reaction to floods has emphasized engineering and land treatment measures—reservoirs, levees, walls, deeper channels, and land and vegetation management—to reduce or block overflow onto flood plains. Hence the term "flood control." The major structures to be recommended by the Corps for the Delaware will reflect this flood control idea, and many engineering enterprises may be built by state and local governments to supplement that system.

There are, however, limitations to flood control measures. (1) Many communities and rural areas cannot be protected economically from floods.[14] (2) No protection works are designed to offer protection against all floods. Any project could experience a flood greater than its capacity, from once in 100 to once in 1,000 years. Yet because this fact is not understood, people develop a sense of false security about flood control works which encourages still more intensive use of potentially dangerous areas. (3) Without land use or other controls, urban growth

---

[13] The first draft of this section was prepared by W. Brinton Whitall, of the staff of the Delaware River Basin Advisory Committee.

[14] In the Tennessee River Basin, for example, it has been found that for every community for which a protective scheme is economically feasible, there are at least 20 additional communities with flood problems in which protective works are not presently justified. See Aelred J. Gray, "Planning For Local Flood Damage Prevention," *Journal of the American Institute of Planners*, XXII (Winter, 1956), p. 1. Though no comparable ratio has been determined, Corps of Engineers data indicate that there are numerous communities in the Delaware Basin that have experienced flood losses for which flood control structures cannot now be justified.

often results in pressure to develop hazardous flood plains.[15] The federal flood control program, focused on high-value property, has generated further demands for public investment in protection works. The Second Hoover Commission commented:

> Present policy leads to a vicious circle. The greater the flood plain development the greater the benefits that can be shown for flood protection. "Let it get really bad so you can get more money" seems to be the prevailing attitude.[16]

An understanding of the nature of floods, however, evokes a concept complementary to flood control: flood damages may be reduced or avoided by human adjustment to flood hazards. As urban-industrial expansion continues on the Delaware, states and localities may reduce potential flood damages by measures like these:

1. establishing channel and flood plain encroachment lines within which construction unduly restricting capacity of the channel or floodway is prohibited;

2. zoning flood plains to realize values from proper land use and to restrict use of high-risk areas to minimize flood damage;

3. regulating subdivisions so development conforms to the degree of flood risk in the area;

4. establishing design standards for permissible structures to prevent use of materials and designs unnecessarily vulnerable to flood damage;

5. establishing flood forecasting and warning systems to increase the time available for relocating movable property, evacuating persons, and taking other steps to reduce flood damage;

6. removing communities, summer camps, and resorts from areas subject to frequent flooding;

7. improving procedures for flood relief and reconstruction funds and services so as to reduce costs of these activities and to help guide reconstruction away from flood risk areas in order to prevent recurrence of such expenses;

8. establishing flood insurance programs to spread the risk over time and thus minimize the financial impact of any single flood.

A few of these practices are found in the Delaware states today. For

---

[15] White, Gilbert F., *et al.*, *Changes in Urban Occupance of Flood Plains in the United States*, Research Paper No. 57, Department in Geography, University of Chicago (Chicago, November, 1958), p. 215.

[16] Commission on Organization of the Executive Branch of the Government, *Task Force Report on Water Resources and Power*, III (Washington, 1955), p. 1255. Cited hereafter as *Task Force Report*.

example, New Jersey and Pennsylvania have laws authorizing regulation of channel encroachments. The joint federal-state flood forecasting service includes the Delaware, while the Neshaminy Valley Watershed Association has its own flood warning system. Zoning, subdivision control, and other guides to flood plain occupancy are frequently discussed but little employed.[17]

Perhaps the chief technical block to non-engineering alternatives to flood control is the lack of proper weather and water data. No readily accessible data indicate flood frequencies on individual properties. No one agency on the Delaware is equipped to advise people or localities about remedial measures. This gap needs to be filled. A basin agency could do it, or finance it, and states and localities then could begin adjustment programs. The result would be a valuable counterpart to the dams, levees, and other control works that will certainly be built.

Withdrawals and Diversions

Toward the end of the Corps of Engineers' Survey, no present or imminent water shortage of a serious nature has been uncovered in the Delaware Service Area. Local shortages in recent years spotted through Pennsylvania and New Jersey will apparently be corrected with the provision of river control facilities. Yet population and water use projections indicate that widespread shortages are not unlikely a few decades hence. And if a water crisis is to develop in the long run, the most significant programs in the area even now may be those concerned with the control of withdrawals for industrial and municipal water supply and for irrigation. They may be the precedents for the establishment of more drastic controls at some future time.

Municipal and industrial withdrawals from ground, reservoir, and channel waters occur all over the Basin today, in the ratio of about one municipal to eight industrial gallons. These withdrawals and diversions, few of which are consumptive, may of course be regulated in a number

[17] In the four Delaware Basin states the powers to zone, regulate subdivision developments, and enforce building codes, for example, are held almost exclusively by cities, boroughs, townships, towns, incorporated villages, and local levy courts. County governments have extremely limited powers to regulate land use, and in some of the states no powers at all. Whether or not this pattern of governmental machinery can be made to function as an effective instrument of flood damage reduction in an interstate river basin is a question that can better be answered after the attempt has been made. If a fair trial period results in failure, then the role of the Basin agency will have to be expanded in the direction of more direct powers to guide developments on the River's flood plain.

of different ways. The State of Mississippi in 1956 attacked this problem by the dramatic means of adopting the appropriation system generally prevalent in the western states. One may admire the courage of Mississippi's legislators while at the same time pointing out that the step taken is difficult to justify in terms of experience, either western or eastern. Short of such drastic action there are means such as those already being employed in a limited way in some of the Delaware Valley states. For example, in New Jersey two laws regulating diversions have been in effect for some years and may be considered as precedents for future laws regulating water use. These and other instances that might be cited provide a beginning for controlling diversions in the Delaware Basin.

Diversions, and thus diversion control, have a close connection with the quality and quantity of surface waters on both the tributaries and the main stem of the river. The case for total control of both surface and ground water diversions in the basin is not as strong as it might be because of the lack of ground water knowledge. Exact effects of ground water withdrawals are often impossible to ascertain. This gap in basic data does not, however, distinguish the Delaware from most other streams in the United States. The study of ground water is so expensive and inconclusive that it has lagged well behind other branches of hydrology. Someday, knowledge and methods may be sufficient to justify advocating complete control of all ground and surface diversions throughout the Basin in order to ensure sufficient water supply. A central research and planning agency can take the lead in deciding when that time arrives.

There is no need to labor the obvious fact that the problem of regulating diversions is one with which individual states will be unable to cope in the long run. Water flows across their boundaries both on the surface and underground. Perhaps by the year 2000 the need for stricter control of withdrawals will be so apparent that a more uniform regulatory system throughout the Basin will have become acceptable. In the intervening period, of course, new sources of water through cheaper de-salination may come into use and slacken the pressure for governmental action. This should be recognized as a possibility, but not assumed. A central planning agency could adjust its operations from time to time as major technological or other developments occur.

This commentary on the potential control of withdrawals and diversions may end with the observation that perhaps the most notable among the gaps in the policies of the Delaware Valley states is the absence of a general policy concerning withdrawals and diversions. In all four, when serious problems arise regarding questions of water rights the resort is to the courts and the rather vaguely defined common law. In the coming era of shorter and shorter water supply in this highly urbanized and economically competitive region, the effects of judicial uncertainties are bound to become serious. The eventual goal of eastern states perhaps should be, and the ultimate outcome almost certainly will be, the imposition of general administrative controls over water use on top of some parts of the existing system—a compromise between the traditional system of riparian rights of the East and the appropriation system of the West.

> . . . a comprehensive water allocation law . . . must be a system that permits unified administration of all the water in the hydrologic cycle and it must be a system that allows for changing use with changing times, without jeopardizing too much both the public interest in optimum use and the expectations of investors. . . . Moreover, the number of occasions for compensation may be reduced and the optimum use in the public interest may be made more certain by advance water-planning to govern all future allocations of water as well as all future water development projects. . . .[18]

It may be that in the years to come a demand will arise in the Delaware for a common system of diversion controls throughout the Basin. If this occurs, a Valley-wide agency may logically administer that function along with research, planning, and operation and maintenance of the dams and reservoirs. In the meantime, the very practical problems of diversion and withdrawal control that state governments will increasingly face may be solved much more rationally if there is a central planning agency with which to advise and consult.

Quality Control

In place of the traditional term "pollution" the term "quality control" is employed here because it includes changes in water quality through temperature rises, salinity intrusion, colloidal or other suspended or bed loads, and other forms of contamination. Water quality should be

[18] David Haber and Stephen W. Bergen (eds.), *The Law of Water Allocation in the Eastern United States* (New York: The Ronald Press Company, 1958), p. xxxvii. See also the interesting conversation on the possible means for state control of diversions in the East and the problems there involved on pp. 617-636. This is not to suggest that the California system should be emulated in the East, for there is a considerable body of opinion that this combination of the riparian and appropriations systems has produced undue confusion.

judged only in relation to the uses in each case. Criteria for the quality of water to be used in a municipal or domestic water supply system need to be the most stringent. Water employed for cooling purposes in a steel plant, on the other hand, may be more contaminated than that used in processing foods and still be acceptable. Standards appropriate to each separate use must be employed.

Better water may be attained by means of programs to offset pollution in all its form—physical, biological, chemical, and radiological. Many different kinds of chemical and mechanical processes have been used to meliorate water quality. Most familiar is control of the discharge of sewage and other wastes either by absolute prohibition or by specifying certain standards of treatment. Once the pollutants enter the channel of a stream, other measures that may be used include the discharge of large quantities of fresh water from upstream reservoirs, construction of desilting and impounding basins, dredging, and so forth. A large array of measures is now employed in the Delaware (as in other basins) by private homeowners, industrial and other business establishments, and municipal systems. There is fairly wide professional agreement today, however, that ". . . the basic engineering principle for the future must be to control pollution at its source and to treat it before it has been diluted, rather than merely flushing it away. . . ." [19]

Traditionally the province of industries and municipalities when performed at all, the fight against polluted lakes and streams was first taken up vigorously by state and interstate agencies in the thirties. In 1936 Incodel was created for the Delaware River, and in the same year the Interstate Sanitation Commission was established to deal with pollution at the mouth of the Hudson River. Incodel's efforts to promote acceptance by the Delaware Valley states of improved standards for pollution abatement proved substantially successful, and improvement in the quality of Delaware water followed. State and local construction of treatment facilities after World War II demonstrated an earnest if underfinanced desire to supplement piecemeal waste treatment on the part of separate industries and municipalities. By passage of the 1948 Water Pollution Control Act, Congress manifested a federal interest in the problem as well; the Water Pollution Control Act of 1956 further expanded the federal program in the water quality field, vested enforcement power in the Public Health Service, and made available grants-in-aid to the states for construction of sewage disposal plants.

[19] Everett P. Partridge, *Your Most Important Raw Material* (Philadelphia: American Society for Testing Materials, 1957), p. 24.

All four states in the Delaware Valley have benefited from the program, under which the Public Health Service approves payment of up to 30 per cent of state expenditures. New Jersey has completed or planned 12 plants; Pennsylvania, 30; New York, 20; and Delaware, 11. Few of these new plants, however, are in the Delaware Basin.

The net result of these and other state and federal programs has been a substantial improvement in the quality of the Delaware water, with continuing progress still being made in the construction of treatment plants by municipalities and industries. Despite hopeful signs, however, it cannot be assumed that these programs will "solve" the problem of water quality for the Delaware. The current Corps of Engineers Survey will formulate a judgment as to Delaware water quality and its prospects, based upon data supplied principally by the U.S. Public Health Service. There is little doubt that the Corps will report an improvement in water quality compared to 20 years ago, but at the same time will warn of a vastly increased pollution load in the future resulting from anticipated increases in population and industrial activity. If these increases develop, it seems likely that present effluent treatment levels will prove insufficient to prevent a deterioration in water quality. If standards of treatment are to be raised, more effective enforcement procedures will be required. Even with secondary treatment fully in effect, used water will not be restored to suitable quality and reservoir releases will be needed to supplement treatment and abate pollution. As a final consideration, the proposal for a barrier dam in the estuary raises the specter of changed and worsened water quality in the lower river unless large-scale anti-pollution measures are instituted.

The field of quality control affords an excellent example of the dependence of operating and regulatory programs in government on a constant flow of accurate and up-to-date basic information. Any of the anti-pollution measures will produce optimum effects only if basic data are adequate and if there is a continuing adaptation to technological developments in sanitary engineering. Sites for applying treatment measures and sites where data on water quality must be collected are scattered over the Delaware Basin, as over any basin. This emphasizes anew the interstate character of a basin anti-pollution program.

The differing definitions of "pollution" employed in the four states were emphasized by a "Report on Definition of the Term 'Pollution' for Use in the Delaware River Basin's Survey Report," presented at the fourth meeting of the Delaware Basin Survey Coordinating Committee.

The administrators involved in the current survey may come to an understanding on a common definition; however, such agreement will leave unchanged the statutes, regulations, and administrative practices of the states. There is disagreement now among state officials as to the relative emphasis to be placed on requiring certain standards for streams or on implementing plant construction and better treatment measures. Differing approaches to the pollution problem among the four states may well be a major block to prosecution of a Basin-wide anti-pollution program in the future, and certainly they will stand in the way of comprehensive water resources planning.

The principal channel of cooperation on interstate pollution matters today is through the instrumentality of Incodel. Since 1939 that agency has based its anti-pollution program upon the passage of parallel legislation in the four states. The Incodel staff members speak of this abatement program as "administered on a concurrent and cooperative basis by the Health Departments of the respective states." [20] Depending as it does upon cooperation for gaining its ends, Incodel has no "teeth," like those of the Interstate Sanitation Commission or the Ohio River Valley Water Sanitation Commission. That is to say, it has no formal power to stop pollution, even in emergencies, nor can it have since it was created only by parallel state legislation.

Pollution will again become serious in the Delaware Basin in the future. As in other eastern areas, ". . . the major water problem is related not to quantity of water, but to maintaining a satisfactory quality of water. Although there are some examples of serious ground water pollution, the chief problem is the pollution of the streams." [21] Population growth will continue and industrialization and urbanization will proceed; consequently the amount of pollution and the number of potential sources of pollution will inevitably multiply. Both the need for further regulation and the interstate nature of the pollution problem will become more apparent. It seems likely that there will be increasing demand for a unified pollution program that will apply fairly uniformly throughout the Delaware Service Area. As matters now stand, the Public Health Service will directly administer that program.

[20] Incodel, *The Delaware River Basin Control and Utilization of Water Resources* (Philadelphia, 1958), p. 12.

[21] C. G. Paulsen, "The Available Water Supply," in Jack B. Graham and Meredith F. Burrill (eds.), *Water for Industry* (Washington: American Association for the Advancement of Science, Publication 45, 1956), p. 9. See also Partridge, *op. cit.*, pp. 24 ff.

Marketing and Distributing Hydroelectric Power

Generation of power at dam sites is potentially an important purpose of the operation and maintenance of major structures in a multiple-purpose system. Firm or peaking power must be tied to the energy requirements of the area,[22] but releases of water to generate power must be integrated with releases for other purposes. Therefore, central control over releases for power, as over other releases, cannot be divorced from the core function of basin water management.

Distribution of power, however, is a function separable from generation which might be handled by existing utilities. It is not customary for a public generating agency to assume responsibility for distribution of the power nor are there strong reasons for it to do so in the Delaware. If distributors buy the power wholesale, there are a number of marketing and power-exchange arrangements that might be used. Clearly, there is no need to duplicate the existing transmission facilities in the area. Who might buy the power and at what price will be discussed in Chapter 11.

Recreation

Far from the frivolous status it once occupied, recreation nowadays is deemed a serious activity by both public agencies and private entrepreneurs. As our population multiplies, urban uses invade rural land, and as the work week shrinks, adequate land and facilities for leisure-time purposes have become progressively more important, more difficult to acquire, and more expensive. All these trends will continue. The plans for Delaware Basin development must include a full measure of attention to recreation.

The term covers many different forms of outdoor sports and pastimes —from picnicking, camping, and simple enjoyment of nature to bathing, boating, hunting, and fishing. Recreation facilities in the modern lexicon include great tracts of wooded and open land, lakes and streams, beaches and bath houses, marinas, food and drink establishments, parking lots, and access roads. These paraphernalia require large capital outlays, ample maintenance budgets, and skilled administration.

Small wonder, in view of these heavy demands, that the future of

[22] Firm power is that available for constant use; peaking power is that available for use during periods of maximum load.

Delaware Valley recreation presently looks dismal. The well-publicized overcrowding of local recreation facilities in Westchester and Fairfield counties deserves mulling over. New Jersey has similar troubles on a summer day when, for instance, 11,000 persons throng to Lake Hopatcong, where the state has parking and beaches for little better than half that number. For some years it has been evident that the hordes of people seeking diversion are destined always to overtax the limited facilities run by local governments. We have Robert Moses' opinion that only state governments ". . . can accommodate such numbers without spoiling everything for everybody . . . ," and that "The best advice is to grab for parks and playgrounds every possible piece of land of fair size where congestion exists or is threatened." [23] And even the states will have trouble coping with the increasingly mobile picnickers, hikers, and boat owners.

State agencies are active in planning and operating recreation programs in the Delaware Basin already, although their funds are too restricted for them to follow Moses' ebullient counsel. In 1956 the four states spent over $19,000,000 on state parks (over their whole land area) and it is likely these amounts will continue to rise. At least two of these state programs would stand near the top in any ranking of park activities in all 48 states. The National Park Service through its expanded research in the East and through its long-time contacts with the state park people will be able to give more advice and assistance as the years pass. The Service directly administers only a few historic sites in the region, since there is no federal grant-in-aid program in recreation.

Local governments and private investors should of course be encouraged to continue expanding their roles in this field. In the Atlantic seaboard megalopolis, however, open areas are ever scarcer and so the opportunities for the local units to enlarge their recreation holdings are becoming increasingly rare. It is most appropriate that the comparatively broad geographic reach of the state governments is being employed to this end.

Although Americans seem to be progressively more addicted to water-centered sports and pastimes, water is but one of the key elements in recreation. The land, the capital structures, the personnel are of equal importance. New recreation areas and programs springing from

[23] *New York-New Jersey Metropolitan Region Recreation for 19,000,000 in 1957,* The New York-New Jersey Metropolitan Regional Recreation Conference, May 9, 1958, p. 10.

Delaware water development need not disrupt the general planning and program patterns already established by the states, which as we have noted have active interests and large stakes in recreation. Lest this point be overstressed, however, it must be affirmed that as Delaware development goes on, new reservoirs and more constant flows will produce potential new recreation resources. If central system operation combined with supervisory measures can keep reservoirs and channels clear and pure, levels reasonably constant, insect pests down and vegetation intact, tremendous recreation values will accrue. To preserve those values for public use from the start, some central agency will need to buy broad belts of land around future reservoir perimeters. Basin water development, indeed, offers a unique opportunity for acquisition of needed recreation tracts in the beautiful hills of the Delaware Valley where urban dwellers may find rest and diversion. Unless sufficient land is gathered into public hands in the beginning, the opportunity will be missed.

If, as is patently wise, the dam-building agency obtains lands suited to these uses, two administrative arrangements are available. First, the Basin's central administrative agency might directly manage the lands. This alternative would require very close gearing of operations with park and recreation agencies in the four states and the local units. Second, the central agency might enter into contracts with states and localities by which the latter would manage the new sites. In the federal experience there are manifold precedents for this procedure. The Corps of Engineers and the Bureau of Reclamation employ this method in roughly similar ways. The Tennessee Valley Authority operates no recreation programs but leases, sells, or otherwise transfers use of its lands to other governmental, quasi-public, or private agencies. Ordinarily, TVA collects no revenue from the operation of recreation facilities.

The point is that the function of recreation may be administered in several different fashions, and further that there is opportunity in this field for allowing the existing state agencies to share directly in basin development. The national government may even be asked for funds to manage a big area or two. The total recreation task ahead is so immense that the combined efforts of all governments, civic groups, and private firms will be needed. The one recreation job a central basin agency can best perform is that of careful planning for the long-range development of facilities. It needs no formal means for realizing its recommendations outside its own lands and reservoirs. It could frame its plans and recommend that state and local agencies work within those plans. If the plans are sound and a spirit of cooperation exists, sensible recreation development centered on the Basin will follow naturally.

Recreation is already a lively topic in this highly urbanized region. Finding money and land therefor is bound to occupy more and more minds. The New York-New Jersey Metropolitan Regional Recreation Conference of May, 1958, which examined recreation needs in an area including much of the Delaware Basin, symbolized the public interest in the subject. The country's concern for recreation is witnessed by the Outdoor Recreation Resources Review Commission set up by the 85th Congress. This temporary body is to inventory and evaluate national resources and opportunities.[24] Before its work is finished in 1961, many additional acres of Delaware land will be occupied and thus withdrawn from future park, playground, or other recreational use.

Fish and Wildlife

One need not be a dewy-eyed sentimentalist, a dry-fly enthusiast, or a frustrated frontiersman to appreciate the importance of governmental and private fish and wildlife programs. As the eastern coastal plain burgeons, this aspect of conservation may become an issue involving the emotions and intellects of much of the population.

Fish and wildlife work has long been recognized as an important part of the whole field of recreation. The case for the engagement of governments in fish and animal management and propagation activities rests upon the same rationale as the case for recreation generally, although the popular base for hunting and fishing is much smaller than that for the rest of outdoor recreation. Total expenditures by the Delaware Valley states for these purposes in 1956 were $12,500,000, a sum which includes grants-in-aid from Pittman-Robertson Act and Dingell-Johnson Act sources.[25] Other federal programs in the Delaware Service Area include the research activities of the Fish and Wildlife Service and the four national wildlife refuges, stations on the Atlantic flyway.

If these federal, state, and local programs in fish and wildlife are to maintain even their present relative status during the next few decades, their absolute financial needs will rise sharply. The load of fishermen and hunters, the demand on hatcheries, and the number of visitors at

[24] P.L. 470, 85th Cong., 2d sess.
[25] The Pittman-Robertson Act (Wildlife Restoration Act of 1937) and the Dingell-Johnson Act (Fish Restoration Act of 1950) provide the only federal grants-in-aid to the states for fish and wildlife purposes.

preserves will increase, and land will become progressively more dear. We are sure to see a drive by all fish and wildlife agencies for higher budgets, more land, expanded professional personnel, more scientific knowledge, and greater public support. This will not distinguish their activities from many other governmental programs one might mention. But the sharp increase in their needs will also coincide with the development of the Delaware for other purposes. New lakes, more stable streams, additional public domains at reservoir sites, new hunting and fishing grounds will all provide both excellent opportunities and vigorous demands for expansion of programs in this field.

Water is of course not the only integrating force in this area of recreation. State recreation programs in the Basin are inextricably related to statewide programs; and one cannot logically argue that these programs should be divided into Basin and non-Basin segments, with the former enjoying special consideration or status. On the contrary, a central agency for the Basin would be directed to plan the physical and research patterns by which programs in and out of the Basin might fit together. It might set broad standards for adoption by state agencies, whose operations would remain the foundation of fish and wildlife work in the Basin. A Basin agency might also be able to provide research funds, expert personnel, lands, advice, and other forms of aid to state fish and wildlife officials.

Fish and wildlife are renewable resources but renewal requires conscious effort. The soil-plant-animal-man relationship exists by a compromise by which man must contribute as well as take. In final analysis, justification for fish and wildlife propagation and management in the Delaware rests on these three hopes for urban man: (1) that the life community of which he is a part may be preserved relatively undisturbed; (2) that constant opportunities for recreation may be afforded him; and (3) that he may continue to enjoy the beauties of nature.

Watershed Management

Basic to the successful development of the Delaware is proper treatment of the land that contributes the water. Simply stated, the objectives of watershed management are to hold the soil in place, improve its quality, and preserve the vegetation at a level and balance deemed proper for the area. There are many techniques by which these ends may be sought. Among them are land use planning, contour plowing, strip cropping, terracing, mulching and fertilizing, the use of proper crops, afforestation, correct grazing and forest practices, other drainage techniques, treatment of old mines and mined land, and retirement of abandoned and maltreated land by public purchase. These and many other kinds of activities compose watershed management as practiced in the Delaware Valley today; they will need to be augmented by new techniques as time goes on.

Some of these measures have long been known, but only in the past fifty years have most of them come into wide use. The creation of the land-grant colleges and the agricultural extension program in the last decades of the nineteenth century, the conservation movement led by Theodore Roosevelt, and finally the renewed conservation efforts of the 1930's have been largely responsible for present agricultural conservation practices.

Much of the upland Delaware Basin has never been cultivated. There is intensive cultivation of considerable areas in the piedmont and coastal plain, although there has been a continuous withdrawal of acreage from cultivation over the past fifty years. Despite a certain continued decline in farm acreage, the remaining lands in the future will receive even more intensive use as new practices, irrigation for example, are perfected. Whether farming, forest, or meadow land, improvement of the thousands of square miles of Delaware Valley soil will always be the first step on the road to better use of its water.

The governmental and administrative patterns by which these watershed measures are applied are established today, and the channels by which new concepts and techniques may be brought into play are well known. The relationship of soil to water is no more close or vital in the Basin than outside, consequently the rationale for removing existing programs from established agencies is not compelling. This is not to say that there is not a continuing need for new research, techniques, ideas, manpower, and money, or that the new Basin agency will not be able to make important contributions to watershed management.

What does not now exist in the Delaware Basin, but might be provided, is an agency to devise a plan to coordinate and supplement the efforts of all individuals and agencies involved in watershed administration, and to relate their activities to water-resources development in broad perspective. Although there is no need for separate Valley administration of these measures, there is a definite place for a coordinating force. A "program of runoff and water-flow retardation and soil-erosion prevention" for the Delaware Basin was proposed by the

U.S. Department of Agriculture in 1950.[26] This was a 20-year plan, and the state and national governments were to share in its administration and to divide approximately equally its $64,382,000 cost. For reasons not relevant at this point, the plan failed to be adopted. It is, however, worth remembering as an example of the kind of planning required to compose, with other water developments, a comprehensive Basin program. It is important that watershed management not become a poor country cousin in the Delaware Basin as it did in the Missouri.

Summary

The dominant features of the Delaware Valley and the determinants of its water problems over the next half century will be growth and change. Dynamic policies and administrative devices will be needed to cope with those problems. There will be constantly shifting and more consumptive uses, changing technologies, increasing re-use, further demands for extra-basin diversions, and a greater and greater pollution load (even after wastes have been treated). The extent of these changes cannot be foretold today, although the Corps of Engineers' Survey will provide estimates.

In this chapter the various parts of the process of water-resources management have been examined, primarily from the standpoints of their innate characteristics and the imperatives they imply about the proper governmental levels, geographic areas, and administrative agencies to perform them. Leaving aside for the time being legal, fiscal, and political considerations, it has been found that there are reasons inherent in the functions for their being exercised variously by certain types of agencies and at certain levels.

There are, to begin with, ample reasons for assigning actual construction of the major structures in the river control system to the Corps of Engineers, at least in the early years of development. At some time in the future, this function may be shifted to a new regional agency more closely identified with area-wide interests in all water uses.

In the coming years the following functions of concern to the whole Basin will best be performed if they are vested in the same new agency. Some of them can be discharged in no other way:

1. research;
2. planning;

[26] 82d Cong. 2d sess., H. Doc. No. 405. This was a survey report made under provisions of the Flood Control Act of June 22, 1936.

3. representation and information;

4. operating and maintaining major structures for all the purposes they can properly be made to serve, including flood control, water supply, power, navigation, recreation, fish and wildlife, among others;

5. setting standards for, advising about, assisting financially with, and occasionally building and operating other structures (and accompanying programs) on the main stem and major tributaries;

6. quality control.

In one additional case it is apparent that effective performance will, somewhat later in the life of Delaware development, demand its being drawn into the orbit of the Basin agency. Control of withdrawals and diversions will surely be required as water use becomes greater and legal concepts and technical and administrative devices prove equal to the task. The few controls of this nature now exercised rest in the states. Because of their limited geographic reach, however, the states will not be able to cope satisfactorily with this function very far into the future.

In the varied and important operating programs examined in this chapter, the four Basin states, their subdivisions, and private enterprise all find their proper places. All should deepen and expand their water-resource operations. There is room for more initiative than ever in planning and providing the many structures auxiliary to the control system, in marketing and distributing hydroelectric power, in building recreation and fish and wildlife facilities, and in performing the very basic processes of watershed management. The expression of the national interest in these operations through such means as grants-in-aid will continue; given favorable conditions within the Basin, this interest will strengthen state and local programs.

What is described here is a logical means of distributing Delaware Valley water functions within the federal system. A new Basin agency providing a focus for regional water-resource interests at the same time will provide a means for rationalizing the plans and programs of all agencies concerned with Delaware River water. In the years to come there will be plenty of work for everyone in the management of water resources. The task is to inventory all administrative resources, to appraise their strengths and weaknesses, and to organize before the problems become acute. The need is immediate.

Part II: Organizing for River Basin Administration

CHAPTER 5

Government and Area: General Considerations

In essence, the prime responsibility of government in a democracy is the satisfaction of program needs. The achievement of program ends involves two basic stages: first, the identification and definition of goals, or program building; and second, the attainment of the goals set, or program execution. The first concerns policy, the second administration. The ends sought are paramount, for they determine the character of the government; but the means through which the ends are pursued are only a little less important, for they determine success or failure in program effectuation. The successful execution of a program is directly dependent on the machinery and methods of administration.

It is axiomatic among students of the subject that the functions (programs) of government are in perpetual motion. The changes reflect both the frequent modification and the occasional abandonment of existing functions on the one hand and the acceptance of new programmatic responsibilities on the other. And every change in function, whether old or new, tends to produce a corresponding modification in administrative organization and practice. The functional change may be a minor one and the resulting administrative accommodation incidental; an important modification in program direction or content, on the other hand, may lead to radical administrative adaptation.

Such adaptation may take either of two principal forms. First, the response may be organizational, in the sense that administrative machinery may be modified to accommodate to new needs. Organizational response to changing demands may assume the character of structural modifications, procedural adaptations, and new or expanded interagency relations, within or among existing administrative units. It may, on the other hand, result in the establishment of new administrative agencies. The quest for "efficiency" in the administration of the myriads of water programs by the agencies of government, national, state, and local, has resulted in an uncounted number of organizational changes within the last decade. The federal structure bears an uneasy relation to the water-resource field, as the several national studies made since 1950 demonstrate. First, then, the machinery of administration is in constant adjustment in response to program stimuli.

Second, administrative reaction to stimulus for change may take the form of areal adaptation. As in the case of organizational structure, the geographical areas of government and administration are in continuous readjustment in search of the most effective areal pattern with which to meet the ever-changing functional needs. In the process of adaptation the relatively simple local government of early days has been elaborated into a complex and multiform system which contains more than 100,000 separate units of local government.[1] Not less significant than the complexity of this system, however, is the steady decrease in the number of local governments, which was 34 per cent from 1942 to 1957. Since the decline occurred preponderantly among rural and the increase among urban units, it appears that the changes came in reaction to the dramatic shift in the urban:rural ratio. For present purposes, however, the central point is not the nature but the fact of areal adaptation to changing demands.[2]

The reconciliation of area and function is one of the major problems confronting administration. The issue is vastly complicated by the fact that its two principal components are in constant change, and by the further fact that the relations between them are reciprocal, with function pressing unevenly on area and area reacting to and in turn modifying function. Obviously there is no final solution to the problem. What is important, however, is not the conclusion that the problem has no permanent solution, but rather the finding that government has both the flexibility and the will to react positively to the ever-changing demands made upon it. The adjustment of area to function is a complex and frequently an annoying problem, but it is by no means one hopeless of reasonable accommodation.[3]

[1] Bureau of the Census, "Governments in the United States," 1957 *Census of Governments,* I, No. 1, p. 1.

[2] For an examination of areal adaptation in local government, see Roscoe C. Martin, *Grass Roots* (University, Alabama: University of Alabama Press, 1957).

[3] A thoughtful analysis of this whole problem may be found in James W. Fesler, *Area and Administration* (University, Alabama: University of Alabama Press, 1949). Arthur Maass (ed.), *Area and Power: a Theory of Local Government*

CRITERIA FOR EVALUATING THE ADEQUACY OF GOVERNMENTAL AREAS

It is not enough to say that there is a constant striving to adapt area to function, and that in its turn function, having sought the optimum in geographical adjustment, must in the end accommodate itself to the persisting areal pattern, with such modifications as it can command. These statements are true as general propositions, but they offer no standard for the evaluation either of the accommodation between the two or of the adequacy of the prevailing system of areas. Fortunately a number of criteria are available for such an appraisal. Some are reasonably explicit in nature, some quite general; but all will prove useful in constructing a framework for appraising the areal adequacy of government and administration.

Congruity of Area and Function

The first criterion has to do with the compatibility of the function to be administered and the area responsible for it. If there is no geographical congruity between the task to be performed and its administrative unit, then it may be posited that the area is not adequate to the task assigned it. Such incongruity occurs frequently (a) when a function outgrows a government to which it has long been assigned, and (b) when a new function arises which requires (or at any rate would profit from) administration by a district which falls outside the accepted geographical pattern. Both eventualities may be instanced by reference to the metropolitan area, where familiar problems long since overleaped established legal boundaries and where new issues, unknown or experienced only in rudimentary form in our undifferentiated society of the past, demand to be recognized. A typical response to an insistent demand for areal adjustment is the creation of a special-purpose district, to which, as we have observed, recourse is had more and more frequently. This study embraces the proposition that the modern needs of water administration place that function in some respects beyond the capacity of existing state and local governments, partly because of their too-limited geographical extent.

(Glencoe, Illinois: The Free Press, 1959), undertakes to systematize thinking on the subject. Chapter 2 of this symposium, Paul Ylvisaker's "Some Criteria for a 'Proper' Areal Division of Governmental Powers," is most directly relevant to the present discussion.

Population Base

A second criterion is found in consideration of the factor of adequacy in population. Size of population is important with regard to such matters as consumer demand and need for services, capacity to support services, vigor and variety of citizen participation, and the provision of a source of civic leadership. We are not required to make the case that the biggest governments are the best governments in order to sustain the contrary point that a great deal of the least effective government is found among the smaller units. The services of modern government, including specifically adequate water supply and satisfactory disposal of wastes, only rarely can be provided successfully or economically by the almost 10,000 municipalities of 1,000 or less, which therefore are open to challenge as viable units for these functions judged by the standard of population adequacy.

Program Scope and Depth

A companion criterion is implicit in the nature of the services to be rendered. For an area to find justification in action terms there must be a significant program, one that makes a substantial difference to people, to be accomplished, and it must be such as to compel popular interest and participation. Further, the functions undertaken must be of sufficient scope and depth to enable the unit to command the technical competence and equipment required for the satisfactory discharge of public duties in this age of specialization. An uncomfortably large proportion of all units of government fails to command favorable judgment when weighed by these standards, for there are many thousands of governments whose activities are artificial or perfunctory, whose "programs" consist in hollow observance of form or obeisance to tradition. A unit of government or administration which performs no important function, or which is ineffectual in what it undertakes, is a worse than useless thing, for it tends to subject all government to popular suspicion and ridicule.

Legal Authorization

A fourth criterion is inherent in the legal authorization or base of a particular district or class of districts. Some areas lack the legal powers necessary to the discharge of the functions for which they were created. Some enjoy a reasonable grant of power within a narrow range of action, but do not have authority to deal with collateral issues. Many do not possess territorial jurisdiction adequate to their task, and others still are lacking in sanctional powers. The history of American government is filled with the chronicles of units which, created in a moment of high purpose (or of desperation), failed to get off the ground for want of legal authority commensurate with their assigned tasks.

Financial Resources

Hand in hand with legal authority goes the standard of fiscal adequacy. The one is as important as the other, for if there cannot be vigorous action in the absence of a sound legal base, neither can there be an energetic program without adequate financial resources. The acquisition and distribution of such resources constitute a basic problem for government, the more because government traditionally relies upon relatively few established sources of public revenue. The problem becomes more and more intense as one moves outward and downward from Washington; it is considerably more urgent at the state capital level; and it is more complex yet in the city halls and the county court houses. With rare exceptions, the units of local government experience the perpetual pinch of poverty. This is due partly to such institutional factors as dependence on general property as the tax base, tax limits, and debt ceilings, and partly to the long-standing popular aversion to energetic local government and therefore to generous, or even adequate, support of local activities through payment of taxes. The normal recourse taken by such governments is not to raise the additional revenue required for a vigorous program, but rather to restrict programs in terms of revenue traditionally available or to seek "outside" aid. For any particular program the result is likely to be limited funds both for capital construction and for maintenance and operation. For some emergent programs without well-established clienteles—the administration of water resources over a broad area, for example—the consequence may be postponement of action past the point required by convenience and into the critical stage. To return to the central point for a conclusion, it is clear that a large percentage of all the units of government do not have access to sufficient fiscal resources to discharge satisfactorily the responsibilities with which they are vested. That their poverty is sometimes imaginary and where real frequently remediable is not sufficient rejoinder to the observable fact that, in the circumstances which prevail, local governments often do not have the money to carry on vigorous programs.

Accountability

Still another criterion for evaluating the adequacy of governmental areas may be stated in terms of accountability, which can be analyzed from two points of view. The first hinges on what may be called administrative accountability; it concerns such matters as internal control over the organization, financial management, and personnel administration. These considerations obviously are foreign to the large percentage of all governments which are too picayune to warrant attention to such relatively technical matters. No way has been discovered to enforce or even effectively to invoke the concept of administrative accountability upon the thousands of petty local and special governments.

Accountability may be defined secondly in terms of political responsibility. Here the issue is primarily that of policy formulation, direction, and control. The principal questions are, how well does the program pursued reflect the will of the people, and how effective is the popular (external) control exercised over the government? These questions are among the most difficult which may be asked about government, and they admit of no easy answers. Two generalizations regarding them may, however, be proposed. One is that the traditional forms of democratic practice—popular election of administrative officials, short terms of office, frequent turnover, government by amateurs —are no guarantees that democracy (that is, responsible government) will result in fact. Another is that, nothwithstanding the American dogma, there is no necessary or inevitable correlation between responsible government and closeness to the people. Certainly the test of the democratic character of a government lies far below the superficial observance of form.

Flexibility

Still another criterion by which to appraise a governmental area is found in its adaptability in the face of changing needs. A unit which is tied exclusively to a particular program is estopped from consideration of needs growing from related developments. This is frequently identified as one of the principal weaknesses of the special district. The most adaptable of local governments with respect to new and changing program needs, the city, nevertheless finds itself seriously limited in its effort to deal with metropolitan problems because of its relatively inflexible boundary. There are in fact few units of government which enjoy the flexibility of program necessary to permit them to shift effectively to meet changing conditions, and there is none possessed of the desired areal flexibility. The legal boundary lines of established units are extraordinarily resistant to change.

Structural Compatibility

Its position in and contribution to the effectiveness of the total paraphernalia of government is a further legitimate standard against which to measure the adequacy of a given unit (or kind of unit). The federal system, though complex, formalistic, and deliberate in movement, nevertheless is a fundamental feature of American government; and the challenge is not to circumvent or undermine federalism but to achieve a working order within the framework which it provides. Thus the criterion of the total effectiveness of government, and of the consequence of any innovation therefor, may quite appropriately be invoked. It is clear that literally thousands of existing units make little contribution either to administration in their immediate area or to the theory or practice of government broadly considered. On the contrary, competition among minuscule governments, both for financial support and for citizen attention, measurably reduces the effectiveness of the total public enterprise. At the same time, care should be exercised in the creation of a new unit of government, which, however justified it may appear in programmatic terms, must be considered with reference to its potential effect on and its prospective relations with existing governments. This is a subtle but significant point, for responsible action requires that due consideration be given to all relevant factors, including specifically the interests and concerns of existing units of government, before moving to the establishment of a new governmental or administrative area.

Contemporariness

Next, government can be appraised in terms of what may be called its contemporariness. A unit which was created a hundred years ago for a particular purpose, which has never pursued any other purpose, and which has not joined in the procession of modern government, can scarcely be expected to undergo a significant renaissance in the face of new program needs. The statute books of the states are full of provisions for districts which enjoyed their brief fling then silently expired, or which, though legally authorized, never came into existence at all.

A considerable proportion of the country's total machinery of government is relatively ineffective because not adapted to the demands currently made upon it. It is well to weigh this fact carefully before vesting in an existing government important responsibilities for new programs. The new-wine-in-old-bottles proverb is particularly applicable
here.

Political Viability

Finally, an area of government/administration must be politically
viable. Political strength is required to gain initial acceptance, and later
to ensure survival. Old and accepted units need concern themselves
only with survival, in which field they enjoy all the advantages of
familiarity, tradition, and popular resistance to change. A proposed
new unit, by contrast, must fight and win an initial battle against
the same resistance to change on the one hand and against entrenched
interests on the other, and in addition must be prepared to wage a
war for survival for many years. More will be said on this subject later;
for the present, it is sufficient to note that the ability to win and hold
political support is an important as well as a quite legitimate standard
by which to judge a government.

Ten criteria have been proposed for evaluating the adequacy of governmental areas. These standards are not equal in value, for some are
basic, others ancillary. The fundamental questions to be asked about
any unit of government are, first, is it effective in terms of program
achievement? and second, is it responsible? All others are secondary
and concern matters which, however important, are contributory. It
follows that, in evaluating a particular government, equal weight cannot be given to the ten criteria; it may be, indeed, that high attainment
by certain basic standards occasionally will warrant passing by some
of those less fundamental. A further caveat must be entered that some,
perhaps most, of the criteria are inexact, which makes their employment a matter of judgment rather than measurement. Finally, it is not
to be assumed that the list is definitive, for another observer will have
his own set of standards which will differ in some particulars from
this one. Nevertheless the criteria offered here may be supposed to
suggest the kinds of questions appropriate to be raised about the
suitability and soundness of a government.

Several conclusions are to be drawn from this analysis. The first is
that, weighed by these criteria, a considerable part of the structure
of government in the United States is found wanting. Many units defy

gravity by continuing in existence while failing to pass muster with respect to several basic standards, enjoying in common the attribute of political viability largely, it may be suspected, through force of momentum. Second, it is proposed as an hypothesis worthy of further examination that little government suffers more than big government through the process of evaluation: that is, that a larger proportion of small governments than of large governments fails to measure up to the standards set. Third and as a corollary, the American tradition of the beneficence of government "close to the people," that is, little government, fails to stand the test of objective analysis. Grass-roots government too often is both administratively ineffectual and politically irresponsible. Fourth, the city is the only local unit which exhibits real vitality, and it has a serious defect in its limited and relatively inflexible boundary. The county, which might (indeed may) develop into an area of general government, is lacking thus far in the spirit required for the discharge of important new responsibilities. An alternative unit, the special district, suffers from certain limitations, chief among them its restricted range of action and its awkward relations with traditional governments. There are situations nevertheless where, in default of effective action by established governments, recourse must be taken to the special district or authority. Fifth, as a result of these and other like deficiencies, important new programs often find it difficult to discover satisfactory administrative bases. This is particularly true of a program which does not fit comfortably into the existing areal pattern. For all the potential flexibility of our governmental structure and for all its constant adaptation, organizational and geographical, to changing needs, the problem of reconciling area and function remains as a continuing challenge to American resourcefulness.

The River Basin as an Administrative Area

One function of great and growing importance which sometimes fails to find a congenial administrative area is that of water-resources management. The water problem assumes a variety of guises, and in some forms it is susceptible of satisfactory administration by existing units of government. Thus there are cities which are so situated that, on the one hand, they can handle their water supply problem without outside assistance, while on the other their activities in the field do not seriously affect others. Such places are few and far between, however, and their number grows constantly smaller; for with the diminishing isolation born of our rapidly growing population and its increasing mobility, there are fewer and fewer water problems which lend themselves to exclusively local treatment. Among those which require a broader view are flood control, navigation, and hydroelectric power development, which clearly call for wider powers and resources than can be commanded locally. Water supply and waste disposal by tradition are local activities, although they, too, increasingly require attention over a broader area, as does water-based recreation. Some of the functions involved in water-resources administration therefore must be addressed on a non-local basis, and others are rapidly reaching the point where local administration can no longer provide satisfactory solutions to the problems posed. More and more the administration of water resources assumes the guise of a regional problem, even as President Theodore Roosevelt characterized it fifty years ago.

Governmental response to emergent river basin needs has been considerably less than spectacular. Historically, the traditional units of government have sought to meet the needs. Thus the towns and cities have dealt with such matters as water supply and waste disposal, and, occasionally, with water-related recreation as well. The states, too, have lent a hand, usually by creating special agencies and districts to deal with parts of the water problem, though sometimes through direct participation, as in the case of New York and the Erie Canal. By the pragmatic test of survival, state and local efforts were successful in meeting the needs of a rural America. As a matter of fact, however, such efforts seldom addressed the larger problems of water management, and they almost never treated of water problems throughout a river basin. There have been occasional attempts by state and local governments to deal with the problem of water management in its natural setting, but these have proved largely unavailing. The spotty experience of interstate cooperation has done little more than emphasize the need for a broader base for the management of some water programs. The states and their local units nevertheless remain active in the field, and they must be taken into account in any plan for basinwide administration of water resources.

In addition to, and usually apart from, state and local activities, a number of federal departments pursue a considerable and growing variety of water and water-related functions, as has been noted elsewhere in this study. The Corps of Engineers has taken the lead in recognizing the validity of the river basin as an area for water-resources administration, and has conducted a series of surveys and drawn up a number of developmental plans based on that recognition. Other federal agencies likewise have accepted the river valley as a useful area for data collection and planning for water resources. In the recent Survey of the Delaware Basin, for example, as many as 18 federal agencies took part. Further, an effort was made to draw the four states and the major local governments of the Delaware Valley into the task of fact-finding and planning. When all was said and done, however, the collaboration sought eventuated in a series of individual undertakings, with the Corps of Engineers assuming final responsibility and the reports of the several participating agencies appearing as appendices to the Corps report. Thus while there was much talk of inter-agency cooperation in drawing up the physical plan for the Delaware, there was actually a minimum of collaboration in the end. In short, the drive for inter-agency collaboration stalled in the face of long-standing agency traditions and commitments, personal as well as programmatic. Nor did the efforts to engage the energies of state and local governments prove successful, beyond achievement of the not unimportant goal of arousing interest in and perhaps enlisting some support for the concept of basin planning.

The experience of the Delaware Basin has been repeated throughout the country, for nowhere have the traditional agencies of government in a river basin been drawn together in meaningful collaboration. This has not been for want of effort, for there have been several attempts both to associate together the federal agencies active in a basin and to bring the state and local governments into a collaborative relationship. Perhaps the most ambitious of these efforts is that found in the Missouri Basin; and the scheme in effect there leaves a great deal to be desired, as Chapter 14 discloses. Indeed, serious doubt may be expressed whether significant results, in terms of basinwide administration, can be expected from the voluntary cooperation of the independent agencies and units of government now active in profusion in the typical river basin. The existing governments, whether federal, state, or local, have too much at stake in their individual programs to warrant the risk involved in cooperating in a truly regional program. Their preoccupation with traditional activities is entirely understandable, but it bodes ill for experimentation nonetheless.

If there is a legitimate regional water-resources program to be executed, and if the task is beyond the reach of the traditional agencies of government, it would appear that a regional administrative agency would have a strong claim to consideration. Such an agency admittedly would face a number of complex and tedious problems, the first inherent in the nature of a water program. Such a program, if it is at all comprehensive, will comprise not a single well-defined operation but a bundle of activities instead, dealing with functions as varied as flood control, water supply, the production and sale of hydrolectric power, and the provision of recreational facilities. These activities may require quite different areas for their proper administration, and in any case not all are related to the river basin equally or in the same way, nor is such relationship as may exist necessarily a vital one in any given instance. In short, the concept of the river basin as an administrative region is open to question in the very beginning, even when the programmatic activities in contemplation are as closely related as the term "water program" suggests.

Second, the river basin exerts and is profoundly affected by powerful influences outside the basin, and this plays havoc with any incipient concept of the valley as a neat, orderly entity. One of the most significant of these for the Delaware Basin is the access to Delaware water granted New York City and New Jersey by the Supreme Court. Here at once is an extra-basin factor that must affect all thinking about a water program for the Delaware Valley. Another is the total metropolitan complex, the "megalopolis" which stretches along the Atlantic seaboard from Boston to Washington. Another is the service area, whose influence tends to destroy the concept of the Valley as an economic region. Another still is the transportation network, which is scarcely more limited by geographical than by political demarcations. These and many like social and economic factors ignore and so obscure regional lines, however they may be drawn. They corroborate the point made above, that there are (or tend to be) as many regions as there are important kinds of action.

A third problem arises from the fact that the river valley does not fit into the existing pattern, either functional or geographical, of government and administration. This means, as an immediate consequence, that any significant basin agency that may be devised at once becomes an orphan, with no strong parent government to look to for encouragement and support, no sister agencies with which to make common cause, no web of established procedure on which to lean, no body of precedent to serve as guide, and no articulate clientele to represent it in the public forum. As a proximate result a basin agency can look forward with some assurance to a protracted period of uneasy relations with existing organizations, particularly with traditional governments and their agencies. Few public bodies are likely to find much that is praiseworthy in a new regional program, and this is true especially of federal agencies in the field.

A regional agency designed to river basin requirements therefore faces a number of handicaps. It does not follow, however, that these weaknesses are fatal; for on the one hand there are demonstrable regional needs presently unmet while on the other a basin agency possesses certain inherent strengths. First among the latter is the fact that its jurisdiction, which extends generally (though not inflexibly) to the limits of the drainage basin, secures to it the very real advantage of reasonable geographic scope, listed above as a basic criterion for evaluating the adequacy of administrative areas. A second point of strength flows from the delineation of its responsibilities in terms of a regional water-resources program, which gives it a center of energy and action not known to any existing government or combination of governments. This provides opportunity for satisfying a second fundamental criterion, that of program scope and depth, for it permits concentration on an important series of related program activities over a significantly broad areal expanse.

A third advantage, consequent upon its jurisdiction and program scope, arises from the fact that a basin agency is in a position to harmonize, or to exert its influence in the direction of harmonizing, the many programs in the region related to water resources. How far it will be able to go in this direction will depend on the powers given it and even more on the skill it develops in negotiation. Fourth, it occupies a strategic position for the advancement of a program related to the needs of the region. Experience has disclosed that, where a number of agencies are active in the same general field, gaps in program are at least as much to be feared as overlapping. The regional agency's situation permits it to appraise ongoing programs on the one hand and regional needs on the other, and to take action to render the composite program adequate to the total need. Fifth, such an agency provides a means for making an over-all plan for the basin and for keeping it up-to-date. A plan is not a hit-and-run thing, but must be kept in focus through continuous study and revision. Only a regional agency can be expected to assume successfully long-range responsibility for regional planning. Sixth, creation of an administrative agency for a river basin makes possible the decentralization of much federal activity to the region. Thus the locus of decision-making and responsibility for action may be shifted from the national capital to the area affected by the decisions and the action taken, namely the river valley. This would seem to represent a considerable basin benefit, so far as federal action is concerned. But a device which from Washington may have the appearance of a decentralizing agent may seem just the opposite to the states and their local units, for centralization and decentralization are relative terms. One's attitude toward a regional agency in this respect therefore may be strongly influenced by one's point of view. It would seem reasonable to hope that such an agency would afford an acceptable compromise between the advocates of federal intervention on the one hand and the devotees of traditional grass-roots government on the other.

Pondering the uneven performance in the face of a problem whose demands grow constantly more insistent, many have drawn the conclusion that a series of river valley authorities provides the only tenable solution. This view rests upon a number of assumptions. The first is that certain identifiable phenomena characterize river basins, which therefore tend to have significant features in common. Second, the inference is reasonable that common features must have as their issue common problems, which in consequence may be expected to recur from basin to basin. Third, it is assumed that regional problems can be resolved by rational action. From these assumptions it is a natural next step to the conclusion that a governmental/administrative structure therefore can be devised for regional adoption *in general and in the abstract.* The logical extreme of this line of reasoning is a series of valley authorities, one for each major river basin, blanketing most of the country. Indeed bills introduced into the Congress in the immediate post-war years would have established federal valley authorities to the number of a dozen or more to administer water programs in the major river basins substantially as the Tennessee Valley Authority administers its program in the basin of the Tennessee.

A contrary view of the problem emphasizes the physical, economic, social, and governmental/political characteristics of the individual basin. It rests upon the conviction that each river valley possesses its distinguishing features, and that each may therefore be expected to have its own particular set of problems. With this conviction as a starting point, the advocate of the second view proceeds to inventory the regional functions to be performed and the institutions and agencies, private as well as public, available for their performance. He seeks next to identify and evaluate the functions that existing institutions cannot administer, or that a valley-wide organization could administer better. If he discovers significant functions that suffer for want of attention or of energetic administration, he proceeds finally to the planning of a governmental/administrative structure adapted to the programmatic needs of the individual region. This approach thus rests not upon the prior conviction that every river basin ipso facto needs an authority on the TVA model, but rather on the hypotheses that a particular river basin is worthy of study in its own right, that certain significant problems are likely to emerge from such study which require regional attention, and that, if this proves to be the case, an administrative agency should be devised especially for the region at hand.

This study accepts the second approach to river basin administration. It recognizes the background value of American experience in the field, and embraces the general conclusions to be drawn from that experience. General lessons, however, must find proof in particular applications, whence the question which recurs throughout this volume concerning the utility for the Delaware Basin of broad propositions distilled from the national experience.

CHAPTER 6

Economic Factors in Basin Development

WATER-RESOURCE development is economic development. This chapter will examine the economic criteria that are available for planning and administering a program for the effective utilization of water. An attempt will be made to assess the importance of water as a factor in economic expansion, the economic characteristics of water, and the elements that influence decisions on water utilization.

ECONOMIC DEVELOPMENT AND PUBLIC POLICY

Economic development means improvement in the material conditions of existence. If the distribution of income and the composition of output are reasonably stable, improvement can be measured in terms of increases in per capita real income for the residents of a country or region. Such increases occur as an economy adds to its stock of capital goods to increase the ratio of capital to labor and as the labor force adds to its skills and productivity.

Increases in investment and improvements in the productivity of labor can be realized either through private action or public action or through some combination thereof. In the last several decades in all countries of the world there has come to be increased dependence on public decision and public organization as a means of development. This trend is not restricted to the so-called underdeveloped countries, for as advanced industrial countries have achieved a higher degree of internal interdependence, they too have come to rely more heavily on public decisions for affecting the conditions of economic growth.

Economic welfare has come to be one of the basic values of the democratic state, along with liberty and equality. In this context welfare does not mean what the word suggests in the popular phrase, "the welfare state." The latter generally connotes government programs to provide expanded services mainly to lower and middle income groups. By contrast economic welfare, in a more general sense, refers to the real national income and the conditions that contribute to its increase. Almost all public programs, whether federal, state, or local, will have impacts on the conditions of economic growth and development.

It is important to distinguish among the purposes of government programs to assist in analyzing these impacts. The economic influences transmitted through government can be classified as falling into three general categories or branches of activity.[1] The first is the allocation branch, which consists of programs that provide goods and services to satisfy public wants such as national defense, the administration of justice, and police and fire protection. The second consists of the distribution branch, wherein decisions are made with respect to an "equitable distribution of income," to alter the relationships among the rich and the poor and among areas within an economy. The third is the stabilization branch, which embraces decisions with respect to aggregate levels of income and employment for the economy as a whole and for segments of that economy.

Public programs for water-resource development partake of the character of all three of these generalized branches of government economic activity. The construction of a system of dams and reservoirs may provide industrial and municipal water for the residents of a valley. This concerns resource allocation, with decisions made on the basis of efficiency criteria relating to the provision of goods and services. The construction of dams and reservoirs will also have distributional implications. The income position of some groups, persons, and firms will be improved in relation to the income position of other groups, persons, and firms. Stabilization considerations may also enter into decisions about the construction of facilities. If there are unemployed resources at any one time it is possible for public construction to be undertaken at a lower social cost than if resources are fully employed. A decline in the level of national income or the income of a region may encourage governmental expenditures to raise levels of economic activity.

Although public expenditures for water-resource development partake of the character of all three branches of the government economy (allocation, distribution, stabilization), every effort should be made to

[1] Richard A. Musgrave, *The Theory of Public Finance* (New York: McGraw-Hill, 1959), especially pp. 3-27.

appraise these sets of considerations separately. The economic evaluation of water-resource problems is complex. Some contribution to simplification can be made by parcelling out and classifying decisions in accordance with their economic impact.

From this broad vantage point, what then may be said about the significance of public expenditures on water-resource development as a general problem of resource allocation? It should be stressed that there is nothing unique about water as a commodity or as an object of public expenditure. Public outlays for water, like outlays for education, transportation, and national defense, should be of such magnitude and in such a time sequence as to maximize the total of public and private benefit.

A water-resource program is important for economic development. Adequate supplies of industrial water or appropriate quality will assist in holding existing industry and in attracting new firms. Provision of navigation facilities will contribute to the development of certain transport-oriented firms and industries. Programs for pollution abatement and for reservoir-based recreation will make a region generally more attractive as a place to work and live. But it is important to avoid over-stating the case. An abundance of inexpensive industrial water, for example, is of greatest importance for such industries as petroleum refining and basic steel. It is of almost no importance for the garment industry. There is no measure of the significance of industrial and municipal water for the location of industry as a whole. Each industry, and indeed each firm within an industry, has its own specific water requirements. Public and private efforts to provide a favorable climate to attract new industry into a region must look not only to water resources but also to supplies of raw materials, availability of markets, labor costs, transportation, and tax rates.

It is important to maintain perspective on the relationship of expenditures for water development to other public and private expenditures for national and regional growth. Eastern river basins are highly industrialized, urbanized complexes where water demand, however measured, is high. In the Delaware Valley, for example, water withdrawals for industrial use are more than 90 per cent of total withdrawals for all purposes, while for the nation as a whole, industrial withdrawals are about half this proportion.[2] All major metropolitan areas on the eastern seaboard are currently concerned with water

[2] Everett P. Partridge, *op. cit.*, p. 3; U.S. Public Health Service, *Municipal and Industrial Water Use* (unpublished manuscript prepared for U.S. Army Engineers District, Philadelphia, 1959), p. 50a.

supply and waste disposal because these services are significant for local economies. Adequate water supplies are important not only to attract additional industrial employment to a region, but also to hold down operating costs for established firms. For example, electric power companies with substantial steam generating facilities cannot relocate out of their service area because of transmission costs. Such installations require an assured and inexpensive supply of water for cooling purposes if costs of operation and power rates are to be kept down; electric power costs in turn are a factor affecting industrial location and expansion.

But for industrialized, urbanized eastern river valleys, water resources are not the key to the whole of development. The Hudson, the Potomac, and the Delaware Valleys are very unlike the Tennessee Valley of 1933. The Tennessee Valley was a depressed area, with substantial unemployment and low levels of family income and welfare. Water-resource investment there, in its direct and indirect impacts, unleashed a major development potential. The public and private redevelopment of water resources in eastern river basins cannot be expected to provide this kind of impetus. These areas are suffering from relative, but not absolute, economic decline; growth rates are positive here, but are lower than in some other parts of the country. Eastern industrial-urban complexes have a heavy investment in social overhead, in such basic facilities as transportation, educational plant, water supply, and waste disposal. Both these areas and the nation as a whole will suffer severe economic losses if basic plant and equipment are not utilized to capacity. Economic growth by way of water-resource investment will bring a more effective utilization of social overhead capital, and lay the basis for further expansion.[3] Growth will bring renewal and replacement of outmoded capital facilities. As population grows, with increased demands for goods and services, investment in such facilities as industrial and municipal water can be integrated, with resulting economies of scale.

Water-resource investment cannot be expected to restore eastern river valleys to a growth rate that exceeds the national average, but expanded water-resource programs, along with other public and private programs, can help maintain existing growth rates and contribute to the economic expansion that the next several decades can bring.

[3] For the development of this concept in relation to water resources investment, see Julius Margolis, "Secondary Benefits, External Economies, and the Justification of Public Investment," *Review of Economics and Statistics*, XXXIX (August, 1957), pp. 284-291.

WATER AS AN ECONOMIC GOOD

Water is a renewable resource. In some instances the renewal process occurs as a part of the beneficence of nature, as when surface and ground waters are replenished by rainfall. In other cases the renewal of water requires economic action as it moves from the status of a free good to a scarce commodity. Water becomes an economic problem of public concern because its use, renewal, and re-use are subject to commonality. The utilization of water in one part of a valley affects the use and cost of renewal in another part of the valley. This commonality of use, and its counterpart on the supply side, interdependence among water purposes, is central and has a great many implications for planning, operating, and financing a system of river control structures.

The relative abundance of water in most eastern river valleys poses special problems for effective future utilization. Industrial water at some locations does not now have status as an economic good; it is often available at zero price (without charge) at the intake. Therefore, there is no experience on which to base estimates of future requirements as water moves to the status of an economic good, that is, as its use is purchased. A great many of the extravagant fears for the future of industrial water supplies in the east have been predicated on this kind of non-economic experience with water use. As long as a zero price prevails for water there is no incentive to economy of use, but water requirements may be expected to shift sharply downward as price is increased.[4]

As an economic good, water is also characterized by a high degree of substitutability on the supply side. There is obviously a minimum biological requirement for water to sustain human life, but at any one time and place there is a very wide range of physical possibilities for substitutes for any one of the purposes which water might serve. For example, there are many alternatives to the use of the Delaware River for domestic water supplies. Water might be imported from the Susquehanna, seawater desalinized, waste waters reclaimed, or weather modified. There is a substitute for the Delaware River as a navigation channel—cargoes could be transported by rail or air or truck. There is a substitute for the control of the Delaware River to prevent flood damage. Property and persons could be moved from

---

[4] Industrial water withdrawals have not increased as rapidly since 1950 as had been expected. This undoubtedly reflects a gradual movement in the status of water from a free good to an economic good.

the flood plain or a flood warning system could be installed. Similarly, the headwaters of the Delaware need not be used for trout fishing. It is possible for fishermen to fly to Canada with their rods and creels. The point is that there are always technological alternatives in the use of water. These may not at any time and place be feasible economic alternatives, for the feasibility of alternatives is always a function of their cost. It follows that the "best use of a river" must always be judged on the basis of best economic use, with as many of the alternatives as possible brought under review as a basis for making decisions about investment in facilities and about the operation of a completed structure for water resources control.

The fact that water use and water derivatives have considerable elasticity of substitution at any one time and place provides a criterion for judging the character and volume of investment to be undertaken. Generating facilities for hydroelectric power should be installed in dams only if costs for such purposes are lower than for alternative power development. Navigation improvements should be undertaken only if the cost of such improvements is less than could be provided by equivalent alternative facilities. Recreation should be developed at reservoirs only when costs are less than for comparable facilities elsewhere.

Water as a commodity is subject to a changing technology that affects the conditions of both demand and supply. Further, it is evident that water and water derivatives cut across all phases of human activity. In consequence, to forecast total requirements for water and total values for use a decade or two hence is as difficult as to forecast the character and variety of human activity. It is this fact—the changing character of water requirements and conditions of water supply—that has led to the stress throughout this report on the need for flexibility in all aspects of planning and operating a water-resource development program.

Emphasis on the uncertainties should not, however, be permitted to obscure the importance of the factors that can be foreseen with at least some clarity. It is reasonable to expect, in eastern river basins and in the Delaware in particular, that the demand for industrial and municipal water supplies will increase sharply, that the control of water quality for use and re-use will assume increasingly larger dimensions, that there will be increased requirements for all kinds of recreation facilities, including water-based recreation. On the other hand, hydroelectric energy as a source of electric power will probably diminish in significance over time, as costs for atomic energy generation are successively reduced. But the time dimensions of these predictable developments cannot be projected with precision.

The period of time between initial planning and the final output of water products is very long and massive investments are involved. Advance planning and sometimes construction to meet anticipated demand is necessary if growth potentials are to be attained. But the uncertainties inherent in future water requirements suggest that emphasis in planning for eastern river valleys should not rest on predictions oriented to a precise development over time.[5] Some binding commitments are of course necessary, since water control structures are long-lived, but where possible emphasis should be placed on an approach that permits postponement of decisions until major uncertainties disappear. If undue emphasis is placed on forecasting the future, policy tends to be bound by that forecast rather than by the necessity for planning for future freedom of action to meet the course of actual events. The history of water-resource development in the United States is replete with cases of inflexible and uneconomic investment. Flexibility in water resource development requires careful attention to the difference between postponable and non-postponable decisions and an effort to balance the cost of flexibility against the cost of committed decisions.

A final characteristic of water as an economic good is the interdependence of water derivatives, a characteristic closely linked with substitutability. Interdependence is the economic justification for multiple-purpose projects. The total value of a combination of water derivatives is maximized when costs can be shared among a number of programs.

Interdependence exists among the various uses of water and its reuse. It exists among project purposes that may be served by a single reservoir or a single release of water and characterizes the relationship between one structure and another in a unified river control system. The pervasive presence of interdependencies in resource development makes for extreme complexity in the planning and administration of river control structures.[6] Very often this complexity can be broken down only by seeking proximate rather than ultimate tests of economic efficiency, by a conscious effort at sub-optimization.[7] This latter requires the acceptance of specific subsidiary goals of development

[5] Professor Jack Hirshleifer, University of Chicago, has made this point.

[6] John V. Krutilla and Otto Eckstein, *Multiple Purpose River Development,* (Baltimore: Johns Hopkins Press, 1958), pp. 52-58.

[7] Roland N. McKean, *Efficiency in Government Through Systems Analysis* (New York: John Wiley, 1958), pp. 27-34.

sufficiently uncomplicated to permit careful assessment of inputs and outputs, and is necessitated in river basin development by the sheer intellectual impossibility of embracing the totality of all possible decisions.

THE WELFARE CRITERION OF ECONOMIC EVALUATION

A recent report by the United Nations points out that economic evaluation of river basin development has four objectives. The first is to determine the feasibility of a particular development in relation to the national interest; the second, to determine the relative economy of variants of a program; the third, to permit a choice among a number of river basin programs; and fourth, to assign responsibility for repayment of the whole or part of development projects.[8] Generally speaking, economic analysis attempts to serve these purposes by assembling data to permit comparisons of benefits and costs of development, both total benefits and costs and marginal benefits and costs. Such comparisons are possible because of the characteristics of water as an economic good and the substitutability of water and water derivatives.

Viewed as a part of the theory and practice of public expenditures, governmental outlays for water-resource development thus stand very nearly in a class by themselves. For large parts of the public sector the measurement of the cost of governmental programs seldom poses severe difficulties, but the measurement of gains is most elusive. The social and private benefits from national defense outlays, for example, are not susceptible of quantification, nor are the total of public and private gains from outlays for police protection and the administration of justice. But many of the values of water-resource development are specific end products susceptible of measurement or estimation.

The strength of economic analysis as applied to project evaluation lies in its use of market measurements. As such this analysis is a part of the established body of concepts known as welfare economics. This approach seeks to maximize individual satisfactions by relating preferences for goods and services, with a given distribution of income, to the technological possibilities for providing such goods and services. The prices that individuals will pay reflect their preferences and these prices direct the quantity and composition of output. The interrelationship between preferences and production possibilities permits

[8] Department of Economic and Social Affairs, United Nations Report by a Panel of Experts, *Integrated River Basin Development*, E/3066 (New York, 1958), p. 22.

the conceptualization of an optimum. Where it is applicable the welfare approach reveals the alternatives that may be followed in achieving this optimum.

In applying this framework to public programs for water-resource development, it is necesary to infer values because market prices are not directly available. This means for water programs that it is necessary to estimate what individuals would pay if there were a market that could reveal their preferences. In the application of economic analysis to project feasibility, the necessity for inferring values poses conceptual difficulties (see next section).

The economics of project evaluation depends on the appropriateness of comparisons between public and private economic activity. Those who favor increased emphasis on this analysis in project evaluation will stress the validity of such comparisons and urge that private market values must serve as the major guideline for economic feasibility in the public sector.[9] This approach, however, is not without its critics. Some economists and most non-economists will urge that the public sector is not an analog of the private sector. There are few who would argue that no attention whatever should be paid to market guidelines, but it is frequently contended that social wants are qualitatively different from private wants, and that decisions about satisfying public wants should not be made primarily in terms of private sector alternatives.[10]

BENEFIT-COST ANALYSIS

In the economic evaluation of water resource projects the first area is project justification, which consists of determining whether or not projects should be constructed and, as components of this determination, of analyzing the optimum scale and the time path of development. For multiple-purpose projects analysis can be used to determine whether it is appropriate to add one project purpose to others and the scale at which such additions should be made. The second area of economic analysis is financial feasibility—the examination of the sources of funds for investment and responsibility for repayment, and funds for operating purposes. This area will be examined in detail in Chapters 9-11.

[9] John F. Timmons, "Theoretical Considerations of Water Allocation Among Competing Uses and Users," *Journal of Farm Economics*, XXXVIII (December, 1956), pp. 1244-1258.

[10] See, for example, S. V. Ciriacy-Wantrup, "Concepts Used as Economic Criteria for a System of Water Rights," *Land Economics*, XXXII (November, 1956), pp. 306-309.

No attempt will be made here to explore all aspects of benefit-cost analysis. The literature and practice of this field are extensive and technical.[11] What is proposed is to survey a number of the conceptual and measurement problems that are encountered in the application of benefit-cost analysis, in order to establish some perspective on the use of this technique as an instrument for planning and administering a basin water program.

The basic approach of benefit-cost analysis is attractive and almost disarmingly simple. It consists of analyzing economic effects "with and without" the project or projects. This calls for a measurement of benefits "to whomsoever they may accrue" and these benefits must exceed costs for the project or projects as a whole to justify investment. In addition, the incremental benefits for any specific project purpose must exceed the separable costs of adding that purpose or level of purpose to the total. If the benefit-cost ratio exceeds 1:1, real national income will be increased as a result of the construction of the project. The larger the amount by which benefits exceed costs, the larger will be the gains in real income from project investment.[12]

The first group of conceptual problems in the application of the benefit-cost technique arises primarily because of the presence of social values that differ from private economic values. In the private sector an optimum use of resources can be obtained if all factor costs

[11] In the Survey of the Delaware Basin the Corps of Engineers had initial responsibility for project justification and hence for the estimation of benefit-cost ratios. In Chapter 18 of this report it is proposed that the staff of DRAW be assigned responsibility for all future project analysis and justification. The Syracuse University Delaware Valley Project does not embrace an examination of the project justification techniques employed by the Corps.

[12] The most comprehensive treatment of this subject is to be found in Otto Eckstein, *Water Resource Development* (Cambridge: Harvard University Press, 1958). Other references include Subcommittee on Evaluation Standards, Inter-Agency Committee on Water Resources, *Proposed Practices for Economic Analysis of River Basin Projects* (Washington, 1958); McKean, *op. cit.,* pp. 25-182; Hubert Marshall, "The Evaluation of River Basin Development," *Law and Contemporary Problems,* XXII (Spring, 1957), pp. 237-257; Arthur Smithies, *The Budgetary Process in the United States* (New York: McGraw-Hill, 1955), pp. 329-359; Eckstein, "Evaluation of Federal Expenditures for Water Resource Projects," *Federal Expenditure Policy for Economic Growth and Stability* (Joint Economic Committee, 85th Cong., 1st sess., 1957), pp. 657-667. An important effort to develop maximization models for planning and administering a river system is in process at Harvard University in a three-year water resource planning and development program. The results are to be published in 1960. See Arthur Maass and Maynard M. Hufschmidt, "In Search of New Methods for River System Planning," *Journal of the Boston Society of Civil Engineers,* XLVI (April, 1959), pp. 99-117.

and all product prices are determined in competitive markets, and if all satisfactions are measured with appropriate price tags attached. But no organized social order tolerates a market determination of all values and all resource allocation. As an extreme example, the administration of justice by the courts is not customarily determined by the interaction between demand and supply schedules in the market place.

In fact, however they may be determined and whatever their relationship to private values, social values do exist, and their existence occasions serious concern in the application of the benefit-cost technique. Private costs and benefits will be very different from social costs and benefits for the same project. These differences may be illustrated in the efforts to compare public and private economic activity. In estimating the value of hydroelectric power in a multi-purpose project it is customary to compute costs of alternative development. But what costs are to be included? If the alternative is private steam electric generation, then the prevailing rate of interest paid for capital would be a part of private costs. But public power projects can raise funds at lower rates of interest. Federal government interest costs are lower than private costs, and development under state auspices could be financed from the sale of securities that would command an even more favorable interest rate because of the tax exemption feature attaching to all state and local government bond issues. It may therefore be inappropriate to impute additional private interest costs to the public development.

The answer to a question of this sort depends on the way economic values are regarded in a mixed economy. To argue that private interest costs should be imputed to public projects is to argue that private market values must be the determinant of economic decision-making. To argue that this cost should not be imputed to public development is in effect to maintain that non-market valuations are as valid as market valuations. Nor are the consequences of this choice unimportant. The imputation of interest charges in the computation of benefits from public hydro will reduce the benefit-cost ratio and reduce the volume of public as compared with private economic activity, with consequent effects on the distribution of income.

A similar and even broader set of considerations is involved in the controversy over the private costs of social financing. This issue has been put in the following terms:

> . . . Federal projects are highly similar in their degree of riskiness to many private projects. It therefore seems reasonable to expect that

Federal investment in these activities should pay off at least at 6 per cent, which, as we have seen, appears to be somewhat below the average return on investments in the private sector of the economy. . . . There seems little or no justification for the Government's withdrawing resources from the private sector unless these will yield as much improvement in levels of living as ordinary private investments.[13]

Other economists have proposed that the social costs of federal financing be computed as the cost of raising capital through taxation and have prepared a set of computations designed to estimate this cost.[14] It has also been suggested that full allowance for alternative private costs might be achieved by putting the minimum justifiable benefit-cost ratio at approximately 1.3.[15]

The case for a private cost approach to social financing is most persuasive when applied to the full employment model. When there are unemployed resources in the private sector, additional public outlay on water-resource projects, or indeed on any other public projects, may be undertaken without a concomitant loss of private goods and services. But when there are no unemployed resources, additional expenditure on water resource projects must come at the expense of private outlay. The private outlay foregone has a cost measured in terms of the goods and services sacrificed in the private sector, and these costs must be balanced against the gains from public activity. At substantially full employment levels, such as those that have prevailed since World War II, it is argued that a private cost concept or a private rate-of-return concept should be applied in benefit-cost analysis.

There are two points that may be made in response to this line of reasoning. The first is that the assumption of full employment may not be reasonable even under economic conditions that appear to represent full employment. Experience in the mobilization programs of World War II and the Korean War demonstrate that conventional notions of capacity can yield to an increase in the level of effective demand. The American economy in peacetime apparently has a large volume of relatively unused or relatively under-employed resources both in labor and in plant and equipment. There is good reason to believe that in most periods of high employment the national economy can absorb an

[13] Arnold C. Harberger, "The Interest Rate in Cost-Benefit Analysis," *Federal Expenditure Policy for Economic Growth and Stability*, pp. 240-241.
[14] Krutilla and Eckstein, *op. cit.*, pp. 78-130.
[15] Eckstein, *op. cit.*, pp. 94-101. See also John V. Krutilla, "Planning and Evaluation," *Journal of Farm Economics*, XL (December, 1958), pp. 1674-1687.

additional expenditure of $2 to $3 billion or more for public investment without corresponding reduction in private outlay and without significant inflation. In these circumstances opportunity cost may not be zero; private economic activity could also be increased.

The second point may be phrased in terms of value structures. Comparisons with private economic values and profit rates rest on an acceptance of the private sector as it now operates, with a good deal of waste and duplication in economic activity, and with producer group influence on consumer demands. The insistence that decisions about public resource allocation be based on interest and profit rates in the private sector implies a value judgment that the private sector as it now operates is a valid measure of economic efficiency. This point has been effectively put as follows:

> The acceptance of the private market standard as a criterion for Federal project justification places the public interest in a peculiar double jeopardy. The private market standard, i.e., justification of public investment on the basis of whether it can yield a return commensurate with private investment, ignores the critical difference between the purposes of private and public economic activities. Moreover, this procedure confers on resource allocation decisions of the private market an economic and ethical omniscience unfortunately not possessed by the market economy . . . It appears strangely inappropriate that the value system of the private market should be accorded such importance in the selection and justification of Federal projects when one of the main functions of government is to initiate or supplement activities that cannot be adequately performed by the market.[16]

A second group of conceptual problems in the application of benefit-cost analysis, related to the first, arises from the production of non-market values by public water development. Such intangibles include the saving of human life through flood control, the improvement in the physical and mental health of citizenry who enjoy water-based recreation, the reduction in disease rates that may accompany an

---

[16] Lawrence G. Hines, "The Use of Natural Resource Expenditures to Promote Growth and Stability in the American Economy," *Federal Expenditure Policy for Economic Growth and Stability,* pp. 699-700. The point has also been made that private costs are often understated because social costs of private activity are not counted. See K. William Kapp, *The Social Costs of Private Enterprise* (Cambridge: Harvard University Press, 1950). The social costs of water pollution are examined on pp. 80-93. See also, W. K. McPherson, "Can Water Be Allocated by Competitive Prices?" *Journal of Farm Economics, XXXVIII* (December, 1956), pp. 1259-1268.

anti-pollution program, and such negative values as the destruction of fish and wildlife or the esthetic losses that occur when a scenic valley is flooded by a reservoir.

Benefits measured in dollar terms are, of course, not comparable with intangible values such as these. But few advocates of measurement techniques will contend that the intangible values of water-resource development are less important than the measurable, tangible benefits.

The presence of intangible values does not, of course, destroy the usefulness of the benefit-cost concept for those elements that can be measured. It does follow, however, that this technique must not become the whole of project evaluation and justification. Project analysis must always include a careful enumeration and description of non-market gains and losses. The door is open and will remain open for non-quantifiable considerations to influence the selection of projects for public expenditure. The technique or procedures used for the analysis of non-market considerations, such as they are, depend heavily on the ingenuity and sometimes the value judgments of expert staff. This is a process of "administrative valuation."

A third area of conceptual importance concerns the treatment of secondary benefits. Secondary benefits stem from the activities of industries that supply the project area with goods or services, or are induced by the industries that process, distribute, or consume the products of the project. From these benefits are deducted (1) costs incurred in such secondary economic activities and (2) net secondary benefits that might be derived from alternative employment of project resources. This computation yields a measure of "attributable secondary benefit." [17]

The controversy over the inclusion of secondary benefits in the benefit-cost ratio has centered on the practices of the Bureau of Reclamation. Outside the Bureau there is general agreement among water-resource and other economists that the inclusion of secondary benefits is inadmissible. It is argued that any investment, public or private, produces a secondary economic benefit and that any broad national view cannot properly attribute more of this kind of economic activity to water-resource investment than to alternative investments that might have been made in the absence of project investment. From this point of view, the argument against secondary benefits would appear to be

[17] *Proposed Practices,* pp. 8-10; see also, *Report of the Panel of Consultants on Secondary or Indirect Benefits of Water-Use Projects* (Washington: U.S. Department of the Interior, 1952).

unassailable, but there may be regional considerations which call for their inclusion.[18]

Apart from the conceptual problems posed by benefit-cost analysis, there is a rather large number of measurement problems. These may be noted but need not be elaborated here. An entirely satisfactory benefit-cost analysis would require knowledge of future prices for water derivatives, factor costs during the period of construction, future operating costs, and future capital costs. None of this kind of information can, of course, be known. Technological change or shifts in relative factor costs or product prices may make uneconomic an investment that earlier appeared to be wholly justifiable. Conversely, changes in relative future prices can enhance the ultimate monetary and social return on water resource investment.

Another type of measurement problem is posed by the so-called spillover effects. As McKean has pointed out, these are both technological and pecuniary.[19] Technological spillover occurs in the familiar case of downstream reservoirs whose effectiveness is enhanced by the construction of additional upstream reservoirs. Pecuniary spillovers are occasioned by shifts in prices that occur as project investment bids up factor costs, raises the price of complementary products, reduces prices of substitute products, or lowers the price of output. Pecuniary spillovers are elusive and may, of course, produce either external gains or external losses.

The presence of the foregoing measurement problems in benefit-cost analysis (and this enumeration is not intended to be complete) has been a factor contributing to sharp disparities in computations of the benefit-cost ratio by different water-resource agencies. Measurement difficulties leave room for differences in judgment and seem to have the effect, on occasion, of encouraging an artificial inflation of the numerator of the ratio.[20]

In spite of conceptual concerns and measurement difficulties, benefit-cost analysis should be retained as a major analytical tool for project evaluation. A great many primary benefits and costs can be ascertained

[18] See below, this chapter.

[19] McKean, *op. cit.*, pp. 134-150.

[20] House Committee on Public Works, *Economic Evaluation of Federal Water Resource Development Projects* (82d Cong., 2d sess., 1952); Fred A. Clarenbach, "Reliability of Estimates of Agricultural Damages from Floods," *Task Force Report*, pp. 1275-1298; Marshall, *op. cit.*, pp. 245-250. Marshall concludes that the resource development agencies are under so many pressures to produce favorable ratios that benefit-cost computations should be subject to an independent central review by a strong unit in the Executive Office of the President.

with dependable accuracy. The analysis should be strengthened, not abandoned. Benefit-cost measurements provide a significant ingredient which helps to channelize and discipline the political process. Benefit-cost sets boundaries for political decisions about water-resource projects and can help to avoid seriously mistaken public investment. The technique encourages additional quantification by water-resource technicians, so that hydrologists, for example, continually search for more accurate measurements of the economic consequences of project development. Improved decisions about public expenditures for resource development, and for other areas of public expenditures as well, depend heavily on further efforts to measure alternative costs and gains. There is, moreover, a neglected but important aspect of the problem in that measurement should extend beyond evaluation in the planning stage to the evaluation of results. This has seldom been attempted by federal or state water-resource agencies, but the staff of a basin agency should include in its responsibilities the examination of benefits and costs after structures are in operation.

Benefit-cost analysis, as used by national government agencies, assumes an undivided national interest in resource development projects. As noted above, it is real national income that is to be maximized. Public investment in projects with favorable benefit-cost ratios, after full allowance for opportunity costs in alternative investments, will contribute to increases in national income. This implicit emphasis on the national interest is an important part of the argument for excluding secondary benefits.

But specific interest groups are well aware that water-resource projects may produce very large increases in localized economic activity. There may be little general understanding of the professional arguments about the techniques for measuring secondary benefits. There is, however, widespread popular agreement that development projects are "good business," particularly if the funds for such projects are provided by the national government with an undetectable fraction of total costs met by an increase in federal tax liabilities imposed on the region itself.

For example, the case for reclamation projects is very different when made on a regional rather than a national basis. At a time of crop surpluses and major expenditures for price supports to maintain farm income, it hardly seems appropriate to spend additional federal funds to bring new lands under cultivation. But from the standpoint of a specific area, there is nothing illogical about this. Federal reclamation expenditures will provide immediate and measurable increases in the income and wealth of an area wherever the national interest may lie.

A similar and even broader point was made by the Cooke Commission in suggesting that the major political and economic stimulus for western flood control and reclamation projects has come as a drive for regional expansion.[21] In these states federal outlays for such programs have been regarded as a necessary offset to the accumulations of economic power and wealth on the eastern seaboard, and as a conscious effort to redistribute income among regions; so viewed, western water programs are the exercise of a kind of countervailing power on a regional basis. And the redistributional consequences of large projects are not negligible, as recent studies have shown.[22]

The question may fairly be asked, what significance does income redistribution among regions have for eastern river basins? These are areas where per capita real incomes are above the national average and thus where considerations of equalitarianism in the regional distribution of income would seem to have little merit. But the fact is that conditions of *relative* economic decline produce a spirit of development not unlike that present in underdeveloped or depressed areas. This is most evidently the case with the New England economy, where in the postwar period there has been much concern over the outmigration of industry, the development of a steel industry, and the reduction of electric power costs—all of this in a context of seeking additional aid from the national government to assist in preventing further decline.

It is reasonable to anticipate that other eastern regions are similarly motivated and will come to understand that federal expenditures for water-resource development will generate substantial increases in regional economic activity. It has often been observed that the national interest is a complex, that a part of this complex consists of strong regional interests, and that these regional interests often conflict one with another. Beyond doubt, a great deal of "wasteful" national government expenditure has been and more could be directed toward the goal of "balanced regional growth." But to assert that an undivided national interest should prevail, or that regional development is of no concern to the national government, is to overlook the realities of our pluralistic order.

Public policy decisions about water-resource development are very

[21] Cited and discussed by Irving K. Fox, "National Water Resources Policy Issues," *Law and Contemporary Problems*, XXII (Summer, 1957), pp. 504-505.

[22] Krutilla and Eckstein, *op. cit.*, pp. 199-264, a case study of the Willamette River.

nearly as complex as those about national defense; and as one observer pointed out recently, in the latter field it is not possible to make reasoned judgments in terms of aggregates, as, for example, in efforts to make comparisons between a 10 per cent reduction in welfare outlays and a 10 per cent reduction in national defense.[23] In the face of this complexity, what happens is that decisions are made incrementally.[24] Only those alternatives are examined that are deemed, rightly or wrongly, to be politically relevant. Decisions are made by reference to policies that have been established elsewhere, and only incremental changes are undertaken. Emphasis is placed on marginal values without insistence on defining ultimate goals and objectives, which would have to be stated so broadly as to have no meaning for specific decisions.

This approach is relevant here. The range of alternatives that ought to be considered in judging the gains and costs from a large multiple-purpose project or series of projects is nearly overwhelming. The necessary comparisons between public and private economic activity are conceptually shaky. The balance between regional and national interests in most intricate. Project evaluation will always contain large elements of uncertainty brought about by changing technologies and changing patterns of human behavior. Nevertheless, an improvement in decisions, as elsewhere in public policy, can come only from continued effort toward systematic evaluation of the range of available alternatives.

This is what makes the case for public planning and development of multiple-purpose water resource projects an unassailable one. Public planning must and does embrace a broader range of values and possible courses of action than private economic planning. In this sense the case for public development rests on the ground that it is more efficient than private development since efforts can be made to maximize a more general set of values.

INSTITUTIONAL CONSTRAINTS ON ECONOMIC DEVELOPMENT

The goal of effective resource allocation should never be lost to sight in planning and administering a system for water-resource develop-

[23] Charles E. Lindblom, "Decision Making in Taxation and Expenditure" (paper for the National Bureau of Economic Research Conference on Public Finances, April 1959).

[24] Charles E. Lindblom, "Policy Analysis," *American Economic Review*, XLVIII (June, 1958), pp. 298-312.

ment. It is important to seek continuously for the highest marginal output of goods and services from each successive input of resources. This chapter has described some of the difficulties that are encountered in the use of the benefit-cost technique in planning for effective resource allocation. It may be useful to touch further on a number of institutional factors that may limit the achievement of optimum development.

First, there are constraints on effective development imposed by the concept of "the national interest." The well-established financial responsibility of the federal government for works of navigation and for flood control may tend toward uneconomic investment in these water programs. Meanwhile, programs for which there is no such strongly established national interest may be neglected and investment in such project purposes as recreation and water supply may fall short of the optimum.

Second, the configuration of voting strength within congressional committees may have the effect of over-emphasizing water development in one region and under-emphasizing it in another.[25] Congressmen in some districts may bargain for support of non-water legislation of immediate interest to their constituents by giving support for water projects in other districts.

Third, state and local governments may be handicapped by their fiscal structures in obtaining the point of optimum investment in water resource development. The inelasticity of state and local revenue sources is well known. When new programs emerge, as water-resource development in eastern river valleys, needs may not appear to be immediately pressing and the kind of interest group support necessary for heroic state and local financial effort may therefore be lacking.

Fourth, there are conflicts among alternative uses of water. Multiple-purpose development itself involves a conflict among project purposes. The water released today for pollution abatement is not available tomorrow to maintain navigation depth. Low-flow augmentation in summer lowers reservoir levels and may destroy recreation values.

Another source of conflict is distributional in nature. Where public funds are spent for resource development, some individuals and firms benefit more than others, with a corresponding enhancement of their incomes, wealth, and economic power positions. The distributional conflict is especially noticeable when development is financed from

[25] The political implications of Congressional leadership and voting patterns are explored in Chapter 19.

general tax sources, since tax burdens will not, of course, correspond with benefits.

Yet another conflict is sub-regional in impact. Some parts of a river basin will necessarily benefit more directly from development than others. Areas whose economic activities depend most heavily on water-using industries may be expected to benefit relatively more than areas where industrial water is unimportant. Those who live near reservoirs will benefit more from recreational facilities than those who live at a distance. There is no way to avoid this kind of sub-regional concentration in the distribution of benefits.

The foregoing kinds of conflicts in development programs cannot be resolved by an appeal to criteria of economic efficiency. Such conflicts, endemic in the economic order, can be resolved only by what Lindblom has called "partisan mutual adjustment." The emphasis on objective criteria for development should not obscure the continued prevalence of such conflicts among at least partially antagonistic interests. It has been said that there is no Republican or Democratic way to pave a street, but there are Republican and Democratic streets to be paved.

Finally, it may be noted that the general presence of institutional constraints on development and the prevalence of inherent conflicts is not altered when development is undertaken in the private sector. Decision-making by private firms in water development may be completely efficient in terms of private sector resource allocation; but private decisions concerning water will also have impact on other economic activity, and distributional and sub-regional effects as well. These effects will be different from those accompanying public development, but private development does not eradicate them. In the private sector the impact of decisions is obscured by the market process. In the public sector the elements that influence decisions and their consequences are more nearly open for all to see.

Water-resource development under public auspices uses market measurements where possible to guide but not control decisions. Public development must also rely on the analysis of alternatives that may be described by staff experts, and must be subjected to the political responsibility that can be assured by adequate procedural and organizational relationships.

CHAPTER 7

Legal Bases for Regional Action

On what legal foundations should the planning and management of water resources on the Delaware, an interstate stream, rest? Any new or expanded activity might be based upon federal statute, state statute, interstate compact, court decree, or some combination of these. Indeed, as in the case of the Missouri Basin Inter-Agency Committee and a few other agencies, administration might rest in part upon less formal arrangements. Legal authority is the starting point, the relatively permanent description of new or changed activity, that will set the tone of future work, establish the forms, powers, and lines of responsibility of any new agencies, and assist in determining the goals toward which their personnel may aim. Any new organizations to cope with the complex functions outlined in Chapter 4 will, in the long run, require the passage of many laws giving new powers and authority and subtracting others. The crucial problems of getting new activity under way and providing it with a firm legal base in its early life are dealt with in this chapter.

No new water resources effort can ignore the obvious and important fact that in several functional fields legal frameworks now exist. For example, in navigation, flood control, and irrigation the national government has established itself both by law and by long practice, and has virtually displaced state activity. In smaller measure, the national interest in pollution control and in fish and wildlife measures has been recognized. New or augmented effort must take advantage of these manifested interests and recognize existing statutes or it must substitute therefor new patterns of cooperation or appropriation.

This is actually a two-sided problem. Which legal base is preferable will in the natural give-and-take of the political process be determined by the existence or absence of certain conditions. For example, desire for speed in getting a new program established will restrict possible alternatives. The support available in the campaign for adoption and the nature of that support will also limit the choices which may be made. These, in a word, are tactical considerations leading to the choice of legal base.

Secondly, the results that may be expected to flow from a given legal base will aid in determining which one shall be chosen. Among the results to be prejudged before the new program is established are the degree of permanence desired for the new program; the difficulty of changing a given base; the powers available to new organizations under alternative legal arrangements; the geographical reach of the various legal bases; who may be committed to participate in a new program under the terms of a given legal form; the kinds of interest groups that in the long run may be expected to rally behind a particular legal authorization; the sources of funds theoretically available under a given legal establishment; and so on. All of these, long-run considerations necessarily impossible of factual determination, might be classified as the strategic aspects of selection of legal base.

EXECUTIVE ORDER OR AGREEMENT

Among less-than-statutory alternatives, direct action by state or federal executives is the most obvious means for sparking water resources activities on a stream like the Delaware. The Delaware River Basin Advisory Committee is an example of how governors of the four states (together with the mayors of New York City and Philadelphia) may, without reference to their legislatures, deal with limited interstate policy issues. DRBAC is confined to a few planning and coordinating functions and is admittedly temporary, yet it probably represents the limits of voluntary, informal action by the governors. For they must scrape together the funds required for collaborative action from sources approved by law, and they are virtually prevented by law from altering agencies or programs by executive order or agreement.

More common is the establishment by the President or by a high federal executive official of a water planning or coordinating organization through the device of executive or departmental order. For example, the field committees by which the Department of the Interior coordinates its activities in seven regions of the United States were set up by departmental order. The nationwide framework for consideration of inter-agency resources problems, headed by the Inter-Agency Committee on Water Resources, is founded on executive action alone. In both cases, the committees are empowered only to study and "co-ordinate" the work of established program agencies. The prestige of neither has been high, and Congressmen have been reluctant to acknowledge their usefulness.

The limitations of the executive order are obvious. Only at the federal level can such orders comprehend interstate issues or areas. Furthermore, they have served as basis only for study or "coordinating" agencies which are usually temporary. Since an executive cannot commit funds over a period of years to an organization based on his own order only, the device is fiscally inadequate. A case can scarcely be made for its use in establishing an administrative organization.

STATE STATUTE

Water management agencies of many different types have been created by state laws. These range from the state bureau, department, or commission, to local governments operating under grant of state powers, to special districts or authorities erected by law to handle various kinds of water problems. Thus more than 162 water authorities and 113 sewer authorities had been created in Pennsylvania to 1957 under the Municipal Authority Act of 1945.[1] In New York in 1957 there were 254 instances in the field of water supply and 65 in the field of sewage treatment and disposal in which two or more adjacent local governments were cooperating under the terms of some six different state laws.[2] Both the Pennsylvania and the New York examples illustrate a common method of state encouragement of local initiative—the permissive law. The state places enabling legislation on the books, but leaves it to local citizens or officials to initiate new functions or organizations. Such legislation usually applies throughout the state.

Special law is resorted to less frequently in the water-management field. Nevertheless such well-known intrastate water agencies as the Massachusetts Metropolitan District Commission, the Metropolitan Water District of Southern California, and the South Carolina Public Service Authority (for the Santee-Cooper Project) have been launched by special state statute.

There are strong limitations to the use of state statutes. The only satisfactory means of employing them on interstate streams is through

[1] "Pennsylvania's Billion Dollar Babies," Federal Reserve Bank of Philadelphia, *Business Review*, March, 1958, p. 17.

[2] *Village Law*, Sections 236 and 276; and *General Municipal Law*, Sections 110-117 and 120.

combining parallel statutes in adjacent states. The uniform state laws movement has led to the adoption of many uniform acts, but most of these have been of a regulatory or criminal nature. In 1957 the Council of State Governments was urging no uniform laws in the field of water resources; instead, in their *Suggested State Legislation Program for 1957* the need was emphasized for federal laws and interstate compacts for "major river basin projects." [3]

Incodel is the prime instance of a water agency created for an interstate stream by parallel state action. The committees on interstate cooperation have as a principal purpose "securing full cooperation among the states in solving interstate problems, both regional and national." [4] Other instances are given by the Metropolitan Rapid Transit Commission, a temporary agency established in 1954 by the New York and New Jersey legislatures to study transit needs in the New York-New Jersey metropolitan area, and the Interstate Commission on Lake Champlain Basin, created in 1956 by parallel action by the New York and Vermont legislatures to plan and carry through a 350th anniversary celebration of the discovery of Lake Champlain. The purposes for which these agencies were established suggest a rather narrow range of activity for commissions created by parallel state statutes. Experience here seems to offer little promise for the development of positive programs and vigorous organizations in the water-resources field from this source.

INTERSTATE COMPACT

The interstate compact and the federal statute are the two legal bases which meet the test of adequate geographic reach.[5] They also meet the criterion of durability, although there are doubts as to the flexibility of the interstate compact device. The ratification of a compact change by two or more state legislatures is likely to be a lengthy process at best; at worst it may constitute an impossible obstacle.[6] Legally speaking, all powers available to the states individually are

[3] *Suggested State Legislation Program for 1957* (Chicago: Council of State Governments, 1956), pp. 144-149.

[4] *The Book of the States 1958-59* (Chicago: Council of State Governments, 1958), p. 201.

[5] On an international stream, of course, the treaty is an additional type of legal basis that would meet this test.

[6] There are numerous examples of amendments to compacts. For example, the Compact between New York and New Jersey Creating the Port of New York Authority has been amended, as have the Tri-State Compact for Pollution Abatement and the Interstate Compact on Juveniles.

available to them collectively through the device of the compact.[7] Where the Congress has enacted a federal law, the states of course may not act in violation thereof, nor is it likely that a compact would envision performance of functions for which Congress has already assumed responsibility or has appropriated money to other states or areas. In the context of a particular time and a given function, as when Congress has consistently refused to act or when federal administrators have repeatedly refused to exercise powers on the statute books, it may be that the sole means of dealing with an interstate problem is by means of the compact. By compact, funds may be made available to an interstate agency from all the sources available to state agencies of other types: appropriation, state lending to the new agency, and borrowing by means of revenue bonds. Federal grants-in-aid and even federal appropriations have been made to compact agencies.[8] That the interstate compact can provide a solid basis for a vigorous program and an organization with high prestige that is able to cooperate actively with federal, state, and local agencies is signified by the records of a few well-known agencies: the Port of New York Authority, the Interstate Sanitation Commission, and the Ohio River Valley Water Sanitation Commission among them.

Interstate compacts ordinarily require several years for preparation and ratification, and this fact alone is cause for hesitation in choosing the compact route. A staff member of the Second Hoover Commission reported that, for 19 successful compacts which deal with various aspects of river management and control, the average time for negotiating, ratifying, and securing consent was eight years and nine months.[9] A new compact covering management of the several important water functions delineated in Chapter 4 would be more complex in its provisions and more comprehensive in coverage than any of these 19. Although many of them were for western states, there is no assurance that an eastern compact would take less time. The issues to be hammered out in drafting and achieving consensus on a compact for a comprehensive planning and operating agency for water would be

[7] Felix Frankfurter and James M. Landis, "The Compact Clause of the Constitution—A Study in Interstate Adjustment," *Yale Law Journal*, XXXIV (May, 1925), pp. 687 ff.

[8] A good case might be made for congressional appropriation to a compact agency of flood control, navigation, or other traditionally federal costs for a dam built on a navigable stream.

[9] Wallace R. Vawter, "Interstate Compacts—the Federal Interest," *Task Force Report*, III, p. 1693. A federal representative participated in most of these negotiations.

most difficult. The difficulties would be increased if some new means of gaining further federal participation were sought. The patience and inventiveness of negotiators would be taxed, and a period of several years might well be consumed in the process.

Experience with the compact device has been examined many times, and no general critique is required here.[10] Instead, attention will be turned to some more specific comments about its use for water purposes and about possible means for gaining closer federal collaboration with compact agencies.

Recent Water Compacts

The central fact about creation of a core agency for river basin development by interstate compact is that the utility of the compact for this purpose remains speculative, for there is no instance of its employment to plan comprehensive water development or to set up a multiple-purpose agency for water. Inferences must be drawn from the cases where pieces of such jobs have been done. Here comment will be limited to some of the recent developments on the compact front.

Two of the more serious attempts to establish multi-purpose basin agencies through compacts—on the Delaware and on the Missouri—were abandoned. The Delaware River proposal, advanced by Incodel, gained wide approval but failed of passage in the Pennsylvania Senate in 1953. The Missouri River draft compact was originally proposed by the Missouri River States Committee with the assistance of a special committee of the Council of State Governments. The governors themselves, acting through the MRSC, voted to drop the compact idea in 1955.[11]

In the eastern states a few water compacts were in effect in 1959, all of them for very limited purposes. The Tri-State Compact for Pollution Abatement represented a pioneering stride in that field.[12] As the legal base for the Interstate Sanitation Commission (ISC), it confers on

[10] See Frankfurter and Landis, *op. cit.;* Frederick L. Zimmermann and Mitchell Wendell, *The Interstate Compact since 1925* (Chicago: Council of State Governments, 1951); V. V. Thursby, *Interstate Cooperation* (Washington: Public Affairs Press, 1953); Wallace R. Vawter, *op. cit.;* Ernest A. Engelbert, "Federalism and Water Resources," *Law and Contemporary Problems,* XXII (Summer, 1957), p. 325; Richard H. Leach and Redding S. Sugg, Jr., *The Administration of Interstate Compacts* (Baton Rouge: Louisiana State University Press, 1959).

[11] See Chapter 14.

[12] 49 Stat. L. 932 (1935); approved by New Jersey in 1935, New York in 1936, and Connecticut in 1941.

that body jurisdiction over the lower Hudson River, New York Bay, much of Long Island Sound, and related waters. There are no federal members on the Commission, which however has good relations with the Public Health Service, Corps of Engineers, and other federal, state, and local agencies. So far, the small staff has focused its attention on research, classifying waters, and cleaning up pollution by municipalities, including New York City. ISC on its own initiative may enforce its standards against any violator. Power of the Commission to order compliance by municipalities has been affirmed by state courts.[13]

Similar compacts are the Ohio River Valley Water Sanitation Compact (effective with eight state members in 1948)[14] and the Potomac Valley Pollution and Conservation Compact (joined by four states and the District of Columbia in 1945).[15] The operating agency on the Ohio, the Ohio River Valley Water Sanitation Commission (Orsanco), has three commissioners from each of eight states and three federal members appointed by the President. Its small staff has established good working relations with many other agencies, federal, state, local, and private. Article IX of its compact gives Orsanco power to enforce its anti-pollution orders in court by about the same procedure as the ISC employs, although no injunction proceedings had been brought by 1958.[16] Orsanco has limited its activities to studying, setting standards, and urging cooperation among municipalities and industries. Like ISC it has had greater success with municipalities than with industries in gaining compliance with its standards.

Incopot, the Potomac agency, has three members from each of four states, three from the District of Columbia, and three federal members appointed by the President. It is noteworthy that the federal government has appropriated $5,000 annually to Incopot, in addition to the $30,000 total each year contributed by the states and the District. Activities to date have been confined to research, public information, and encouragement of cooperation, for Incopot has no enforcement powers.

---

[13] Interstate Sanitation Commission, *Report, 1956* (New York, 1957, mimeographed); and Stanley Kollin, "The Interstate Sanitation Commission: A Discussion of the Development and Administration of an Interstate Compact" (unpublished master's thesis, Syracuse University, 1954), pp. 92-96. First action was taken against Union City, West New York, and Weehawken, N. J. in May, 1948.

[14] 54 Stat. L. 752, 1940.

[15] 50 Stat. L. 884, 1937, and 54 Stat. L. 748, 1940.

[16] Suit for enforcement against Gallipolis, Ohio, was discussed in 1956, as were other possible injunctions in other years. Orsanco, *8th Annual Report* (Cincinnati, 1956), p. 11. A majority of commissioners from the state where the polluter is located must vote in favor of injunction proceedings, by terms of the Compact.

Proposals to broaden the scope of the Commission's powers to include coordination and planning for multiple-purpose use were considered in the period 1956-1958, and a new compact was being drafted in the spring of 1959.[17]

The records of these three organizations provide excellent illustrations of the concrete but limited results achievable for single water purposes under an interstate compact. The burden of anti-pollution work is still shouldered by the relevant anti-pollution agencies in the member states.[18] Enforcement steps against large industrial polluters have yet to be taken, and compliance normally depends upon negotiation and persuasion.

Another school of thought about the function of water compacts in the East is revealed in the Connecticut River Flood Control Compact (1953), signed by Connecticut, Massachusetts, Vermont, and New Hampshire. On its face, the compact does two things. First, it specifies the dams that the three upper basin states "agree" to allow the United States to construct from among those authorized for the Corps. Second, it provides for downstream states to reimburse upstream states for portions of the taxes lost by reservoir flooding and other damages thus incurred. There is no federal representation on the Commission. The functions here may be considered planning or operating only in a narrow sense. The compact obviously is viewed by its signers as a weapon to be employed in longstanding arguments with the national government.[19]

Four compacts recently effected in the western states—in 1950, the Canadian River (New Mexico, Texas, and Oklahoma); in 1953, the Sabine River (Louisiana and Texas); in 1957, the Klamath River (California and Oregon); and in 1958, the Bear River (Utah, Idaho, and Wyoming)—illustrate the kinds of interstate water agreements that

[17] See Incopot, *Compact Revision Report* (Washington, 1957); and Abel Wolman and John C. Geyer, *Consultants' Report to the Interstate Commission on the Potomac River Basin* (Baltimore, 1958, mimeographed).

[18] A Tennessee River Basin Water Pollution Control Compact was approved by Congress in 1958. It calls for a Commission of three members from each state and one appointed by the President for "liaison and reporting." It is to have power to enforce its orders like that possessed by ISC and Orsanco, 72 Stat. L. 823.

[19] 67 Stat. L. 45. The Merrimack River Flood Control Compact has similar features (71 Stat. L. 18, 1957), as does the Thames River Flood Control Compact (72 Stat. L. 364, 1958). See also the Tennessee-Tombigbee Waterway Development Compact (72 Stat. L. 608, 1958) for an instance of an eastern water compact that falls far short of meeting many of the criteria applied in this book.

have gained support in the West in recent years.[20] None of these contemplates a basin development agency of a multiple-purpose nature. The central aim of all is to provide for the equitable use and distribution of water resources within the respective basins. To this end, each compact carefully spells out the terms of interstate water allocation, provides a framework for settling future disputes, and authorizes collection of hydrologic data by the commission. The Klamath River Basin Compact deals with data collection and pollution control by leaving them to the separate states; but it gives the commission authority, in cases of disputes over pollution, to issue "orders for correction thereof." Additional purposes of the Sabine River Compact are declared to be ". . . to encourage the development, conservation and utilization of the water resources . . ." of the river and ". . . to establish a basis for cooperative planning and action by the States for the construction, operation and maintenance of projects for water conservation and utilization purposes on that reach of the Sabine River touching both states, and for apportionment of the benefits therefrom."

Federal government representatives were present at negotiations for these compacts, and provision is made for the non-voting chairman of each commission to be appointed according to federal law. It will be interesting to observe in coming years how effectively federal members are able to participate in these organizations. Federal interests are often immediate and tangible in western river basins, quite apart from the fact of the frequent use of federal funds in actual reservoir or other construction.

Among the older water compacts providing for federal representation on the commission is the Upper Colorado River Basin Compact (Colorado, Arizona, New Mexico, Utah, and Wyoming, 1949). The compact gives the Commission power to perform several planning functions, but no study of the operation of this grant is available. The federal commissioner, who serves as chairman, is entitled to vote, although the Commission reportedly operates by the "consensus" method.[21] This compact, like the four previously mentioned, is primarily intended to

[20] 64 Stat. L. 1124, 68 Stat. L. 690, 71 Stat. L. 497, and 72 Stat. L. 38. The Sabine River of course flows through a wet area.

[21] Congressional committee discussions before passage of the Upper Colorado River Basin Compact neglected the problem of the powers of the federal representative, but hours were spent discussing whether and how Congress would commit the national government by signing the Compact in the first place. 81st Cong., 1st sess., "The Upper Colorado River Basin Compact," *Hearings before a Subcommittee on Irrigation and Reclamation of the Committee on Public Lands* (Washington, 1949), especially pp. 59 ff.

settle the issue of which states get how much water. When that division is accomplished,[22] the major point of interstate friction in most of these basins is settled, at least for the immediate, post-negotiation period. It can be argued that this type of agreement is a first step in planning, but it may also be viewed as constraining subsequent planning.

Federal Work with Compact Agencies

The Council of State Governments has encouraged state governments to use the interstate compact ". . . as a vehicle for sharing with the federal government in the development of major river basin projects."[23] Wallace Vawter found, furthermore, that in 29 instances of proposed compacts, ". . . the Federal interest in the negotiations was felt to be important enough to warrant appointment or designation of a Federal representative to participate or assist and encourage." Of these, 25 compacts ". . . were to be concerned with agreements for allocating water supply or controlling pollution."[24] There are thus a number of precedents that point toward more experimentation in federal participation in compacts and possibly more substantial commitments by the federal government in compact-based enterprises.

A regular procedure for federal participation in compact negotiation is prescribed in a letter from the Director of the United States Bureau of the Budget.[25] No method of appointing a federal representative in compact negotiation is specified,[26] but it is stated that any such representative, among other things:

> a. . . . has the duty of assuring that the complete range of Federal or national interests is considered in the negotiations, . . .

[22] In terms of their responsibility to maintain specified minimum flows, in terms of total acre feet of consumptive uses, in terms of water needed to irrigate certain acreages of land, or by other standards.

[23] See *Suggested State Legislation Program for 1957, op. cit.*, p. 145; also Frederick L. Zimmermann and Mitchell Wendell, *op. cit.*, pp. 60 ff., for a brief but imaginative discussion of further federal participation in interstate compacts. See also Zimmermann, *op. cit., passim.* Details of 23 water compacts are listed in *State Administration of Water Resources* (Chicago: Council of State Governments, 1957), p. 19.

[24] Vawter, *op. cit.*, pp. 1694-5.

[25] "Guide to Federal Participation in Interstate Compact Negotiation" (Washington, January 3, 1956, duplicated).

[26] Congressional authorization for compact negotiation often sets a method for choosing the federal representative. Vawter, *op. cit.*, pp. 1693-5.

b. . . . is responsible to the President through all stages of the compact's negotiation and final clearance. He will report to the President through the Director of the Bureau of the Budget.

Many different federal agencies work closely with compact organizations. Relations of the Public Health Service with the various interstate compact water pollution control agencies, for example, are today integral parts of the pattern of cooperative federalism. The U.S. Fish and Wildlife Service is named in the compact as the research arm of the Atlantic States Marine Fisheries Compact Commission,[27] and it has carried out several research projects for the Commission.

Beyond this point, however, there is no standing guide to the type or extent of federal participation that may be written into a compact. The Upper Colorado River Compact is evidence that the federal representative may have a vote in compact agency deliberations. But how far may he commit his government? Obviously federal funds could not be allocated through the means of a compact, nor could a Congress or President be committed beyond the present moment in any substantive, procedural, or other matter. Presumably, federal representatives could never be outvoted. In so far as history provides a guide, the sovereign character of the federal government would always be the over-riding fact in any discussion of terms for such a compact.

This problem is not novel, even if it is relatively unstudied. A minority of three in the 1953 report of the Missouri Basin Survey Commission thought a new agency for that basin ". . . should be established by a compact to which the basin States and the Federal Government are parties. Its members, moreover, should be selected by and represent each basin State and the United States."[28] They spoke no more precisely of the relationship, believing that the duties and powers of a new organization could best be worked out in the compact negotiations. The Commission majority, however, concluded that:

. . . its report should come before the President and Congress as free as possible of unsolved constitutional questions . . . an attempt to establish a State-Federal Compact would raise constitutional questions which would require prolonged litigation. . . .[29]

[27] *Atlantic States Marine Fisheries Compact,* Article VII. The Fish and Wildlife Service "shall act as the primary research agency . . . cooperating with the research agencies in each state for that purpose."

[28] Missouri Basin Survey Commission, *Missouri: Land and Water* (Washington, 1953), p. 13.

[29] *Ibid.,* p. 10. James W. Fesler assumes that ". . . a truly joint regional instrument of the states and the federal government . . . [is] unavailable . . . on a

A Northeastern Water and Related Land Resources Compact drafted for the Northeastern Resources Committee (an agency of the New England states) in 1958 called for one member from each state (presumably any state in the northeast might join) and seven members representing unspecified federal resources agencies, all members to have a vote.[30] In discussions before a subcommittee of the Inter-Agency Committee on Water Resources the problem of constitutionality figured prominently—this despite the facts that the proposed compact agency was to have only coordinating and research functions, that no mention was made in the draft as to how federal funds would come to the agency, and that the position of the federal members appeared to be little different from that of the federal member on the Upper Colorado River Basin Compact Commission, which has operated for nearly a decade.

In the absence of a Supreme Court decision that no interstate compact can establish a water resources agency which contemplates a greater federal part than now exists, there is wide leeway for discussion and good reason for exploration of such arrangements. The paramountcy of the national government is the undeniable major premise of the discussion. The challenge is that of finding a formula recognizing that sovereignty but permitting closer state-federal collaboration on crucial water-resource issues.

A compact could pledge the lasting good will of the federal establishment. It could acknowledge state-federal collaboration as wise public policy. Methods of bringing requests for appropriations annually through regular budgetary channels to President and Congress might be spelled out. Decisions might be taken only when federal representatives voted with a majority, and/or there might be a majority of federal members. These suggestions, however, are just that. Compact negotiations would produce more. The interstate compact has been called a major device for smoothing the rough edges of the federal system in practice. Surely there is room for fresh thinking and experimentation here.

---

nation-wide basis." "National Water Resources Administration," *Law and Contemporary Problems*, XXII (Summer, 1957), p. 445. See also Frederick L. Zimmermann and Mitchell Wendell, "Representation of the Region in Missouri Basin Organization," *American Political Science Review*, XLVIII (March, 1954), pp. 152-165.

[30] The draft provides that no action on other than internal management matters can be taken unless majorities of state and federal members are present and majorities of both majorities vote in favor thereof. Article VII of the Compact.

We must not deny ourselves new or unfamiliar modes in realizing national ideals. Our regions are realities. Political thinking must respond to these realities. Instead of leading to parochialism, it will bring a fresh ferment of political thought whereby national aims may be achieved through various forms of political adjustments.[31]

Summary

There are no full-fledged precedents for multiple-purpose planning or development by a compact agency, with or without federal participation. The compact remains the most acceptable vehicle for state participation in the management of interstate waters. Why has it not yet been effectively used? Specific reasons can be named for specific compact failures. One may speculate as to more general reasons. First, there is the fear on the part of its critics that the compact agency is the route to little or no action—that it will magnify what are believed to be the conservative or laissez-faire tendencies of state governments in the resources field. Second, the states often are reluctant to step in where ambitious programs already are operating under Corps of Engineers or other federal agency direction, as for example in the Missouri basin. Next, a serious problem at the very heart of the basin water controversy is that of the division of water between states. Officials may hesitate to specify concrete allocations of water for the future, and this tendency is heightened when there is uncertainty as to quantities of available water. Apparently this unwillingness to cut up the water pie over the long term has been a major factor in the Missouri Compact stalemate, as also on the Delaware.[32] Whether litigation or

[31] Frankfurter and Landis, *op. cit.*, p. 729. On p. 688 these authors repeat, "Creativeness is called for to devise a great variety of legal alternatives to cope with the diverse forms of interstate interests." C. Herman Pritchett in "Regional Authorities through Interstate Compacts," *Social Forces*, XIV (December, 1935), pp. 205-6 goes somewhat further: "Some sort of federal control over the activities of interstate authorities would be inevitable and essential. The federal government would exercise influence in the actual drafting of the compact. . . . The compact should make provision for continuing federal influence in the affairs of the authority. . . . Some sort of federal control over the developmental plans of the authority would be essential, so that they would not be out of line with the national program. . . . Federal grants-in-aid to the authority would furnish an effective method of influencing the execution of its program. . . ."

[32] Cf. Wallace R. Vawter, *op. cit.*, p. 1693, where he reports that average negotiation time for 19 river management and control compacts is much longer than the averages for other types of compacts. Vawter's article gives a fairly complete catalog of the pros and cons of the compact device.

compact negotiation is the more time-consuming, costly, and nerve-wracking remains a moot question. They usually, in fact, go together. Some litigation has been terminated in much briefer time than that on the Colorado, but experience there stands as an eternal reminder that compacts are no guarantee litigation will end.

There may be a tendency for compact agencies to reflect some of the faults of the state governments, their progenitors. There is no way of guaranteeing that personnel will be of high quality, and possible mediocre staff may be reflected in disappointing agency performance. If state legislatures are unrepresentative in character, any compact agency they help to create is likely to be similarly unrepresentative. The lesson here is that state appointments to any compact agency should be made by the Governor, the most representative of state officials. This is in fact common practice. The dearth and uncertainty of methods for assuring the responsibility of compact commissioners, once selected, makes it that much more important that their choice be made by a politically responsible authority.

FEDERAL STATUTE

Few objections may be raised to the federal statute as a basis for water-resources administration on an interstate stream with regard to adequacy of geographic coverage, permanence, and adaptability to changing conditions. Furthermore, the criterion of adequate powers is better met by federal statute than by any other legal basis. Among the water resources functions outlined in Chapter 4, only that of the power to allocate water is questionable as to exercise by the Congress through statute, and even there recent developments signalize a growing exercise of federal power.

An additional and very important consideration lies in the fact that a federal statute theoretically would make available all the financial resources of the national government. The principal potential sources of funds for water-management uses include direct appropriation from Congress, authority to issue revenue bonds, and loans from the national government. So deeply committed is the federal government to construction activities in navigation, flood control, and irrigation, that it may well be useless even to consider looking elsewhere for support for these functions.

The TVA, the Bonneville Power Authority, and the Southwestern and Southeastern Power Administrations, all based on federal statutes, are continuing evidence of the efficacy of federal statute as a basis for river basin administration. That they rest on federal law and do not formally depend upon state instrumentalities for their operation means that the specter of "states' rights" may always be raised in opposition to them. On the other hand, each of these agencies has carved out for itself a permanent niche in the federal system, and in so doing has learned to work closely with state and local governments.

Can some means be provided for direct state participation in an agency created by federal statute? In the new Southeastern River Basin Commission and Texas River Basin Commission, formal state representation is provided on the commission by requiring the governors to nominate candidates and the President to choose appointees from among these nominations. This would seem to be a practicable way of recognizing state concern while preserving the national interest. Direct appointment by the governors to such federally-based commissions might be held unconstitutional by the courts.

To sum up, the federal statute offers many advantages as a legal basis for interstate administration of water resources: sufficiently broad geographic jurisdiction, permanence, adaptability to change, adequate powers, fiscal adequacy, prestige, and possibilities for fitting well within the framework of federalism. If in the past it has left unresolved the basic issue of federal-state collaboration, that may be because of excess of caution in probing the possibilities the device affords.

THE SPECIAL PROBLEM OF WATER ALLOCATION

Legal bases for controlling withdrawals and diversions of interstate waters have been examined so often that they need no extended discussion here. Potential bases include United States Supreme Court decree, federal law, and interstate compact. They are not mutually exclusive, and any of them may provide for an administrative agency to manage withdrawals and diversions within specified limits.

Court Decree

After negotiations at the administrative level or in pursuit of a compact have failed, the Supreme Court on occasion has allocated water among contending states by decree.[33] Thus the 1931 allocation of Dela-

---

[33] See the cases included in T. Richard Witmer (comp. and ed.), U.S. Department of the Interior, *Documents on the Use and Control of the Waters of Interstate and International Streams* (Washington, 1956), pp. 457-732.

The term, "allocate," is used synonymously with "apportion" to mean a single

ware River water was re-opened in 1954 when New York City sought more Catskill water. The method followed by the Court was that of appointing a special master to adduce evidence and encourage cooperative study and mutual concession. Taking cognizance of population and economic growth, the Court revised its earlier decree, granting both the New York and the New Jersey requests for additional water. It also appointed a river master to administer the decree, and stipulated that the case might be re-opened when any interested party might wish.[34]

Here are displayed at their best the qualities of judicial settlement of a water dispute: (1) careful sifting of data and other evidence by an ad hoc special master; (2) lengthy, well-organized conferences between contending parties, initiated by the master; (3) a fairly prompt and clear decision; and (4) the prestige of a Supreme Court action. Add to these attributes provision for review on petition by an interested party, and an impressive case emerges for continuing the method and applying it elsewhere.[35] A court decree, however, is a dispute-settling device. Moreover, a decree tends to emphasize the states as major parties to the division of interstate waters, and this emphasis unfortunately does not tend to maximize the economic value of water.

As early as 1907 in *Kansas* v. *Colorado*[36] the Supreme Court recognized that water use is related to economic development and based its division of Arkansas River water on its judgment of the economic situation. In so doing the Court engaged in broad planning for the economies of the two states, and in nearly all water allocation cases in recent years it has done the same thing. This is planning on an ad hoc basis, with no special regard for any plans that legislatures or administrators may have formulated. Only a narrow range of possibilities is raised in making decisions that may have profound future economic impact.

---

act. "Control of withdrawals and diversions," includes these terms, but is also intended to include a process that may be administered by a governmental agency.

[34] *New Jersey* v. *New York*, 283 U.S. 336 (1931); 347 U.S. 995 (1954). See also Chapter 16. There is a federal court-appointed water master for Lake Tahoe on the Truckee River, California and Nevada.

[35] See the excellent discussions of division of water between states in William A. Schnader and Samuel A. Greeley, "Discussion of a Difficult Allocation Decision," *Engineering News-Record*, Jan. 13, 1955, pp. 35 ff.; and Maynard M. Hufschmidt, "The Supreme Court and Interstate Water Problems: The Delaware Basin Example" (Cambridge, rev. 1958, duplicated), especially pp. 65 ff.

[36] 206 U.S. 46, 99 ff.

The Court insists that a real dispute must be present before it will take jurisdiction.

When dealing with other water functions than allocation, the Court also becomes involved in planning. For example, in early 1959 the U.S. Solicitor General asked the Supreme Court to appoint a special master to ". . . reevaluate the needs of all parties and to make recommendations as to the future pattern of development . . ." for purposes of sewage disposal in the Chicago area.[37] He was demanding environmental planning of a broad nature. Ultimate resort to the courts can never be denied, but it is highly doubtful that they are suited to exercise of the planning function. The Supreme Court itself has urged caution in these words:

> We cannot withhold the suggestion, inspired by the consideration of this case, that the grave problem of sewage disposal presented by the large and growing populations living on the shores of New York bay is one more likely to be wisely solved by co-operative study and by conference and mutual concession on the part of representatives of the states so vitally interested in it than by proceedings in any court, however constituted.[38]

Federal Law and Interstate Compact

The virtues and shortcomings of the decree method are best appraised in comparison with two alternative devices: federal law, by which priorities might be accorded to water uses;[39] and interstate compact, by which rights to water use have often been apportioned (among western states). Some relevant considerations may be examined briefly.

1. Under any of the three methods a carefully prepared body of data will be required. In the past, the collation and interpretation of data have usually been performed ad hoc, in preparation for making more or less permanent divisions of interstate water. This has been true whether the deliberations were by the Court in equity, by negotiators of a compact, or by congressional committee. More rare has been the creation of a permanent staff to perform these duties after an

[37] *Chicago Daily Tribune*, April 15, 1959.

[38] In *New York* v. *New Jersey*, 256 U.S. 296, 313 (1921). On this point see also Frankfurter and Landis, *op. cit.*, pp. 706 ff. ". . . most questions of interstate concern are beyond . . . all court relief . . ." p. 707.

[39] No instance has been found where water has by law been allocated among states, and Congress' authority to do so is questionable.

allocation decision has been made. That step was taken on the Tennessee and Missouri Rivers in pursuance of federal law and on the Upper Colorado River by compact terms. The Delaware river master also exercises this function with regard to specific directives in the 1954 decree. Presumably a federal law or a compact could provide for periodic re-setting of allocations between states or even between other geographic areas or users, and for a permanent staff to collect and study data and recommend such re-allocation as well.[40] Such procedure, however, has not yet been adopted.

2. Conferences among all interested parties might be convened from time to time under all three methods, with rules recognizing the best of both legal and social science procedures.

3. Where one state's need is clear, the Supreme Court can settle allocation disputes quickly. Some litigation, however, has been protracted, for example in the Arkansas and Laramie allocation cases[41] where state need was not readily demonstrable. Examination of a number of compact negotiation experiences suggests that very pressing needs by most or all states in a basin must be manifest before a water division formula can be reached.[42] Congress arrived readily at the 1944 Missouri priorities when various factors coincided to create what was apparently overwhelming pressure for action. Given favorable conditions, therefore, it would seem that a prompt decision is obtainable under any of the three devices, although the requirement of unanimity probably makes the compact procedure slowest.

4. The decree method is stamped with the authority of the Supreme Court, undoubtedly a more awesome hallmark than that of a federal law or a compact. Eastern water uses from now on are going to shift and grow rapidly, however; and a decree might confer too much prestige on a given division of water. Its immunity from criticism could slow down needed re-division and unduly skew economic development as between states or parts of states. With its need for consensus, the compact route is perhaps even more inflexible.

5. By means of all three devices continuous opportunity can be provided for re-opening and changing a division of water. New demands for water will continually arise as economic conditions change, and no allocating device will ensure an agreement permanently pleasing to all concerned.

[40] But see Article IIIB of the 1944 draft of a Yellowstone River Compact, in T. Richard Witmer, *op. cit.*, p. 254.

[41] See T. Richard Witmer, *op. cit.*, *passim*.

[42] Schnader and Greeley, *op. cit.*, pp. 36 ff.

Allocation by Administrative Process

A better means of controlling withdrawals and diversions may be derived from the fund of experience on rivers like the Missouri, the Tennessee, the Upper Colorado, and the Delaware. This experience stems from the work of the administrative staffs on these rivers, who continuously collect and interpret data, in some cases direct operation of principal control structures, and oversee withdrawals and diversions that have been set by higher authority. On the Missouri and Tennessee that authority comes from priorities stated in federal laws; on the Upper Colorado, from division among the party states in a compact; and on the Delaware, from division between states fixed by Court decree.

A new Delaware Basin agency, created by federal law or compact, could exercise this function as an *administrative* responsibility. A Basin agency exercising several other vital water functions could endow its apportionment decisions with a great deal of prestige, although appeal to Supreme Court and Congress would remain available. In such an appeal the intermediate agency could develop its own case, with records and opinions distinct from those of other parties. Any final Court allocation therefore would be on even firmer ground. And if the administrative allocation were sound the agency would be upheld by the Court and its prestige thereby enhanced.

Administrative control of diversions and withdrawals offers prospects of greater flexibility and speed than any other method. The staff of a basin agency might continuously discuss and decide water allocation. The lengthy, formal re-negotiation required for amending a compact, a law, or decree could thus be obviated, or at least the means of obviation would be provided.

Only through administrative processes can control of withdrawals and diversions be dynamically related to planning by the Basin agency. Maximization of effectiveness in water use will occur only where allocation among users is studied in conjunction with management of mainstem dams, quality control, and all major water-related activities. The water budget mentioned in Chapter 4 would be an integral part of this complex planning process. The Basin agency's power to allocate would make of the water budget a vital action instrument. All this is to emphasize the basic significance of planning for the function of allocation. The Supreme Court decree of 1954 provided water to New York and New Jersey, for their needs were clearly established. At the same time the economic future of the Delaware Basin was placed in jeopardy, for it was weighed by a temporary staff on a one-shot basis. The dynamics and the continuing nature of planning were largely ignored. Water allocation is too intimately related to other water functions, its proper performance ties in too closely with changing economic conditions for it to be done without reference to long-range water planning. Such continuous attention to basin planning is best provided by an administrative agency.

Administrative settlements could be made among actual water users—municipalities, industries, private persons. The Supreme Court and interstate compacts have traditionally settled controversies and apportioned water among *states*, and they may be expected to continue to do so. The issue properly phrased, however, is not "Which states shall get how much water?" but rather "Where or to what users should how much water go?" The latter question is more likely to develop from an administrative process, given favorable auspices and strong support, than from a court, congressional committee, or compact negotiating body.[43]

An administrative agency, finally, can make democratically responsible allocations of water. It can adopt quasi-judicial rules and regulations to assure regularity of procedure, and give adequate notice of its decisions. It can offer continuous opportunity to change plans and shift water uses. Appeals channels can be kept open, and the whole process can be carried on under the eyes of the press, elective officials, and citizens groups.

If state or other interests are so strongly committed to the permanent allocation idea that the only practicable course of action on the Delaware seems to be a long-term allocation by law or compact, there is still a chance to put the idea of administrative allocation to limited use. The opportunity arises from the fact that in 1959 there is no water supply emergency on the River. Therefore concrete allocations for current proved needs, including those of New York City and New Jersey, or priorities supporting the needs could be settled by a law or compact. The unused increment of water within stipulated limits could then be allocated administratively from time to time by a new basin agency. This would recognize existing vested interests yet allow the agency some flexibility in prosecuting its program. In 1959 there is still much unused and re-usable water in the River.

[43] Another variant that might be considered for adoption for the Delaware is allocation by state courts among users, as in some western states. This would still require gross division among states, however; and the idea is rejected here as undesirable on this and several other grounds, and on the ground that state courts are not suited to this type of planning.

Summary

The system established by judicial decree has worked well on the Delaware in performing the limited task for which it is intended. If, however, comprehensive planning and development are to be introduced for that stream, it is hard to see how a court decree can serve satisfactorily as its permanent legal basis. The compact method of dividing water leads to inflexible allocations and thus is also unsuitable for a central role in dynamic and comprehensive development. Priorities set by federal law offer little more promise, although they could be used to fix the limits of administrative allocations.

A basin agency created by compact or by federal law could be empowered to make administrative allocations of water. This would ensure a desirable flexibility in allocation. At the same time, all legal rights would be preserved through appeal to the courts. Such an agency could employ quasi-judicial procedures in taking its decisions—procedures like those used by the special master in the 1954 Delaware decree proceedings. The political climate may be such that this power cannot be worded to include all water in the Basin. A wise alternative then would be first to pin down present, proven needs by division in a law or compact; and second to leave to the new agency power to divide administratively among users the water not clearly required as of the time of original allocation. If the allocation process is to be connected in any meaningful way with the comprehensive development of the Valley, it must be significantly related to the function of water-resource planning. Such a relation can be best established by vesting responsibility for both in the administrative agency to be created for the Delaware Basin.

CHAPTER 8

Organizational Forms

SINCE before Alexander the Great adopted the phalanx, the importance of organizational forms in government has been evident and the close relationship between form and function has been recognized. This chapter is based upon the assumption that structure is one of the important determinants of the continuing effectiveness of an organization's administration of a program. There are four separate but interdependent points to be made in this connection:

1. Organization or form to some extent is determined by and in turn determines function. This idea has been examined in Chapter 4 and is mentioned here only for re-emphasis.

2. The general public, disparate publics, and interest groups often cling to myths or beliefs about specific organizational forms which, true or untrue, set limits to political possibilities. For example, slogans and myths unfavorable to valley authorities in general, bolstered by specific myths about the TVA, were used effectively in the Columbia and Missouri Basins to prevent adoption of valley authorities.

3. Specific structural details are crucial in establishing the lines of democratic control over policy-making. Thus it is important whether the members of the board of a new agency are appointed by and responsible to the President, a federal department head, or a governor, as distinguished from appointment by several such executives or from "responsibility" to a legislature or Congress. The more diffuse the lines of responsibility are, the less certain it is that consistent policies will be formulated and followed over the long pull. The formal position of the Bonneville Power Authority under the Secretary of the Interior tends to make it a more responsible organization than another which may not be so clearly in the executive establishment—the so-called independent commissions, for example. This is not to make excessive

claims for the importance of formal lines of authority in determining responsible policy-making, but it is to insist that such lines significantly affect responsibility.

4. Structure has important meaning for the internal management of an agency. Clear lines of administrative authority from the top to the bottom of an agency assist greatly in establishing and carrying out policy. This key tenet of public administration needs no further elaboration. If an organization is plainly laid out, it is easier for the influences of public opinion, higher executive authority, professionalism, and organizational pride to be balanced one against another.

To offset these claims as to the importance of structure, it is well to remember that ". . . many arguments about form and structure are really rationalizations or concealments of arguments about substance." [1] Thus any public investment at all in water development may be attacked on the grounds that the federal government or a valley authority should not be involved. "States' rights" may become a cloak for the position of interest groups who feel they can exert dominant influence on a program if it is a state responsibility. This caveat is only the traditional one that motives may be devious and that ". . . things are seldom what they seem."

Notwithstanding these and other qualifications, organizational form palpably is highly important to the field of water resources. Many different types of structure have been tried, and there is a wide variety in existence today. The bulk of this chapter is devoted to a discussion of these organizational forms as they have worked and in theory might work at federal, state, and local levels.

GOVERNMENT CORPORATIONS

In most democracies today the suggestion that the government launch a new program in resources development would immediately evoke the idea of a government corporation for that purpose. *Étatisme* has not expanded as consistently in the United States as in many other countries, but it has commanded wide acceptance nevertheless, especially in time of war and depression. The Tennessee Valley Authority (federal) and the Port of New York Authority (interstate) are the best-known examples of the public corporation, although state-created corporations like the Erie County Water Authority in New York and

---

[1] Herbert A. Simon, Donald W. Smithburg, and Victor A. Thompson, *Public Administration* (New York: Alfred A. Knopf, 1950), p. 44.

the Turnpike Authority in New Jersey are familiar to the people of those states. All are ad hoc organizations, brought into being by superior governments for specific, limited purposes.[2]

Government corporations possess most or all of the following characteristics:

1. separate legal existence and substantial autonomy;
2. authority to determine and make their own expenditures;
3. a commercial or private-business system of accounting;
4. an annual budget approved *as a whole* by Congress or legislature;
5. a commercial-type audit, not extending to review of the legality of each expenditure;
6. financing by means of revenues and revenue bonds, or in the case of federal corporations by direct annual appropriations from Congress which may be carried over from year to year;
7. exemption from ordinary civil service requirements;
8. flexible boundaries which may be defined to fit the function to be performed or purposely left vague.[3]

Public corporations, then, operate in a domain between the private and public sectors. They evidence growing recognition that expansion into certain fields requiring the flexibility of commercial operations is a proper function of government. Corporations have not often engaged in other kinds of activities.

The generic term "corporation" applies to agencies known variously as authorities, boards, corporations, commissions, and so on. Commonly, corporations created by state or local governments are referred to as authorities. The 36 federal corporations with few exceptions are known as banks or corporations. Most of the 78 corporations active in New York State in 1956 were called authorities. The approximately 1200 corporations (mainly local) extant in Pennsylvania in 1957 were termed authorities. These variations in usage need not be confusing, although the differences from state to state and even from corporation to corporation are such as to necessitate examination of individual cases. Federal authorities operate under the terms of the Corporation Control Act of 1945, while in the states there are often general acts that determine the methods of creating corporations and the limits within

[2] The special case of TVA is discussed in Chapter 14.

[3] Sidney D. Goldberg and Harold Seidman, *The Government Corporation: Elements of a Model Charter* (Chicago: Public Administration Service, 1953), pp. 5-7.

which they may operate.[4] Federal corporations generally are in the
executive branch and report to one of the department heads: only the
TVA and the Export-Import Bank report directly to the President. The
few interstate corporations report to their governors or legislatures. At
the state level a usual pattern is for authorities to report to the legislature, on the ground that they are distinct from the executive departments.

A desire for greater independence—from legislative and other popular controls, from executive direction, from civil service requirements, from the legislative appropriation process, and from standard
financial controls—along with the need for large amounts of capital
have been the primary motives in the establishment of most corporations. There is every prospect that their number will continue to
increase.

The growth in corporations and authorities has come about in the
face of increasing fears that more and more of the public's business is
being removed from direct popular control. Many critics have ques-
tioned the wisdom of having wide-ranging policy decisions made and
tremendous sums of money handled by officials who are not subject
to the periodic check of the ballot. How, it has been asked repeatedly,
can the rates charged by corporations be better synchronized with the
over-all tax structure? How can their physical plans be better ac-
commodated to the manifold plans of general government at all levels?
How, in short, can the operation of authorities in the public interest
be assured? [5]

Corporations continue to fulfill a need that other organizational
forms cannot meet, or at any rate have not met. Foreign observers
have often commented favorably on the records of American governmental enterprises. The TVA, for example, is one of the features of
our federal system most admired and envied by other countries.

---

[4] *Ibid.*, p. 8; State of New York, Temporary State Commission on Coordination
of State Activities, *Staff Report on Public Authorities under New York State,*
Legislative Document No. 46, (Albany, 1956), pp. 4 ff; "Pennsylvania's Billion
Dollar Babies," Federal Reserve Bank of Philadelphia, *Business Review,* March,
1958, p. 17. For general comments on corporations and their underlying phi-
losophy, see A. H. Hanson (ed.), *Public Enterprise,* (Brussels: International
Institute of Administrative Sciences, 1955); and W. Friedmann (ed.), *The Public
Corporation* (Toronto: The Carswell Company, 1954).

[5] See, for instance, Temporary State Commission on Coordination of State
Activities, State of New York, *op. cit.,* Chap. XI; and W. Friedmann, *op. cit.,* pp.
576 ff.

Responsible American students, however, have usually endorsed Luther Gulick's view:

> An authority should be the last resort, not the first bright idea. If there is any doubt, use the regular machinery of government, a machinery which has been developed over many years of experience to guarantee democratic control, the coordination of political decisions and the protection of daily operations.[6]

"The Regular Machinery of Government"

A second common suggestion when a new water program is mentioned is that its conduct be vested in an existing agency of government. The rationale is precisely that stated above by Mr. Gulick, and is self-evident. What may not be so obvious is that such a course of action involves grave risks. The call for a program to go to such-and-such a department may rest on the secure knowledge that there it will operate under a low ceiling—that innovation and expansion will be limited. In an old department policies, attitudes, and workways can be so impervious as to smother new ideas. A water-resources development program aimed at comprehensiveness may be out of place in an organization where such technicians as irrigation engineers, soil conservationists, flood control experts, and navigation engineers have long been dominant. Adequate appropriations for a new program may not be forthcoming if it is put within an existing agency, where budget limits have long been hardened. And in the case of some established agencies, decisions may be so subject to the influence of private interest groups as to preclude proper carrying out of the policies implicit in the new program. Many writers believe a new program should be kept organizationally separate until it is firmly established, at which point it may be shifted into a regular department if a congenial home can be found for it. At any rate, the character of existing agencies and their abilities to perform adequately the programs they already have are good, if general, criteria of their suitability for coping with new programs.

Federal Departments

The idea of putting a new water program for an interstate river somewhere in the established framework of federal administration is convincing in logic but puzzling in practice. For many years the dis-

[6] Luther Gulick, " 'Authorities' and How to Use Them," *The Tax Review,* VIII (November, 1947), p. 51.

persion of responsibility for national resources administration and water resources administration in particular has been a target of criticism. The Programs and bits of programs are scattered among many different agencies ranging from the bureaus in a number of executive departments to the virtually independent commissions and corporations.[7] "The federal government's relation to water resources is perplexingly complex," in great part because "water" is not a clear-cut organizing idea,[8] but for other reasons also. Half a dozen official study commissions since World War II have echoed this finding and formulated proposals for correcting it. Among them were the two Hoover Commissions, the President's Water Resources Policy Commission, the Missouri Basin Survey Commission, the Temple University Survey, and the Presidential Advisory Committee on Water Resources Policy.

The First Hoover Commission, to illustrate, recommended that the Department of the Interior should be thoroughly reorganized into the principal natural resources department with primary responsibility for water programs. It suggested that the flood control and rivers and harbors functions of the Corps of Engineers be transferred to Interior. A Board of Impartial Analysis was proposed for the Office of the President to review all engineering and architectural project proposals, including those relating to water projects.[9] It is hardly necessary to add that nothing came of this recommendation. Year after year the confusing organization continues, and there can be little doubt that water and other natural-resource programs suffer from the inter-agency conflicts thus perpetuated.

The situation confronts the proponents of new programs with a serious dilemma. If a comprehensive water program for the Delaware Basin is to be created by federal law, where should it be located in the federal administrative structure? Should it be associated with the Corps of Engineers? The Corps has coordinated and led the current Delaware survey. Once the survey report is filed with Congress in 1960 or 1961, a strong case can and probably will be made that the Corps should build the key water control structures specified in the survey. This raises the question whether the Corps should become the central agency for long-term development of water resources in this

---

[7] See Perry R. Taylor, "Inventory of the Federal Agencies Handling Water Resources and Power Development and Conservation," *Task Force Report,* III, pp. 1003-1049.

[8] James W. Fesler, "National Water Resources Administration," pp. 444-445.

[9] U.S. 81st Cong., 1st sess., H. Doc. No. 122, *Department of the Interior* (Washington, 1949), *passim.*

eastern Basin. The Corps might find it exceedingly difficult to prosecute a balanced, multiple-purpose program, in the face of its long commitment to and emphasis on flood control and navigation. From the standpoint of theoretical desirability, a number of objections to long-term Corps leadership on the Delaware may be raised. First and foremost among these is the impressive bill of particulars prepared by Arthur Maass and Albert L. Sturm, among many students of these problems, to the effect that the Corps should have no civil functions at all.[10] Their case is built in part upon the location of civil activities in a military department, in part upon specific policies and engineering practices of the Corps, in part upon the traditional influence of non-governmental interests in this agency's work, and in part on the anomalous organizational situation that has just been stressed above. It would be difficult to justify placing a new Delaware program in the hands of the Corps for reasons other than expediency.

Is the idea of a new eastern water program vital enough and is its public and congressional support strong enough to warrant attempting to put the program in the Department of the Interior, thus taking a giant step toward making that Department in truth the major federal water agency? A new program might founder on that proposal alone. Should the areal aspects of a new program be emphasized by having it report directly to the President, outside regular departmental lines, as the TVA and the Export-Import Bank do? The idea is attractive, given the lack of a national water policy and of a rational federal organization for water administration.

Beyond this point, if prime responsibility for a new program is to be placed in a federal agency, the cooperation of other water agencies must be obtained—the Geological Survey, Public Health Service, and Soil Conservation Service, for example. State and local participation in policy-making and administration is also an urgent need.

Inter-Agency Committees

Inter-agency committees have originated at the federal and federal-interstate levels as partial solutions to the problems of divided responsibilities and of coordination with state and local governments. Familiar examples of the inter-agency device include committees for the Mis-

---

[10] Arthur Maass, *Muddy Waters*; Albert L. Sturm, "Civil Functions of the Corps of Engineers—Relation to Military Mission," *Task Force Report*, III, pp. 1473-1578.

souri, Columbia, Pacific Southwest, Arkansas-White-Red, and New England-New York, along with the current Delaware River Survey Coordinating Committee. These committees have come about in two principal ways: (1) Those for the Columbia, the Pacific Southwest, and the Missouri stemmed from the initiative of the old Federal Inter-Agency River Basin Committee and from state desire for participation in federal agency deliberations; and (2) the NENYIAC, AWRIAC, and Delaware committees stemmed from congressional committee or presidential directive. The latter category has been considered temporary and those committees have usually disbanded operations when a survey report was finished. In 1958 two new inter-agency study committees were created by law for the southeastern states and for Texas.[11]

Some of these committees have served moderately well as mechanisms for communication and discussion of problems that cross agency lines. Whether they have been able to "coordinate" federal agency and state efforts is open to serious question, as is also their utility as devices for producing comprehensive, multiple-purpose studies or plans or for operating control systems.[12] Members find it virtually impossible to surmount loyalties to their superiors and to the ideas and traditions of their agencies; various professionals—engineers, soil specialists, sanitarians—find difficulties in communicating with each other; incomplete technical knowledge and data continually present obstacles to agreements. There are no permanent staff officials to assist members. Nor have states ". . . exercised a very influential role in those basins where they are participating on the committee."[13]

If inter-agency committees are to be more effective, program and organization lines among federal agencies and between federal and state agencies will have to be relaxed somehow. The committees have insecure legal bases, however; and it may be impossible for them to exercise more powers than they now do.

[11] 72 Stat. L. 1058 and 1090. The President is to appoint all members of both study commissions, but state members will be nominated by governors. On the Texas commission there will be 7 federal (a chairman and 6 representing agencies) and 7 state (representing basins in Texas) members. On the southeastern commission there will be 7 federal (a chairman and 6 representing agencies) and 4 state (representing separate states) members.

[12] Cf. Wallace R. Vawter, "Case Study of the Arkansas-White-Red Basin Inter-Agency Committee," Commission on Organization of the Executive Branch of the Government, *op. cit.*, pp. 1443, ff.; and Henry C. Hart, *The Dark Missouri*, (Madison: University of Wisconsin Press, 1957), pp. 197-199 and 205-206.

[13] Ernest A. Engelbert, "Federalism and Water Resources Development," *Law and Contemporary Problems*, XXII (Summer, 1957), p. 343.

State Departments

Studies and judgments about state water or natural resources administration are less frequent and less well-known than those about federal. This is especially true of states east of the Mississippi. Somewhat more attention, therefore, will be directed at state problems and in particular at the four Delaware Basin states. Three considerations are especially pertinent: (1) water-resource planning, (2) management of specific water or water-related programs, and (3) the general condition of water policy. Assessing these points will aid in appraising the capabilities of the Delaware states to join in planning and managing an expanded water program through their established governmental institutions.

If the states are to take an active part in the administration of a water program, they should participate in water-resources planning from the beginning. So far as can be determined, no eastern state government has prepared a comprehensive plan for a major basin. And because virtually all major rivers in the East drain more than one state, it seems unlikely such a plan will ever appear. An authority with broader geographic jurisdiction than the state will have to produce it, as in the current Corps of Engineers survey of the Delaware. State officials are taking part in the Delaware survey, though primarily as observers.

State and local governments have engaged in water planning activities in a few intra-state basins in the East. Examples include work on the Muskingum (Ohio) and the Santee (South Carolina) and related basins. To the west, activities in Oklahoma and the Lower Colorado of Texas may be noted. In all these cases the federal government assisted materially. The New Jersey proposal for the South Branch of the Raritan might loosely be termed a basin plan. Also Pennsylvania in 1958 prepared a plan for the Brandywine Creek (by contract with a private firm), but in this case the lower reaches of the basin are in Delaware and that state did not participate.

The existence of active, well-manned planning agencies in Washington and the willingness of Congress to pay for basin planning go far to explain state avoidance of the water planning function. Eastern states do not now have the technical personnel or the organization to perform the complex tasks of basin water planning.[14] When Delaware

[14] A Pennsylvania legislator has used an apt simile to describe the situation. The people of the states consult the Corps about water developments as they consult a doctor about bodily ills. On the basis of the Corps' plans, they may then

Basin states face a detailed planning assignment, they contract it to a private firm.[15] Incidentally, the technical aspects of Incodel's Delaware plan of 1950, sponsored by an interstate agency, were also prepared by consulting engineers.

In the West and South where state governments are more active in dealing with water, proposals have been made for state or local planning, and/or operation, with the national government contributing those portions of the costs it customarily contributes on a nonreimbursable basis. This is the plan adopted with reference to the flood control costs for the Oroville Dam in California. Such an arrangement is also included in the Markham Ferry authorization in Oklahoma (Grand River Authority) and in the Priest Rapids project on the Columbia where the Grant County Public Utility District is to build and operate the facilities.[16]

Other basins have been planned and/or developed chiefly with federal funds by the Corps or the Bureau of Reclamation, or by one of these agencies jointly with state or local authorities, and subsequently turned over to the state or locality for operation. This happened in the case of the Lower Colorado River Authority, and it was an early proposal for the Muskingum, where eventually the Corps took over the operating job. These and some other similar agencies had PWA, WPA, or RFC assistance.

In the approaching era of fuller development of eastern rivers, it will be crucial that the states engage in comprehensive planning of their intrastate basins. For intrastate basins the state planning effort, given adequate funds and trained staffs, may be sufficient. Again, obviously, single states, no matter how skilled their planners, cannot deal effectively with interstate rivers. But the agencies (regardless of their nature) that eventually produce working plans for interstate rivers should be able to consult state water plans and confer with state water planning agencies. As the Hudson, Delaware, Susquehanna, Potomac,

---

go to the state government to do the building, just as they take the doctor's prescription to the druggist. This is the pharmaceutical theory of partnership in water resources.

[15] A New Jersey example is Legislative Commission on Water Supply, *Survey of New Jersey Water Resources Development* (New York, 1955), prepared by Tippets-Abbett-McCarthy-Stratton, Engineers. In a few respects this document meets the requirements for a state water plan, although its shortcomings as a comprehensive statement of policy are obvious.

[16] U.S. House of Representatives, 84th Cong., 1st sess., *Hearings*, Committee on Interior and Insular Affairs, "Discussion of Budget Bureau Circular A-47 and the Related Power Partnership Principle" (Washington, 1955), p. 44.

and other basins parallel each other down the eastern seaboard, so intelligent water plans for each must sooner or later be laid out alongside those for their neighbors.[17]

These observations serve to accent the minor, piecemeal role that the states have played in the past in planning water developments. If the states are to take part effectively in water development, they must first look to the planning function and get their houses in order. Planning and action must go closely hand-in-hand.

Limited-Purpose Programs

In Chapters 2 and 3 organization for water administration in the Delaware states has been described and virtues and shortcomings noted. More can be said, however, about execution of water programs in further evaluation of state capabilities.

An over-all standard of a state "comprehensive water program" has been proposed by the Council of State Governments.[18] Such a program would cover these facets: hydrologic data research, over-all water resource planning, clear-cut water use rights, water pollution control, careful review of federal projects, assistance to local governments, and state developmental activities. No program priorities are named by the Council. A canvass reveals that the four Delaware Basin states measure up to the suggested standard in few respects. In the gathering of hydrologic data and in pollution control they would probably rate best, and these are program areas where the federal government has provided leadership. There is practically no systematic coverage of water law problems in any of the four states, nor is there even a high-level attorney who gives his full attention to that field.

Water is a comparatively recent policy area of major concentration by eastern state governments. The groundwork of governmental activity in most aspects of water problems has been done by the national government and by localities. Some measure of future state ability to take part in ancillary parts of basin development may, however, be

---

[17] State plans also provide a framework for local developments. Indeed they may make more evident the need for local projects to be multi-purpose and thus for state aid to localities to make possible building the more expensive structures thereby entailed. One is reminded of the great New York City system in the Catskills where power, recreation, and other uses play little part. See *The California Water Plan, op. cit.*, p. 227.

[18] *State Administration of Water Resources* (Chicago: Council of State Governments, 1957), pp. 66 ff.

found in the character of water-related programs they are now operating. Interesting examples in the Delaware states are the navigation and hydroelectric power programs in New York, the flood control program in Pennsylvania, and the diversion control and water supply programs in New Jersey:

1. The New York Department of Public Works operates a system of over 524 miles of canals, parts of which are more than 150 years old. Not only are millions of tons of cargo annually still carried on this system of waterways, but it serves as a valuable recreational resource as well. Long regarded as an outstanding example of a vigorous state program in a field in which the federal government elsewhere reigns supreme, the canal system was dealt a heavy blow as a state enterprise when, in the general election of 1959, the people of New York authorized the legislature to take steps to turn the system over to the federal government. Presumably this vote portends the end of state activity in the domain of navigation.

2. Another example of New York's vigor in administering water developments is found in the work of the Power Authority of the State of New York, created in 1931, which began the generation and sale of power from the St. Lawrence in 1958. It is also currently constructing a major generating plant on the Niagara River. When this latter comes into service after 1961, the Authority will have an installed capacity of over 2,900,000 kw, placing it well up on the list of hydroelectric power producers in the United States.[19] The five trustees of the Authority are appointed by the Governor, with consent of the Senate, for five-year terms. Financing is entirely by revenue bonds; the first issue of $335,000,000 was offered in 1954. It is far too early in the active life of this agency to attempt to gauge the quality of its performance.

3. In the face of a vigorous program of flood control on the part of the federal government, the Commonwealth of Pennsylvania today has an active flood control program which is unusual among the states. The Department of Forests and Waters for many years has had statutory authority to engage in such work, and as early as 1943 it was clearing debris from stream channels in the wake of flash floods.[20] This aspect of its program was given added significance by Hurricane Diane and other 1955 floods, so that the cost of projects planned or completed

---

[19] *New York Times,* June 29, 1958, Section 11; New York State Power Authority, "St. Lawrence Power" (Albany, August 10, 1954).

[20] Current legal authority is in Act 195, 1947.

since that year totals $16,951,000.[21] This activity is financed by a one-cent tax on cigarettes which yielded $12,000,000 for channel rectification and small works, principally in the Delaware Basin, and by miscellaneous funds from other sources (including proceeds from oil and gas leases, which the Secretary of Forests and Waters may devote in part to this work).

Projects are planned, designed, approved, contracted, and supervised during construction by the Department. Ordinarily local governments are assessed part of the cost of a structure in the form of assistance in estimating flood damages, provision of land and easements, and guaranteeing the state against liability—provisions similar to those the Corps of Engineers has employed in its projects. In many respects, the methods used in the Pennsylvania program derive from the practices of the Corps. The engineer in charge of the program in 1958 was a former Corps employee, while the Chief Engineer for the Department of Forests and Waters was a long-time Bureau of Reclamation engineer.

Some rather large structures have been built by Pennsylvania; for example, the single-purpose George B. Stevenson Dam on the West Branch of the Susquehanna River cost $14,000,000 and has a capacity of 75,800 acre feet (acre foot: the amount of water necessary to cover one acre to the depth of one foot). Further, there is a current policy of using these dams for recreation purposes whenever possible.

Whether this program duplicates or conflicts with the federal flood control program in Pennsylvania is a difficult judgment to make. Three large dams have been built at sites where the Corps was authorized by Congress to build, but where actual appropriations for construction seemed to be far in the future. Among the smaller works the Commonwealth has built or intends to build, several have been refused approval by the Corps. Forests and Waters engineers claim that they are able to use more economical (yet still safe) designs than is the Corps. Furthermore, land enhancement benefits are included in benefit-cost computations by Pennsylvania to a much greater extent than Corps regulations permit. Otherwise, benefit-cost calculations on the larger Pennsylvania projects closely parallel Corps' procedures, while small stream clearance is carried out when costs do not exceed the total of damages over the past five years.

How is the existence of this relatively expensive program explained? For the answer, one must look to diverse political, historical, and phys-

[21] Department of Forests and Waters, Commonwealth of Pennsylvania, "Interim Report on Emergency Flood Control Work" (June 7, 1957, mimeographed).

ical factors. The floods of 1936 and succeeding years and especially those of 1955 profoundly affected Pennsylvania thinking and rendered the public more willing to devote money to flood control work. The state is characterized by many narrow river valleys, heavily urbanized and inclined to torrential flooding by mountain streams. Whether this is more characteristic of Pennsylvania than of other states along the Appalachian chain is, however, debatable. In any event, here is a state program that is a counterpart of a federal program. Currently the relationships between the two are fairly clear: Pennsylvania builds nothing included in the Corps program for reasonably early construction. The state program can be expected to remain at a high level of expenditure for an indefinite period.

4. If an eastern water crisis is in the making, it may be that the most significant state programs in the Delaware Basin are those in the broad area of the control and provision of industrial and municipal water supply. Severe water shortages from drought and inadequate provision of facilities have led New Jersey to launch three such programs that may prove significant precedents for future eastern basin developments. The first of these concerns the control of ground water withdrawals, to an extent somewhat greater than in other eastern states. This program is described in Chapter 16. The second involves the management of the Delaware and Raritan Canal to transport and sell a monthly average of up to 100 mgd of Delaware River water to municipalities and industries in the rapidly growing urbanized area about New Brunswick. The Department of Conservation and Economic Development has collected over $100,000 annually from these sales in recent years.[22]

Third, in the fall of 1958, New Jersey voters approved a proposal for a $45,850,000 bond issue that will place the state even further in the water supply business. Most of this money will go to construct two large reservoirs to alleviate at least for the next twenty years the domestic and industrial water shortages in the mid-Jersey portion of the New York-Northeastern New Jersey metropolitan area.[23] Raw water will be sold by the state to local distributors and the bonds retired from the proceeds. It is physically possible for this system at some future date to be integrated with operation of a comprehensive Delaware River control plan.

[22] State of New Jersey, *Annual Report of the Commissioner of Conservation and Economic Development* (Trenton, 1954-55 and 1955-56).

[23] About $6,000,000 of the bond issue will finance ground water studies and investigations into other means of replenishing surface flows. Chapter 34, P.L. 1958.

State Water Policy

Perhaps the cardinal point of this discussion of water programs in four eastern states is that, like most states, not one of them has a comprehensive water policy regarding the uses of water, their priorities, and their control by government. In certain substantive areas, as has been seen, their official stand is marked out and well-financed programs exist on solid bases. But when serious problems arise regarding questions of water use and water rights, the resort is to the courts and the rather vaguely defined common law. In the coming era of shorter and shorter water supply, the uncertainties of judicial administration through adversary action are bound to have serious effects.

Criticism of the absence of a comprehensive water policy can be carried one step further. In none of the Delaware Valley states is there convincing evidence that a search for such a policy is under way. The framework of thinking employed in dealing with routine affairs is characteristically unsuited to placing the varied pieces of the water-resources programs side by side and balancing them with one another. The concept of the watershed or drainage basin is rarely incorporated in routine operations in an important way. Questions arise and are settled in terms of individual projects.

Yet examples may be drawn from each of these states of the significance of the watershed concept. All P. L. 566 small watershed projects are perforce couched in watershed terms. Water pollution studies sometimes are done by drainage basins.[24] Pennsylvania's flood control structures must be planned in accordance with the drainage areas they control. A new optional water planning law in New York State permits policy formulation along drainage basin lines.[25] There are, however, only a few such instances. The general absence of thought and action in drainage basin terms precludes the optimum conditions for consideration of water-resource problems from coming into play.

The Delaware Basin states likewise have far to go in employing multiple-purpose concepts, although here, too, a beginning has been made. As one might expect, New Jersey, where the pressure of population is great and where land is progressively more dear, is deeply involved in this problem. The issues facing a Land Use Committee in the Department of Conservation and Economic Development have been described thus:

[24] Yet in Pennsylvania the regions used for enforcing anti-pollution measures have no relation to the state's watersheds.
[25] Chap. 843, L. 1959.

The significance of the Committee lies in the fact no state in the Union goes so far as New Jersey in supporting a large population on extremely small land area. The state can ill afford the luxury of employing land for one particular purpose to the exclusion of other compatible uses. Some tracts can be utilized for a variety of purposes—for water supply, for timber production, for hunting and fishing, and for such forms of recreation as hiking, camping and water sports. Government is under obligation to study all the potentialities of the public domain. . . .[26]

The purchase in 1956 of the 90,000-acre Wharton Tract southeast of Camden has given new reason for threshing out a land-use policy.[27] The sandy barrens provide excellent catch basins for extensive ground water aquifers, wildlife thrives there, and folk from the teeming city find the stunted pines and clear streams relaxing to their nerves. Should roads, beaches, and tourist facilities be built to pollute the water and mar the natural beauty? Should controlled burning be adopted to improve deer habitat? These and similar issues are being vigorously debated, both by officials and by the various publics involved. It is significant that, in this debate, the importance of planning for multiple-purpose development is recognized.

The future will bring more such controversies to state water and other natural resources officials in the crowded East. The concepts of multiple use of land and water are bound to be examined and reexamined countless times. Whether created by federal law or by interstate compact, a water planning and management agency for the Delaware Basin will find ample opportunity to provide leadership and guidance to these disjointed state efforts.

SUMMARY

In view of the considerations raised in this chapter and the one preceding, it is evident that the choices of legal bases and organizational forms to be employed for a new Delaware water agency are limited. Either federal statute or interstate compact, all factors considered, is the legal base which would best assist in meeting the criteria set forth in Chapter 5. On the basis of experience federal law would be the more expeditious of the two, although a compact possibly would offer the states opportunities to play fuller roles in a Basin water de-

[26] State of New Jersey, *Annual Report of the Commissioner of Conservation and Economic Development*, 1954-55, p. XIII.
[27] *Ibid.*, 1955-56, pp. 25 ff.

velopment program. Both legal bases fit well into the framework of evolving federalism, and both afford an adequate legal foundation for performance of the functions outlined in Chapter 4. There is, indeed, good reason for believing that *both* federal statute and interstate compact could be employed to advantage in stages over a period of time to gain optimum water development in both the regional and the national interest.

Upon either legal base an administratively unified Delaware Basin water organization could be set up. By federal law, a corporation or other independent agency could be created for the region. It might report directly to the President, and both federal and state members might sit on its governing body. There is ample precedent for these arrangements. By interstate compact with federal participation (a federal-interstate compact), a like organization could be created to perform comparable operating functions. Some inventiveness will be demanded to design the means of federal participation in a federal-interstate compact. There are, however, some precedents for such a partnership. There is good reason for wishing to increase federal participation in the Delaware Basin development and also good reason to believe it can be done. The two agencies (one resting on federal statute, one on compact) might be employed in sequence, in the manner suggested in Chapter 18.

Finally, many state and federal agencies are active and many programs are going on in the Delaware Valley today. Most of these activities are constructive in their effects and should be continued. It is highly desirable that ways be found to gear in existing programs closely with the work of the new Delaware Basin agency.

Part III: Financial Considerations

CHAPTER 9

Financial Responsibility
for Basin Development

THIS chapter will survey the guide lines that are available for assigning financial responsibility for investment in and operation of public water resources—the financial philosophy of development. After an examination of the general concept of financial responsibility, broad principles specifically applicable to the Delaware Basin will be proposed. The following two chapters will then examine in detail the possible sources of finance that might be available for Delaware development.

THE ANALYSIS OF FINANCIAL RESPONSIBILITY

As noted in Chapter 6, the economic evaluation of river basin development can be expected to assist in assigning responsibility for repayment of a whole or a part of development projects. The measurements of benefits and costs that are so significant in project evaluation can also serve, at least in part, as the basis for allotting financial obligations.

Project evaluation stresses efficiency considerations—the effective use of resource input. Cost sharing rests on an analysis of the distribution or incidence of the benefits from water-resource development.[1] The assignment of financial responsibility may also and indirectly serve an efficiency purpose. The willingness of project beneficiaries to pay for the gains serves as a kind of check on the benefits estimated in project evaluation.

It was proposed in Chapter 1 that the financing of water-resource

[1] Mark M. Regan, "Sharing Financial Responsibility of River Basin Development," *Journal of Farm Economics*, XL (December, 1958), p. 1690.

development in the Delaware Valley be based on a broad concept of benefits received. This is the traditional basis for financing water programs at all levels of government in the United States. Economists find in the benefit approach to public finance a theoretical principle that guides decisions in the public sector in such a way as to contribute to the maximization of resources.[2] A charge exacted from water project beneficiaries discourages wasteful use and serves a function comparable to that served by prices in the market sector. The utilization of charges in the public sector, where users can be appropriately identified, thus provides a principle that is or may be common to both the public economy and the private economy.

Groups that are concerned with inter-governmental relations find in the benefit concept a criterion for dividing public expenditure and hence taxes among the levels of government.[3] Also, there is a general public acceptance of the benefit approach as applied to resource development. Support is widespread for the proposition that public expenditures should occasion no unjust enrichment, and that public funds should not be exploited for private gain. The prevention or control of private enrichment may be extremely difficult where project beneficiaries cannot be specifically identified, but there is reason to expect that public policy will support efforts to define beneficiaries and exact contributions therefrom.

The general concept of benefits received, then, is well-established and broadly-supported as a basis for apportioning financial responsibility for water projects. But, as with the application of benefit-cost analysis in project evaluation, the transition from an idealized concept to operating reality is fraught with problems.

A number of these are identical with those discussed in Chapter 6, above. Benefits are difficult to isolate and measure because of the absence of objective market prices and the presence of intangibles. The interdependence of water uses and project purposes and of structures within a river control system produces a highly complicated pattern in the distribution of economic consequences, so that the most competent staff of analysts has great difficulty untangling the gains and losses.

But apart from these difficulties, some of which are inevitable, there are other limitations on the application of the benefit concept. The national government's responsibilities for some water programs, notably

[2] Richard A. Musgrave, *op. cit.*, pp. 61-89.
[3] *Report by the Presidential Advisory Committee on Water Resources Policy*, H. Doc. No. 315, 84th Cong., 2d sess. (Washington, 1956), pp. 29-35.

navigation and flood control, are undertaken without assessment against the gains of specific beneficiaries. On the other hand, state and local governments might gain from a water-resource program but be unable to contribute to its cost because of general fiscal infirmities.

An additional limitation on the application of the benefit principle resides in its inherent conflict with another well-established concept of public finance—ability to pay. Expenditures by governments for water-resource programs are not separable from other public expenditures or from generalized political and economic value judgments about the distribution of income. It is reasonable to expect, therefore, that water-resource programs will reflect prevalent attitudes concerning an appropriate distribution of income and general public policies directed toward its implementation. A good example in point is the much controverted 160-acre limitation in reclamation projects. This limitation is a political expression of attitudes toward speculative activity in our economy, the family-size farm, and the distribution of income among the rich and the poor. The 160-acre limitation is not intended to make for the most effective use of resources; that is, it is not intended to be an economically efficient control, but it is nevertheless a legitimate political constraint on the use of public funds for development. Similar kinds of policies, although possibly less controversial, may be expected to influence financial responsibility for every water-resource development.

BENEFICIARIES AND COST ALLOCATION

The literature and practice of water-resource project analysis has not directed as much attention to principles for sharing costs as to principles for estimating the benefit-cost ratio. In the practical applications of cost-sharing there seems to be an inevitable if understandable tendency to justify as much as possible under the head of federal investment in order to minimize the contributions of non-federal interests. In the literature most of the discussion has centered on allocation as a basis for apportioning the cost of specific water programs in a multipurpose project.

Starting with the concept of benefits received, there are two possible approaches to measurement.[4] The first is described in terms of the value of services to beneficiaries. The market value, estimated or imputed, for each water derivative is calculated and a pattern of charges established to assure that the calculated values are covered into the public

[4] Regan, *loc. cit.*

treasury. Where administrative or equitable considerations do not permit the collection of charges, the treasury assumes the financial burden out of general revenue. The application of this technique does not require the calculation of the cost of providing each water program; emphasis is placed on the values received by beneficiaries. The value-of-services approach to financial responsibility has never been employed. For some water programs, such as flood control, values can be estimated with accuracy. For others, such as recreation and pollution abatement, the problem of estimating and imputing values resists solution, since there is no way of measuring the preferences of beneficiaries.

The second general approach has been more commonly used. This calls for the measurement of benefits on the basis of cost. This procedure is harmonious with the conceptual pattern generally employed for the measurement of government product, which, in the national income accounts, is valued at cost rather than at its estimated worth to households and business firms. Apportioning financial responsibility on a cost basis can be implemented by (1) sharing costs in proportion to project benefits of all kinds, or by (2) assigning the full cost of specified project purposes to particular classes of beneficiaries or levels of government.[5] The full application of the first would mean that all identifiable beneficiaries would pay charges or assessments in accordance with costs measured by benefits. Specific recipients of flood control protection or the users of navigation facilities would contribute to financing such programs. Under the second, financial responsibility is allotted in accordance with costs, but part or all of the costs of some programs are assumed by the national government. It is this approach that has become traditional practice. Cost allocation policy has evolved in response to a changing concept of the national interest, influenced by the concerns of organized interest groups. In some cases, this has had the result of favoring water programs that are financially weak. In others, programs have been favored because their supporters were well-organized.

The analysis of financial responsibility in terms of project costs under either of the foregoing alternatives requires a method for allocating such costs. This problem made its forcible entry on the scene of public policy in the allocation of project costs among the multiple purposes of the Tennessee Valley Authority. Controversy centered on the cost that had been assigned to the power program, and out of this came

[5] Regan, *op. cit.,* pp. 1694-1696.

the first systematic efforts to devise workable techniques for allocation.[6]

At some level of theoretical abstraction, cost allocation for a multiple-purpose project is impossible. There is simply no logical method of dividing common costs; there is no logical method of apportioning overhead costs in a manufacturing firm producing a number of products. But the practical requirements for apportioning financial responsibility have dictated some solutions that are at least workable and that have an appeal on the basis of a kind of internal logic.

The generally accepted method in federal water-resource programs is that known as separable costs-remaining benefits.[7] The application of this approach is intended to prevent costs allocated to any purpose from exceeding benefits, to require each project purpose to carry at least its separable cost, and to provide for proportional sharing of the savings from multiple-purpose development.

In the application of the separable costs-remaining benefits technique, separable costs are defined as the difference in total project costs occasioned by the inclusion or deletion of any specific project purpose. This cost is then charged to each project purpose. The difference between the sum of the separable costs and the total cost constitutes the common cost attributable to all project purposes. The common cost is distributed to each purpose in accordance with the excess of its benefits over its separable costs. Where alternative costs are less than benefits, these are substituted.[8]

The prevailing federal practice, then, in the assignment of financial responsibility has been in terms of project benefits measured by classes of water users or by project purposes. This serves to link, quite appropriately, concepts of financial responsibility with project planning and justification. Running alongside the project purpose analysis, however, is the measurement of benefits, and cost allocation therefor, in terms of level of government. On the one hand, this reflects efforts to enlist additional financial support from the national government; on the other, it recognizes the realities of the federal-state-local fiscal system.

The assignment of financial responsibility by level of government proceeds in terms of the concept of reimbursement. A water-resource pro-

[6] Martin G. Glaeser, "Water Resources," *Federal Expenditure Policy for Economic Growth and Stability,* Joint Economic Committee, 85th Cong., 1st sess. (Washington, 1957), pp. 668-682.

[7] Subcommittee on Evaluation Standards, *op. cit.,* pp. 47-51.

[8] Regan, *op. cit.,* p. 1694.

gram is said to be reimbursable if the national government constructs the facilities but requires payment by state or local interests. A non-reimbursable program is one for which the national government assumes all capital and operating costs. Reimbursement may be accomplished in two ways. First, the specific end-products of water development, such as industrial and municipal water supply or hydroelectric power, may be sold to provide revenue to meet operating expenses and amortize capital investment. Second, state or local appropriations may reimburse the national government, although this practice is not widespread. More commonly, state or local governments assume financial responsibility for specific water-resource programs or segments of programs, or appropriate funds to agencies that assume such responsibilities. In this way the national government is not required to provide funds for initial development, and reimbursement is not required.

The measurement of benefits and the division of financial responsibility on a federal-nonfederal basis opens the door to recognition of the secondary economic benefits that may accrue to a specific state or region as a result of generalized increases in economic activity occasioned by local construction, and of operating activities stemming from project investment and the additional economic activity that may be attracted to the development area. The presence of such secondary benefits, which may not be appropriately recognized in project evaluation that seeks to maximize real national income, may nevertheless justify state or regional financial support to meet a part of project costs.[9] In other words, state or regional secondary benefits provide a justification for state and local government financial support of water-resource projects out of general fund revenues. The practical aspect of this is that water-resource development may be expected to increase levels of state and regional economic activity, add to the income and wealth of persons and firms, and thus augment state and local tax bases.

The analysis of financial responsibility by level of government requires an effort to delineate broad classes of national benefits, state and local benefits, and benefits that may accrue to specific individuals and firms, where these last can be subjected to appropriate assessments or user charges. There are a number of difficulties that may be encountered in efforts to parcel out benefits in this fashion. The growing controversy over low-flow augmentation will serve as a case in point.

Low-flow augmentation, as has been noted elsewhere, is the provision

---

[9] The subject of secondary benefits was discussed in Chapter 6.

of water releases to increase the minimum stream level during periods of reduced flow. It cuts across and influences almost all other water programs. It may give rise to specific benefits in terms of pollution abatement, navigation, power, irrigation, recreation, or fish and wildlife. It may result in a reduction in treatment costs for municipal and industrial water users. Augmented flows are used for many purposes by many users. Low-flow augmentation is not, then, a separable project purpose with distinguishable beneficiaries apart from other classes of project beneficiaries.

In recent years congressional committees dealing with water-resource projects have become interested in increased national responsibility for low-flow augmentation. The 85th Congress adopted and the President subsequently vetoed an Omnibus Rivers and Harbors and Flood Control Act that would have provided for specific federal financial support for projects with low-flow features. The President objected to the inclusion of substantive legislation in a general project authorization bill, and averred that the complex issues involved had not been fully explored. As a result of the veto, this provision was deleted in the statute ultimately enacted. The proposal, however, continues to receive strong support from the House Committee on Public Works; the provision was endorsed by the Chief of the Corps of Engineers; and similar legislation has been introduced in the 86th Congress (H. Res. 2920, S. 863).

The approach adopted by Congress was contained in the following section of the vetoed legislation (S. 497): ". . . storage may be included in any reservoir project . . . without reimbursement to increase low flows downstream to the extent warranted . . . by widespread, general and non-exclusive benefits from such increases in low flow." The controlling phrase here is "widespread, general and non-exclusive benefits." Nothing in the legislation would have required federal financing where low-flow augmentation was found to be specific and measurable. Given the history of federal participation in water-resource projects, however, if the measure is ultimately adopted the proposing agency—the Corps of Engineers or the Bureau of Reclamation—will probably find at least a part of any low-flow benefits to be widespread and non-specific and hence non-reimbursable.

Storage for low-flow releases is important in projects for the development of eastern river valleys because of the significance here of industrial and municipal water supply and pollution abatement. Experience in the determination of low-flow benefits is limited, except where such benefits have been estimated under other headings, as in the provision of water supply. The leading specific case is the West Branch Mahoning project in the Ohio Basin.[10] This development has been authorized by the Congress with the requirement that 50 per cent of project costs be assumed by low-flow beneficiaries. Assessments have been made, but the levies have not yet been collected nor has the Congress appropriated the authorized federal share of the project. It may well be that the delay in this case is occasioned by a hope on the part of beneficiaries that the national government will assume a greater financial responsibility in the near future.

The vagueness of prevailing concepts of federal financial responsibility is well illustrated by the controversy over low-flow augmentation. Where there are specific beneficiaries who can be singled out and assessed for low-flow benefits, there is no apparent reason why such assessments should not be made. Since low flow in many instances is so closely tied to industrial and municipal water supply, for which storage costs are deemed to be reimbursable to the federal government, it would seem to follow that there is no very strong case for the national government's assuming financial responsibility here. On the other hand, navigation and flood control works also give rise to some very specific measurable benefits, and there are a great many project beneficiaries in the history of water-resource development in the United States who might appropriately have been asked to contribute to the cost of such programs. But this has not been the practice. Flood control and navigation are deemed to be in the national interest and little or no assessment is made against beneficiaries.

Low-flow augmentation also presents some intricacies in measurement. Some specific beneficiaries can undoubtedly be identified with little difficulty. But low-flow storage will, in most instances, provide some "widespread, general and non-exclusive benefits." The improvement in the esthetic quality of a river in the summer months, the improved living and working conditions along its banks, the increased enjoyment of the river for pleasure boating—all of these benefits could appropriately be described as widespread and general. To the extent that the national government has a generalized interest in the improvement of interstate waters, a case may be made for federal support. On the other hand, it can be argued with equal force that the cost of such widespread benefits could appropriately be met out of the general funds of state and local governments.

Financial responsibility for the division of development costs among national, state, and local governments and specific beneficiaries there-

[10] *Mahoning River Basin, Ohio West Branch Reservoir,* H. Doc. No. 191, 85th Cong., 1st sess. (Washington, 1957).

fore is by no means settled. There are, indeed, fundamental obstacles in the way of any long-range solution of this intricate problem, whose issues ramify throughout public water policy. Meanwhile, it may be noted that there is an inescapable political-economic tendency to move more and more of the costs of water-resource development to the national government.

Financial Policies for Delaware Basin Development

The foregoing general background will serve as the basis for an analysis of policy to be followed in financing a Delaware Basin water program. Such policy, together with the proposals for specific revenue measures developed in the two succeeding chapters, are intended to be harmonious with the proposal for organization of a Basin agency and with the functions to be undertaken by that agency. Considerations relating to organization for the administration of water resources cannot be divorced from those which concern financial responsibility; and both organizational and financial policies for the Delaware must be developed as extensions of long-established governmental policies and activities in the water-resources field. Adaptations may always be made for specific river valleys, but they must proceed from a base of established public policy and program.

The financial philosophy expressed in the revenue proposals of this report rests on four propositions: first, the sources of revenue for Delaware Valley development should be diversified; second, the control of funds should be centralized insofar as possible in the hands of a Basin agency; third, it is appropriate for the federal government to provide funds that are subject to a measure of state or regional control; and fourth, there should be flexibility in the application of revenue to program. These propositions warrant further discussion.

The necessity for diversified revenue sources is an almost self-evident proposition stemming from the fact, noted above, that the beneficiaries of some water programs may be expected to contribute to the cost of development and operation, and that national, state, and local governments all have assumed and will continue to assume financial responsibility for specific programs. It may be hoped that in financial diversity there is financial strength and stability. The diversification of revenue sources should make it possible for a Basin agency to adapt its financial requirements to the changes imposed by variations in water use and water programs. The principle of diversification should also embrace the possibility of devising new sources of revenue as water use, particularly for industrial and municipal purposes, increases and as water becomes more valuable.

The centralized control of funds by a Basin agency will contribute to its strength as an independent organizational entity. The application of this principle will be complicated in the case of the proposed Basin agency both in its federal and in its compact phase by the fact that existing national and state local water programs are not intended to be displaced. Therefore, the Basin agency will have direct management control over only a part of the total financial resources that are to be devoted annually to Delaware Valley water development. The Basin agency should undertake, as one of its responsibilities, the preparation of an annual information statement to set forth present and prospective expenditures by all governments on programs affecting Delaware water.

The third proposition requires a partial separation of the sources of funds from the control of funds. This may have the appearance of departing from what is sometimes thought to be fiscal virtue. Writers and practitioners in the field of public finance have sometimes argued that the level of government that raises revenue should have sole responsibility for its expenditure and, conversely, that governments should have expenditure authority only when revenues have been raised from taxpayers within their jurisdiction.[11]

But the existence of a federal system with the differing fiscal capacities that are inherent therein has required major and long-standing modifications in the notion of a rigorous unification of fiscal responsibility for revenue and expenditure. The grant-in-aid device, by which a higher level of government makes funds available for expenditure by a lower level, represents a significant modification in the practice of fiscal unity. The grant-in-aid is one of the major instruments that has been employed to adjust fiscal capacities among governmental levels.

What is proposed here is to build on the philosophy and practice embraced in established patterns of federal grants-in-aid. A Delaware Basin agency will need substantial financial support from the national government, even as other interstate streams have required federal assistance. In its first phase of operation under federal statute it is proposed that the Basin agency be responsible to the national government.

---

[11] For an application of this philosophy to water resources see Henry C. Hart, *op. cit.*, pp. 180-182. This would appear to be the position underlying some of the recommendations of the Second Hoover Commission. See Commission on Organization of the Executive Branch of the Government, *Water Resources and Power* (Washington, 1955), pp. 35-39, 51-55.

In the second phase, under a federal-interstate compact, the degree of participation and hence control of funds by state, local, or regional representatives will be increased.[12] This combination of federal and state-regional responsibility is in accord with the distribution of governmental concern for water-resource development, particularly in eastern basins. It is also in accord with experience in other basins, where federally-financed facilities have been turned over to state management. States and regions have interests in valley development that are not measured alone by their ability to provide the capital and operating funds necessary for development. It may be noted that the proposed partial separation of the sources of funds from the control of funds reflects the philosophy underlying a policy position taken by the Council of State Governments in 1956: "The initial capital for large-scale river basin projects should come from the federal government, because of its greater fiscal resources." [13]

The fourth proposition, that there should be flexibility in the application of revenue to program, is a corollary of the concept of comprehensive development. If water resources are to be treated (insofar as possible) as a unified whole, and if water supply, navigation, hydro power, recreation, and other water programs are to be planned and administered jointly, it follows logically that they may be financed jointly, with a surplus of revenue from one water program made available to support other water programs.

The controlling precedent for this approach is to be found in the practices of the Bureau of Reclamation.[14] In irrigation project planning estimates are made of the ability of irrigators to repay investment. Costs above ability to repay may be attributed to the power program, so that power customers, in effect, pay a part of irrigation costs. This practice has resulted in a larger volume of federal expenditure on irrigation projects than would otherwise have been found justified. The policy is highly controversial, and its opponents charge that irrigators are thereby subsidized in uneconomic operations.[15] Those who favor this

[12] See below, Chapter 18.
[13] *Suggested State Legislative Program for 1957* (Chicago: Council of State Governments, 1956), p. 145.
[14] Peggy Heim, "Financing the Federal Reclamation Program: Reimbursement Arrangements and Cost Allocation," *National Tax Journal*, IX (March, 1956), pp. 35-45.
[15] The Collbran formula is now sometimes used for this purpose. This provides that power investment shall first be liquidated and, thereafter, that power revenue shall be applied to meet irrigation costs. See Charles D. Curran, "Application of

approach to irrigation project financing reply that the irrigators themselves are very often the consumers of hydroelectric power, and that in any event there are generalized resulting increases in regional economic activity (secondary benefits) that more than offset the added costs of power.[16]

In recent years the practice of supporting irrigation projects from hydroelectric power revenues has been expanded into what is known as the basin account. This concept has been employed in the Upper Colorado River Basin.[17] A master account has been established in the United States Treasury. The account receives all appropriated funds for the Upper Colorado plus all operating revenues. These receipts are available to meet the costs of operating and maintaining river control structures and to reimburse the investment of the United States Government, with interest, in hydroelectric power facilities. Revenues beyond these financial requirements are then allotted annually to the four Colorado basin states by formula, and these funds are available to meet the costs of irrigation projects that exceed the ability of irrigators to repay. This has the effect of supporting some irrigation projects that would not otherwise be feasible. The use of a basin account also has the effect of providing for larger investment in irrigation projects in those areas that have substantial hydroelectric capacity.[18]

In the Delaware Valley hydroelectric power will be valuable and its effective utilization will be of great importance for water development. There are a number of possible uses to which this hydroelectric potential might be put. One would be to market the hydro power in a single block to an electro-chemical or electro-metallurgical firm. Benefits would thus be concentrated at a specific location, with localized employment and income increased as a result of this industrial development. However, the firm power potential of the Delaware is limited;

---

the Interest Component of Power Revenue from Reclamation Projects Under the Solicitor's Opinion and the Collbran Formula," *Task Force Report*, pp. 1205-1213.

[16] There are other cases where governmental agencies use net revenue from operations to support specific facilities that incur deficits. This has long been the practice of the Port of New York Authority. The Delaware River Port Authority is empowered to use toll revenue from bridges and tunnels to support harbor improvement and other transportation facilities under its jurisdiction. See Committee on Public Works, U.S. Senate, *Delaware River Port Authority—Supplemental Compact between New Jersey and Pennsylvania*, 82d Cong., 2d sess. (Washington, 1952).

[17] P.L. 485, 84th Cong., 2d sess.

[18] Roy E. Huffman, *Irrigation Development and Public Water Policy* (New York: The Ronald Press, 1953), pp. 173-174.

the highest economic value of the hydro lies in its utilization for peaking purposes. Therefore, the marketing of hydro to attract heavy power-using industry could not be expected to produce the results for the Delaware that it has brought to the Tennessee, the Columbia, and the St. Lawrence.

A second possibility for the use of Delaware hydro would be to market the power at minimum assignable cost with no surplus of revenue, and thus to contribute to reductions in electric power rates for such customers as might be served. The benefits of Delaware hydro power would thus be spread broadly in accordance with electric power consumption. The danger here is that such rate-reduction benefits would be widely dissipated and would produce no significant increases in economic activity or water-resource development.

The third possibility is to market the power to existing distributors at rates that will achieve a surplus of net revenue, and to utilize this revenue for the general support of Delaware Basin water-resource development. This proposal assumes that a competent and well-financed Basin agency can contribute more to the economic welfare of the Valley than would be contributed by general but slight reductions in charges to electric power consumers. It seems probable, although it cannot be demonstrated conclusively, that this financial policy will make the maximum contribution to the economic development of the Delaware Valley.[19]

The utilization of net revenue from hydroelectric power for the general support of a Basin agency may well turn out to be crucial for its financial success. The proposition that there should be flexibility in the application of revenue to program would require the abandonment of rigid concepts of cost as determinative of the prices of Delaware Valley water products. For cost would be substituted a bargaining concept and the Basin agency would seek to maximize the net revenue obtainable from hydroelectric power.

The foregoing four propositions are suggested as the basis for financial policy for the development and management of Delaware Basin water resources. A policy resting on these propositions would go far to assure the financial stability and flexibility that a Basin agency must possess if it is to measure up to its program responsibilities.

[19] See Chapter 11 for a further discussion of hydroelectric power.

CHAPTER 10

Sources of Funds for a Basin Agency

A Basin agency, whether organized under federal statute or under a federal-interstate compact, will need stable and dependable sources of finance. The capital funds needed for construction may be expected to be provided initially by the national government.[1] Apart from capital construction, the first requirement is for income to maintain the central staff. As a minimum definition of duties this staff will have responsibility for plans and surveys, for information and education on water resource problems in the Valley, for managing the system of control structures, and for providing technical assistance to communities and industries on problems of water utilization and control. The budget for a staff with these functions will be substantial if salaries are to be paid at a level to attract professional personnel of high competence. Furthermore, it is reasonable to anticipate that the size of the staff will increase during the first decade of operation.[2]

[1] The rough magnitudes of capital outlays required for major structures are indicated by the tentative proposals announced by the Corps in October 1959. These call for the construction of six dams as they are needed. The largest of these is Tocks Island, estimated at $89,000,000 including power facilities. The remaining five projects are estimated to cost $87,000,000, for a total of $176,000,000. All six are multiple-purpose, and each structure embraces project purposes deemed to be at least partially federal in character.

[2] Some idea of staff requirements may be deduced from the experience of other basins. The Corps of Engineers' Reservoir Regulating Section for the Missouri River, with offices at Omaha, spends about $250,000 annually on staff for river control alone. The Ohio River Valley Water Sanitation Commission, with responsibilities for pollution abatement, budgets about $120,000 annually for staff. The Upper Colorado River Commission has annual operating expenses of about $100,000 and the Lower Colorado River Authority about $462,000 for administrative and general expenses. Costs of the Office of the River Master of the Delaware River are about $40,000 per year. All of these agencies have narrower responsibilities than are

In addition to the annual requirements for staffing, a Delaware Basin agency could effectively utilize income for two purposes. The first is the promotion of those aspects of water-resource programs that, by their very nature, are either non-revenue-producing or productive of minimum revenue. Programs for pollution abatement and recreation fall into this category. Investment here may produce handsome returns for the long-run economic development of the Valley, with corresponding generalized increases in property values and incomes.

A second added need for revenue will arise from the desirability of controlling or acquiring lands at and around prospective reservoir sites. Population growth and urbanization will inevitably bring about private development and raise land costs unless preclusive action is taken. Land acquisition or control is particularly important if recreation potentials are to be eventually realized.

Revenues to meet these requirements may be provided by endowing the Basin agency with authority to derive income from the sale of the end-products of water development, and possibly to levy general charges on water use or withdrawals. In the first decade of development it appears likely that the most important source of net revenue will be hydroelectric power. In later years water supply and possibly recreation may be put on at least a self-sustaining basis, and there may be limited possibilities for net revenue from these programs. It is reasonable to expect that as Delaware water becomes more valuable over time, revenue resulting from the control of water will increase.

Financial requirements, particularly for central staff, may also be met at least in part from annual appropriations by the national government. General appropriations from state legislatures may be possible in the first phase of organization under federal statute, or alternatively the states may be willing to assume responsibility for specific programs, such as recreation. The compact organization could certainly anticipate support from appropriations by state legislatures in the Basin.

To endow a Delaware Basin agency with authority and responsibility for producing net income from the sale of the end products of water is to endow it with a prerogative that must be carefully defined. The effective utilization of revenue from the sale of water products will be necessary for the optimum use of Delaware water. And the charter for a Basin agency must be written to assure, so far as possible, a high standard of financial responsibility.

---

proposed for the new Delaware Basin agency. A minimum staff budget of $500,000 annually, rising to perhaps $1,000,000 within a decade, would appear to be a modest estimate for that agency.

This chapter will examine the specific responsibilities of the national government for non-reimbursable water programs and analyze possibilities of revenue from industrial and municipal water. The following chapter will survey revenue potential from hydroelectric power, recreation, and other possible sources.

State Water-Resource Programs

The participation of the four Basin states in water-resource programs for pollution abatement, recreation, and flood control was touched on in previous chapters.[3] Those states are now committed to major financial responsibility for these programs, and in some instances have developed competent staffs for planning and administration. Substantial expenditures for water-resource programs have been undertaken. This suggests that the governors and legislatures of the four states may be willing to assume additional commitments as needs arise. At the same time, the Basin agency will have responsibility for arranging its organizational structure, program planning, and administration and finance to establish a pattern of working relationships with the existing financial and program responsibilities of state and local bodies.

Federal Financial Responsibility

The national interest in water-resource programs is an expanding one.[4] In the current fiscal year the federal government will spend about $1,000,000,000 on water-resource development. It will be the responsibility of a Delaware Basin agency to relate its own activities to established national programs and to assume financial responsibility for Basin development with attention to and respect for existing and emerging national government interests.

There are three water-resource programs where federal financial responsibility has traditionally been limited, but where recent expressions indicate an expanding national interest. These are water supply, recreation, and low-flow augmentation. All three have major financial implications for the Delaware Basin and its new water agency,

[3] See especially Chapter 3, the section entitled "State and Local Agencies and Programs."

[4] Federal water programs are examined briefly in Chapter 3 in the section entitled "Federal Agencies and Programs."

although the true nature of their impacts cannot be known until federal policy has become more clearly defined. Likewise there are three programs for which the national government will provide appropriations for the original investment in facilities, with the requirement however that this investment be repaid with interest by state or local interests. These are water supply, hydro power, and, in some cases, recreation. Existing and emerging federal financial responsibilities in these areas, together with the specific character of the programs in the Delaware Basin, will be examined in detail.

INDUSTRIAL AND MUNICIPAL WATER

Providing for adequate supplies of industrial and municipal water is undoubtedly the most important long-range economic objective to be served by a water-resource program in the Delaware Valley, for an adequate water supply is one of the basic conditions of economic growth. Adequate supplies of municipal water will also influence the location of residential areas and commercial activity within specific sub-areas of the Valley. The Corps' Survey will emphasize that water supply and flood control are the two major needs for development.

Planning for water supply may well become the most significant activity of the Basin agency, more especially because it will increase in importance over the next several decades. Within twenty or thirty years revenue from the sale of water may constitute a major source of income for the agency. Careful planning for water supply and careful analysis of water requirements will be necessary if uneconomic investment is to be avoided. As noted above, construction must be planned and land acquired in anticipation of need, but experience with water supply projects in other parts of the country suggests that there is ever-present danger of overbuilding and wasteful investment.[5]

It is most difficult to forecast accurately a future supply or demand schedule for industrial and municipal water. There is no single quantity of water to be supplied. Water must be differentiated with respect to quality—chemical, bacteriological, physical—and geographical locus. Water supply has a time dimension; availability may fluctuate from week to week or from season to season. Further, water supply can

---

[5] Possibly the outstanding case of uneconomic investment in water supply facilities has occurred in a water shortage area in Southern California. See Jerome W. Milliman, *The History, Organization and Economic Problems of the Metropolitan Water District of Southern California* (unpublished doctoral dissertation, University of California at Los Angeles, 1956).

always be augmented by recourse to higher-cost alternatives. A "water shortage" in the Delaware Valley might some day be met by diversions from the Susquehanna, or by the adoption of techniques for the reclamation and treatment of waste water.

The demands for water of a given quality and quantity at a specific location are similarly incapable of quantification. The next several decades may bring drastic modifications in Valley water requirements from such developments as the New Jersey Ship Canal, a fifty-foot navigation channel to Trenton, a barrier dam in the estuary, or major increases in water requirements for irrigation. Even in the absence of such dramatic developments, changes in industrial water technology to increase re-use and re-cycling will have a major impact on requirements. And, of course, policy decisions will influence the demand for water. New York City, other segments of the New York Metropolitan Area, and other out-of-Basin areas may seek additional Delaware water at some time in the future. Decisions with respect to such diversions will have major impact on total requirements.

Efforts to reduce the degree of uncertainty with respect to future water supplies and requirements are handicapped by the absence of data. Almost nothing is known about the water uses and costs and not much about the water technology of the self-supplied industries in the Valley. Little is known about the extent of ground water utilization, or about the relationship between ground water and surface water. The establishment of a Basin agency to strengthen data-collecting activities will overcome some of these difficulties in time, but additional data alone will not make possible reliable forecasts. The uncertainties in this situation can be offset only by the design and construction of a flexible system of water storage and control, and by the establishment of a centralized agency for the administration of the Basin's water resources.

Projecting Industrial Requirements

An ideal economic analysis of water supply and the revenue that might be obtained therefrom would proceed in a series of steps. First, a schedule would be drawn up to show demand for specific qualities and quantities of water at stated prices and exact locations in time. Second, a schedule would be constructed to show the quantities and qualities of water that might be made available at stated costs over time at specific locations. Third, if the supply schedule were under the control of a single agency, inter-relationships could be analyzed to show the revenue that might be derived from the sale of storage for industrial and municipal water in reservoirs and the charges that might be made for withdrawals from surface supplies.

The formidable difficulties in the preparation of supply and requirement schedules for industrial and municipal water have been stressed. But even if these difficulties could be overcome, it would not be possible to move directly to an estimate of revenue to be derived from sale of water since the Basin agency probably will not, in the foreseeable future, be endowed with authority to control water supplies from both surface and ground sources. Moreover, charges for water, particularly for industry, will lead to a shift in the demand schedule. An increase in the price of water to industrial users will elicit a technological response. Cooling towers and other re-use equipment will be installed to reduce gross water requirements. Self-supplied industrial water from surface sources is now available to most users at a zero intake price, that is, as a free good. The response of water-using industries to a charge for water will certainly be in the direction of economizing its use, but the magnitude of this response cannot be predicted.

In planning for water supply in the Survey, the Corps of Engineers has necessarily reckoned with the foregoing difficulties. The projections of storage requirements show very large general increases in industrial and municipal water needs as of 1980.[6] The Corps has not carried water supply planning to the point of ascertaining that specific water companies and municipalities in the Valley are willing and financially able to contract for storage at a price adequate to pay for it. This kind of planning may not be possible for several years, and in any event may be appropriately assumed by a Basin agency.

Because of the crucial importance of industrial and municipal water for the development of the Delaware Basin, and because of the difficulty in translating the projected general shortages into area and industry shortages, three specific research projects were undertaken to provide additional data.

First, under a contract with the Delaware Valley Project the Bureau of the Census tabulated, from the *1954 Census of Manufactures,* the water use patterns of five industrial classifications for firms in the Delaware Basin.[7] The results appear in Tables 5 and 6. The categories

[6] These data are now classified but will be published, together with historical data on industrial and municipal water characteristics, in the Survey report.

[7] Bureau of the Census Project No. 9002, February 3, 1959. The tabulation consists of a break-out of the Delaware from the Census' Delaware and Hudson Region.

TABLE 5

Industrial Water Use in the Delaware River Basin for Selected Industries By Establishments Using 20,000,000 or More Gallons of Water During 1954 (In Billions of Gallons)

Industry name and region*	Number of establishments	Water intake		Process	Cooling and air conditioning	Boiler feed, sanitary service, and othe uses
		All purposes				
		Total	Treated prior to use[1]			
Total Use	144	470.8	250.3	51.5	332.8	86.5
Pulp, paper and products	46	35.2	23.2	24.6	6.9	3.7
Delaware Estuary	24	20.6	12.4	12.5	5.8	2.3
Schuylkill	14	4.9	2.1	3.6	.4	.9
Lehigh[2]	—	—	—	—	—	—
All other[2]	8	9.7	8.7	8.5	.7	.5
Chemicals and products	76	131.4	63.7	16.0	98.2	17.2
Delaware Estuary	60	124.2	62.0	15.1	92.6	16.5
Schuylkill[5]	16	7.2	1.7	.9	5.6	0.7
Lehigh[5]	—	—	—	—	—	—
All other[5]	—	—	—	—	—	—
Petroleum refining	6	112.0	9.9	1.0	69.6	41.4
Delaware Estuary	6	112.0	9.9	1.0	69.6	41.4
Schuylkill	—	—	—	—	—	—
Lehigh	—	—	—	—	—	—
All other	—	—	—	—	—	—
Blast furnaces	5	40.5	21.0	2.5	30.3	7.7
Delaware Estuary[7]	—	—	—	—	—	—
Schuylkill[7]	—	—	—	—	—	—
Lehigh[7]	—	—	—	—	—	—
All other	—	—	—	—	—	—
Steel works and rolling mills	11	151.7	132.5	7.4	127.8	16.5
Delaware Estuary[8]	—	—	—	—	—	—
Schuylkill[8]	—	—	—	—	—	—
Lehigh[8]	—	—	—	—	—	—
All other	—	—	—	—	—	—

Detail may not add to totals because of rounding.

* The regions include the following counties: For the Delaware Estuary—New Castle, K« and Sussex in Delaware; Atlantic, Burlington, Camden, Cape May, Gloucester, Mercer a Salem in New Jersey; Bucks, Delaware and Philadelphia in Pennsylvania. For the Schuylkil Berks, Chester, Montgomery and Schuylkill in Pennsylvania. For the Lehigh—Carbon, Leh and Northampton in Pennsylvania. For "All other"—Delaware and Sullivan in New Yc Hunterdon, Warren and Sussex in New Jersey; Monroe, Pike and Wayne in Pennsylvania,

[1] Includes both simple and complex treatment.

[2] Water used in the Lehigh region (less than 100 million gallons intake) was combined w the "All other" region to avoid disclosure of individual company data.

[3] Less than 50 million gallons.

| Water discharged | | Water required if no water was recirculated or reused | Water intake, by kind of water | | | | |
| Total | Treated prior to discharge | | Total | Fresh | | | Brackish |
				From public water system	From company surface water system	From company ground water system	
446.7	148.0	818.9	427.9	23.6	380.7	23.6	43.0
31.0	12.8	115.4	33.2	1.1	27.9	4.2	2.2
17.5	8.3	78.9	18.7	.8	17.2	.7 [4]	2.1
4.4	2.8	17.1	4.9	.3	3.0	1.6	0.1
—	—	—	—	—	—	—	—
9.1	1.7	19.4	9.6	[3]	7.7	1.9	—
126.3	38.8	169.2	90.6	16.8	61.7	12.1 [6]	40.8
120.4	37.6	159.0	83.5	14.3	59.7	9.5	40.8
5.9	1.2	10.2	7.1	2.5	2.0	2.6	[7]
—	—	—	—	—	—	—	—
106.2	43.1	319.1	111.9	1.3	109.6	1.0	[4]
106.2	43.1	319.1	111.9	1.3	109.6	1.0	[4]
—	—	—	—	—	—	—	—
—	—	—	—	—	—	—	—
38.7	8.0	44.8	40.5	1.7	38.8	[3]	[4]
—	—	—	—	—	—	—	—
—	—	—	—	—	—	—	—
—	—	—	—	—	—	—	—
144.5	45.3	170.4	151.7	2.7	142.7	6.3	—
—	—	—	—	—	—	—	—
—	—	—	—	—	—	—	—
—	—	—	—	—	—	—	—

A quantity of brackish water (less than 100 million gallons) was included with "Pulp, er, and products" in the Delaware Estuary to avoid disclosure of individual company data. Establishments in the Lehigh and "All other" regions were combined with the Schuylkill on to avoid disclosure of individual company data.
Adjusted to exclude a quantity of brackish water (between 100 and 500 million gallons) void disclosure of individual company data.
Establishments in the Delaware Estuary, Schuylkill, and Lehigh regions were combined to id disclosure of individual company data.
Schuylkill and Lehigh regions were combined with the Delaware Estuary to avoid disclosure ndividual company data.
ource: Bureau of the Census unpublished tabulation from the 1954 Census of Manufactures pared for the Syracuse University Delaware Valley Project (May, 1959).

TABLE 6

Industrial Water Use in the Delaware River Basin for Selected Industrie
By Establishments Using 20,000,000 or More Gallons of Water
During 1954: Summary by Regions (In Billions of Gallons)

Region*	Number of establish-ments	Water intake				
		All purposes		Process	Cooling and air condi-tioning	Boiler feed, sanitary service, and other uses
		Total	Treated prior to use			
Total Use	*144*	*470.8*	*250.4*	*51.5*	*332.8*	*86.5*
Delaware Estuary	97	343.3	160.1	32.9	245.0	65.4
Schuylkill	26	50.0	20.0	7.3	38.8	3.9
Lehigh	11	66.8	60.7	2.6	47.7	16.5
All other	10	10.7	9.6	8.7	1.3	.7

* For definitions see Table 5.
1 Adjusted to exclude a quantity of brackish water (between 100 and 500 million gallon
to avoid disclosure of individual company data.

employed are pulp, paper and products; chemicals and products;
petroleum refining; blast furnaces; and steel works and rolling mills.
The industries so classified account for nearly 50 per cent of the total
industrial water intake for the entire Delaware and Hudson Region for
1954. Water use and re-use in relation to total intake is also high in the
Delaware Basin as compared with other regions.[8]

Second, Alderson Associates, Inc., of Philadelphia prepared a study
of locational patterns for the five major water-using industries that are
now and that may be expected to be significant in the future of industrial water requirements in the Valley. The results of this analysis
are summarized in Table 7. Conclusions are based on data from public
and industry sources, supplemented by interviews with officials in
selected firms. The findings reveal that capacity in petroleum refining,
chemicals, basic steel, and thermal power is expected to expand sub-

[8] For comparisons see *1954 Census of Manufactures* (Washington, 1957), Vol.
I, pp. 209-32 to 209-41. The data are for firms using 20,000,000 or more gallons
of water during 1954.

Water discharged			Water intake, by kind of water				
Total	Treated prior to discharge	Water required if no water was recirculated or reused	Total	Fresh			Brackish
				From public water system	From company surface water system	From company ground water system	
446.7	148.0	818.9	427.9	23.6	380.7	23.6	43.0
327.6	128.1	649.6	300.5	16.7	269.3	14.5	42.8
47.0	9.4	71.4	50.0	2.2	43.8	4.0	.1 [1]
62.2	8.8	77.5	66.7	4.7	59.6	2.4	—
9.9	1.7	20.4	10.7	[2]	8.0	2.7	—

[2] Public water (under 100 million gallons) included with surface water to avoid disclosure individual company data.
Source: Bureau of the Census, unpublished tabulation from *1954 Census of Manufactures* prepared for the Syracuse University Delaware Valley Project (May, 1959).

stantially between now and 1980. Paper and pulp, however, will increase only modestly. Most of the anticipated expansion will come along the Delaware estuary below Trenton. This is important since a considerable increase in industrial water use could take place in the estuary without significant effect on water quality.

Third, Paul H. Cootner utilized the Census data and the Alderson study of industrial location to project water requirements for the five major water-using industries for the year 1980.[9] Statistical techniques were supplemented by interviews with industrial water technologists in selected firms in the Basin. These projections are based on the assumptions that (1) there will be no shortage of plant sites on the river or its tributaries; (2) the quality of water withdrawals will remain approximately at present levels; (3) fuel costs will remain stable over the period of projections; and (4) no significant charges will be im-

[9] Dr. Cootner, formerly of the staff of Resources for the Future, Inc., is now a member of the faculty of the Massachusetts Institute of Technology.

TABLE 7

Growth of Five Water-Using Industries in the Delaware Valley
Projected to 1980

Petroleum Refining[1]	1958	1980
Thousand bbl/day	875.5	1784.3
Employment (thousands)	21.3	29.4
Chemicals[2]	1957	1980
Employment (thousands)	70.0	106.8
Basic Steel [3]	1957	1980
Capacity (millions of net tons)	8.8	14.0
Employment (thousands)	54.8	51.6
Paper and Board [4]	1957	1980
Production (millions of short tons)	1.14	1.58
Employment (thousands)	3.6	3.9
Thermal Power[5]	1955	1980
Energy requirements (million kwh)	29,456	108,400

[1] Almost all growth will come in the estuary.
[2] Growth in the estuary, on the New Jersey side.
[3] Major growth at Fairless; modest growth at Bethlehem.
[4] Little or no additional capacity anticipated; growth limited to existing sites.
[5] 50-54 per cent of increase in kwh will come from plants located in the Basin; it is difficult to determine locations as between the upper Delaware and the estuary.

Source: Alderson Associates, Inc., *Growth Projections for Five Selected Industries in the Delaware River Basin, 1960-1980,* unpublished memorandum prepared for the Syracuse University Delaware Valley Project (January, 1959).

posed for withdrawals during this period. The summary projections are set forth in Table 8.

The steam-electric power industry is expected to about double its water demand between 1954 and 1980. Capacity will increase at a somewhat greater rate. Fuel efficiency is expected to increase as older plants are replaced by newer installations and since water is used primarily for cooling, this technological improvement will result in a reduced use of water per kilowatt hour. It is not anticipated that re-

TABLE 8

*Water Use of Five Water-Using Industries in the Delaware Valley
Projected to 1980*

	Production 1980	Water Use/Unit 1980	Water Use, Billion Gallons, 1980	Water Use, Billion Gallons, 1954
Steam-electric power	55 billion kwh	38 gals/kwh	2090	1025
Petroleum refining	651 million bbls	500 gals/bbl	325	112
Paper and board	1,580,000 tons	25,000 gals/ton	39	35
Chemical	400 (1954 = 100)	900 million gals/ton	360	131
Steel	12,600,000 tons	35,000 gals/ton	440	191
Total			*3254*	*1494*

Source: Paul H. Cootner, *Delaware River Basin Water Projections,* unpublished memorandum prepared for the Syracuse University Delaware Valley Project (May, 1959).

cycling will increase substantially for steam plants. It is expected that petroleum refining will about triple its water use between 1954 and 1980. Water technology is expected to improve gradually but not dramatically in this industry, with recycling in 1980 at 1.9 times the 1954 rate. Changes in refining processes, however, are expected to increase fuel utilization and thus increase the demand for water per unit of output. The projections reflect a balance among these and other forces affecting future water requirements for the industry. The paper and board industry is expected to increase its water use roughly in proportion to increases in output, with only moderate savings from improved water technology. The chemical industry is the most difficult to analyze because of the absence of a homogeneous unit of output. The projection, which shows an almost three-fold increase in water requirements, attempts to make allowance for the changing structure of the industry (a shift to petro-chemicals by firms in the Delaware Basin), and for anticipated improvements in cooling processes. In the steel industry water requirements are expected to increase somewhat more rapidly than the growth in capacity. The reason for this is that major additions to capacity are expected at sites where water use per ton of steel is high and where there is no reason to anticipate a change in existing water use technology. The water requirements for these five industries are expected to more than double betwen 1954 and 1980, as Table 6 shows.

Projecting Municipal Requirements

The Philadelphia Bureau of Municipal Research-Pennsylvania Economy League, by arrangement with the Delaware Valley Project, undertook a detailed investigation of water use experience for the City of Philadelphia and selected water companies in the Valley.[10] Data for this investigation were taken from the published and unpublished records of water companies.

Selected findings from these studies are set forth in Tables 9, 10, and 11. The general conclusion to be drawn from the tables is that per capita water demand has not increased in recent decades as much as is commonly supposed. This is particularly evident in Tables 9 and 10, which show that Philadelphia per capita water demand in the 1950's is almost identical with that of the 1920's. The data for specific companies in Table 11 would suggest that there was a substantial increase

TABLE 9

Filtered Water Produced per Capita, City of Philadelphia Average per Day by Decades, 1921-1958

Decade	Average Number of Gallons Per Day
1921-30	173.4
1931-40	161.6
1941-50	168.6
1951-58	173.3

Source: Philadelphia Bureau of Municipal Research, *Philadelphia Water Use Trends,* unpublished memorandum prepared for the Syracuse University Delaware Valley Project (February 2, 1959).

[10] These data were prepared by Mitchell J. Hunt and Martin P. Klingel of the staff of BMR-PEL.

TABLE 10

Per Capita Water Use, City of Philadelphia
For Selected Years, 1921-1958

Year	Gallons Per Day*
1921	167.6
1926	180.8
1931	161.1
1936	166.8
1941	168.2
1946	169.5
1951	168.6
1955	179.7
1956	171.2
1957	171.8
1958	164.4

* Measured in terms of filtered water produced.
Source: Same as for Table 9.

in per capita water use between 1940 and 1950, but no pronounced trend since. It was found that the inclusion of industrial water demand increased the total but did not substantially alter the trend of per capita consumption. Apparently at some point water conservation measures in the major cities arrest the trend toward increased household use.

From these data it would appear, therefore, that increases in total demand by water distributors will result from the increase in the number of customers and not from increased per capita use. It follows that increases in the demand for water that might be sold to water companies will be a function of the growth in the Basin's population. This growth, of course, is expected to be considerable. The Office of Business Economics has projected a population increase for the Valley of 3,000,000, or about 50 per cent, between 1955 and 1980. For the Delaware Service Area the population increase is projected at 8,400,000 for the same period, which amounts to about 40 per cent.[11]

Unfortunately, it is not possible to move readily from a general projection of water demands to specific area requirements. A study of

[11] Office of Business Economics, U.S. Department of Commerce, *Economic Base Survey* (Washington, 1958), p. 18.

TABLE 11

Per Capita Water Demand in Gallons per Day by Class of Service
Selected Water Companies for Selected Years, 1940-1957

	1940	1950	1955	1956 [1]	1957 [2]
Easton					
Residential	32	64	62	70	72
Commercial	14	21	13	12	19
Industrial	23	33	26	22	23
Other	2	7	2	2	1
Total	*71*	*125*	*103*	*106*	*115*
Philadelphia Suburban Water Co.					
Residential	38.0	49.2	50.7	48.9	53.2
Commercial	5.7	7.5	7.3	7.3	8.0
Industrial	5.4	8.4	6.2	6.1	6.0
Other	16.7	20.2	15.6	13.8	14.0
Total	*65.8*	*85.3*	*79.8*	*76.1*	*81.2*
Ambler Borough					
Residential	n.a.[3]	36.7	54.7	41.0	46.5
Commercial	n.a.	30.4	4.9	3.6	5.1
Industrial	n.a.	10.9	10.1	12.8	15.4
Other	n.a.	0.9	0.4	0.9	1.6
Total	*n.a.*	*78.8*	*70.1*	*58.3*	*68.6*

[1] Wet year
[2] Dry year
[3] Not available

Source: Philadelphia Bureau of Municipal Research, *Water Use Experience for Selected Water Companies, Delaware River Basin,* unpublished memorandum prepared for the Syracuse University Delaware Valley Project (December 22, 1958).

major demand centers for water suggests that the generalized increases will probably not be felt for some time. Both the cities of Philadelphia and New York estimate that their system requirements will be met by existing facilities and those under construction until approximately the turn of the century. The recent study and recommendations for the Brandywine, sponsored by the Pennsylvania Department of Forests and

Waters, proposes a cooperative federal-state-local development that will satisfy needs in this area, including Wilmington, until approximately the year 2000.[12] Although the Brandywine projects affect only a small portion of the Delaware Basin and may be constructed independently of its new agency, the need for unified water-resource management will one day require a pattern of integrated control for the whole of the Valley.

Apart from the Brandywine, the areas of most immediate need are southeastern Pennsylvania (except for Philadelphia) and the lower Schuylkill and lower Lehigh Valleys. By 1980, plus or minus five years, it may be anticipated that there will be need for water in northern Delaware (excepting Wilmington), northeastern New Jersey, Mercer County, and the Raritan Valley, although this last will depend on the intensity of Raritan River development in the next twenty years. Philadelphia, New York City, the New York City Metropolitan Area, and the upper Lehigh and Schuylkill Valleys will probably not be in the market for additional water until some time around the turn of the century.

All of this underscores the fact that the new Basin agency will have a major responsibility for the detailed study of emerging water needs. It is evident also that the agency will need to cooperate with public and private groups throughout the Valley to bring about the most effective utilization of Delaware water.

Financial Considerations

It is a long-standing policy of the national government that financial outlay for water supply is fully reimbursable with interest. Until recently this meant that federal multi-purpose projects embracing water supply could be authorized by the Congress, but construction of water supply storage could not proceed until distributors (public or private) assumed responsibility under contract for the purchase of water at rates sufficient to liquidate the federal investment. The Omnibus Rivers and Harbors and Flood Control Act of 1958 (P.L. 500), however, enlarged the financial responsibility of the national government with respect to future water users. The Corps of Engineers and the Bureau of Reclamation may now propose the construction of storage for future use not to exceed 30 per cent of total costs in multiple-purpose projects.

[12] *Recommended Plan of Development for Brandywine Creek Basin in Pennsylvania.* Bourquard, Geil and Associates, for the Department of Forests and Waters (1958).

Local interests must give "reasonable assurance" that this storage will be utilized and eventually paid for. Construction cost plus interest must be reimbursed within the project life or within fifty years after the project is first used for water storage, whichever is the shorter period. Payment may be in lump sum to cover the first costs allocated to water supply or an equivalent annual payment. Local interests must also assume a proportionate share of operation, maintenance, and replacement costs. No payment need be made until the storage is actually employed, and no interest is charged until the supply is first used, or after ten years, whichever comes first. The controlling phrase in this legislation is "reasonable assurance," and neither the Corps nor the Bureau of Reclamation has yet attempted a careful definition. Previous practice suggests that the form of assurance required will be progressively more binding as the date for committing construction funds approaches.

The implementation of P.L. 500 with respect to the Delaware Valley would be greatly expedited if the Basin agency were to assume responsibility for proposing Basin-wide standards to meet the intent of the law and for effectuating these standards by securing commitments from water distributors. Indeed, it may be asserted that this responsibility will be basic to planning and meeting the needs for future water supply in the Valley. Federal investment in anticipatory water supply storage can make a major contribution toward meeting future water needs, but this contribution must be carefully balanced against the cost of fallow investment, a cost that must eventually be assumed by water users.

It is difficult at this time to define the precise limits of the Basin agency's physical responsibility for future water supply. For surface water the agency will be in a position to market an increment of water quantity and/or quality, that increment to be provided by releases from the structures under its management. As the agency assumes control over the maintenance and operation of Delaware Valley structures, it would seem logical that it should also assume responsibility for the provision of facilities for the distribution of water from reservoirs, or at the least for construction of diversion dams and conduits at specified points in the river or its tributaries. The federal agency with most experience in water supply—the Bureau of Reclamation—generally provides storage capacity and facilities such as canals or pipelines to take untreated water to the user, but the Delaware agency may wish to adopt a different pattern of operation in accord with the specific water supply needs of its region. Eventually, perhaps by the turn of the century, it may be desirable for the then agency to organize and construct inter-connected sub-basin systems to assure unified water supply in specific areas. Feasibility studies of an integrated wholesale water distribution grid would need to be initiated long before this time.

Future water rates for the Delaware Valley cannot be projected because of the uncertainties of supply prices and because the Basin agency will not, in the foreseeable future, control all diversions or withdrawals of water from both ground and surface sources. For the next several decades ground water and existing surface supplies will continue as alternatives to water provided by the Basin agency, and public and private water companies will explore these alternatives. Wholesale water rates that may be charged by the agency will be limited by the costs of these alternatives.

It is not now possible to forecast that water rates can be set at a level to return a surplus of revenue to the Basin agency. The financial goal for the agency's water supply activities, however, is clear and unmistakable. Rates charged for water use must be set at a level high enough to return the full cost of providing such water, including essential overhead staff costs. Long-term contracts with users can eventually give the agency the financial stability necessary for the flotation of revenue bonds. The proceeds of such bond issues would then be available for retiring any remaining federal investment in water storage and for financing the construction of additional reservoirs and conduits.

CHAPTER 11

Sources of Funds for a Basin Agency

(continued)

HYDROELECTRIC POWER

PROGRAMS for the generation, transmission, and distribution of power from multiple-purpose government projects are highly controversial. Few areas of domestic economic policy have involved so much political tension. This controversy frequently has destructive consequences, preventing the construction of projects that are justifiable and blocking the achievement of optimum utilization. For the development of Delaware Basin water resources, a workable pattern of relations between public and private power is of utmost importance. Fortunately, the grounds for prospective agreement in the Delaware vastly exceed the probable grounds for disagreement.

The proportion of potential Delaware hydro to existing total electric power capacity in the Valley marketing area is small, amounting to only about 5 per cent. But revenue from the sale of hydroelectric power is of great potential importance to further Basin development, and particularly to the proposed new water-resource agency.[1] Pre-

---

[1] Estimates of the value of hydro depend on load factors; the daily, weekly, or seasonal availability for peaking; and the load curves of prospective purchasers. None of this information is now available for the Delaware Valley. For illustrative purposes, if the following conditions obtain (and they are believed to be conservative):

Installed capacity	500,000 kw
Capacity cost, under public financing	$21 kw per year
Capacity value, sold to distributors	$25 kw per year
Energy value, assumed to be required by pumped storage	zero

Then

Gross annual revenue would amount to	$12,500,000
Annual cost would come to	10,500,000
And annual net revenue would be	2,000,000

liminary calculations indicate that in the first stage of physical development installed hydroelectric capacity, primarily pumped storage, may amount to 500,000 kw. Maximum utilization, with additional pumped storage, might double this capacity. Revenue from the sale of this power could be a significant source of income to a Basin agency, particularly during its early years.

Power for Peaking Purposes

In recent years hydroelectric power usually has found its most efficient utilization for peaking rather than for base load. Hydro power has technological flexibility not possessed by thermal power. The recent development of supercritical thermal units suggests that this pattern will continue; that is, that the incremental value of hydroelectric power for peaking purposes will increase rather than diminish over the next several decades.

Since hydro power normally is most valuable for peaking purposes, it is prevailing practice among federal agencies, except in the Pacific Northwest, to plan installations for peaking and to estimate power values on this basis. This assures optimum development. If these values are to be subsequently realized, however, the power must be utilized by a distribution system with substantial peaking requirements. In the Delaware Valley this suggests the sale of power to one or more of the private companies in the Pennsylvania-New Jersey-Maryland interconnection, a system embracing eight major electric light and power companies operating both within and well beyond the borders of the Valley. There are other large private systems in New York State within feasible transmission distance of the Valley but no other fully integrated systems.

The effective development of the hydroelectric potential of Delaware Valley structures will necessitate the construction of pumped storage facilities. These facilities are designed solely for peaking purposes and must be integrated with steam generation that is capable of providing off-peak power to return the water to the upper reservoir.

Power Marketing under Federal Statute

In the first organizational (federal statute) phase of the Basin agency, if power is marketed in accordance with existing national government policies, Section 5 of the Flood Control Act of 1944 will be controlling.

Here it is stated that the Secretary of the Interior has responsibility for marketing all power produced by installations at structures built by the Corps of Engineers; that rates are to be set to recover the cost of producing and transmitting such energy, including, in practice, amortization with interest; that rate schedules are to be approved by the Federal Power Commission; and that public bodies and cooperatives are to be given preference in the sale of such power. Of these policies, the most significant for present purposes are the preference clause and the requirement that rates be set at cost.

The federal preference clause is a much-controverted subject.[2] This controversy need not be explored here. The fact is that present policies seem to be firmly established, regardless of the political complexion of the administration or of the Congress. There is no realistic ground for anticipating any substantial change in policy as applied to the Delaware.

There is, of course, the possibility that a type of partnership arrangement might be negotiated between the Basin agency and private power companies, with the former selling rights in falling water and the latter assuming financial responsibility for investment in generation and transmission facilities. Although there has been extensive discussion of partnership in water resources development in recent years, only one small project involving the partnership principle has been approved since the Flood Control Act of 1944. This is the Waterbury project in Vermont, where the Green Mountain Power Corporation, in 1953, constructed generating facilities with an estimated value of $550,000 in a Corps-operated dam. The partnership arrangements were not a part of the original authorization; the project was first approved as an emergency work relief measure in 1933.[3] In the last few sessions of Congress policy debate has centered on the Trinity River development in California and the proposals of the Pacific Gas and Electric Company to purchase rights in falling water at that project. The failure of the Congress to approve the contracts that have been proposed suggests that partnership arrangements of this type are not likely to be accepted in the immediate future.

The applications of the preference clause of most significance for

[2] For a history of experience see John B. O'Brien, Jr., "The Preference Clause in Federal Electric Power Development and Distribution," *Task Force Report*, III, pp. 1107-1150; Henry P. Caulfield, Jr., "Federal Electric Power Policy" (Washington: Resources for the Future, Inc., 1958, mimeographed).

[3] Information from correspondence with Eugene W. Weber, Special Assistant to Assistant Chief of Engineers for Civil Works, U.S. Corps of Engineers.

the Delaware Valley are to be found in the experiences of the Southeastern Power Administration and the Southwestern Power Administration. SEPA was organized by the Secretary of the Interior in 1950 to market power produced at structures built by the Corps of Engineers in ten states. SEPA has negotiated contracts with private utilities in the area to wheel and firm with supplemental generation the power produced at some ten reservoirs.[4] The contracts assure that the hydro capacity will be used for its most efficient purpose, that is, for peaking. The interests of the preference customers are met by the exchange of peak power for an equivalent amount of base power; in other words, the private utilities agree to serve the preference customers in accordance with their requirements. The limits of preference customers' entitlement are set by the estimated firm power that could be produced. SEPA reimburses the private companies for the expenses of wheeling and firming.[5] It may be noted that in 1955 Attorney-General Brownell ruled in the Clark Hill case that the Secretary of the Interior was required to negotiate such contracts to satisfy the needs of the preference customers.[6]

A similar pattern of wheeling and firming has been negotiated by the Southwestern Power Administration. The first of these contracts dates back to 1947, and in fiscal 1957, 40 preference customers were served under such arrangements with private utilities.[7] SWPA, unlike SEPA, owns, leases, and operates transmission lines in addition to utilizing the transmission facilities of private companies.

Numerous other public agencies have negotiated satisfactory arrangements with both private utilities and preference customers. The Pacific Gas and Electric Company has contract arrangements of this type with the Bureau of Reclamation. Also, the Bureau of Reclamation has a central dispatching system at Phoenix, Arizona, that embraces some of the facilities of the Arizona Public Service Company and the

---

[4] Wheeling is the transmission of energy generated by one company or agency over the lines of another. Firming is the provision of sufficient capacity, over and above that available in a specific system or project, to produce a given output 100 per cent of the time or to meet a given load demand 100 per cent of the time.

[5] See, for example, *Contract Executed by the United States of America, Department of the Interior, Acting by and through the Southeastern Power Administration and Virginia Electric Power Company*, August 8, 1952; *Annual Report Southeastern Power Administration, Fiscal Year 1957* (Elberton, Georgia).

[6] Reported in U.S. Senate, *Committee on Public Works, Power Rates—Southwestern Power Administration*, 84th Cong., 2d sess., 1956, pp. 680-687.

[7] *Annual Report of the Southwestern Power Administration*, 1957 (Tulsa, Oklahoma).

Southern Nevada Power Company and thus provides an effective power interchange among preference customers and private companies. The New York State Power Authority has negotiated a number of wheeling contracts with the Niagara Mohawk Power Corporation to serve several small municipally-owned electric companies outside the immediate St. Lawrence project area. The Grant County Public Utility District is financing construction of a major project on the Columbia on the basis of contracts with private utilities in its area.

For the Delaware Valley it is difficult to appraise the significance and the power needs of preference customers. Thirty-five municipally-owned distribution systems and five REA cooperatives operate within 100 miles of potential hydro sites in the Valley. For the group in the 100-mile radius the FPC has estimated that 1957 peak demand requirements were about 130,000 kw.[8] It is anticipated that load requirements for the Valley as a whole will increase by 1980 to two and a half times 1957 requirements. If this group of public bodies and cooperatives grows at the same rate, their peaking demand requirements will increase by 195,000 kw to approximately 325,000 kw. The installed capacity of structures to be built in the Valley in the next twenty years may be provisionally put at approximately 500,000 kw; therefore the application of continuing preference for the 195,000 kw might claim approximately 40 per cent of the total of Delaware River hydro capacity installed over this period. Public bodies and cooperatives have other sources of energy, however, and may not seek to meet their entire load requirements from Delaware River installations. On the other hand, there may be preference customers outside the 100-mile radius but within feasible transmission distance that could be economically served, as well as some who may wish to substitute Delaware power for their existing sources of supply.

In the practices of SEPA and SWPA the legal limit of preference is measured by the amount of firm power that could be produced if the structures were designed solely for this purpose. If this limit were applied to Delaware hydro, the preference customers might be entitled to no more than 10 per cent of installed capacity, or about 50,000 kw, since the firm power potential of the river is quite limited. The significance of pumped storage for the Delaware suggests that if preference is to be applied its limits may need to be defined in terms other than alternative firm power. In these circumstances it may be ap-

---

[8] Information provided by New York Regional Office, Federal Power Commission. The municipalities included are those with populations of 2,500 or more.

propriate for preference customer entitlement to extend to whatever combination of firm or peaking power they can utilize effectively. The marketing arrangement for Delaware River power under the provisions of federal preference, utilizing wheeling contracts with private utilities, should seek to maximize the hydroelectric values that may be obtained. Whether this maximization can in fact be realized through wheeling and firming contracts depends on a number of factors whose significance cannot now be appraised. For example, if the preference customers interested in firm power are so widely scattered as to occasion considerable transmission costs, there will be resulting net revenue loss to the Basin agency. The price that preference customers will be willing to pay for firm power or for such limited peaking power as may be required will depend on the shape of their load curves and the cost of alternative sources of supply. On the other hand, sales of peaking power to the private grid may require expensive high voltage transmission lines that would again reduce the Basin agency's realizable net revenue. In the absence of specific data it is not possible to estimate the "price of preference," that is, the potential net revenue loss that might be occasioned by selling to preference customers by way of wheeling and firming contracts, as compared with selling all Delaware power direct to the private grid.

The requirement of Section 5 of the Flood Control Act of 1944 that power from federal projects be marketed at cost will be seriously detrimental to the long-run interests of effective Delaware water-resource development. The standards set by the 1944 Act for hydro power rates apparently permit, as a part of the cost to be recovered by rates, only those administrative overheads specifically chargeable to power operations. If the sale of hydro power by the Basin agency is to return a net revenue to support at least partially the central staff and to contribute to other programs in the interests of effective long-run development, it will be necessary to seek congressional modification of this portion of Section 5 as applied to the Delaware.

Power Marketing under Interstate Compact

A compact agency would not be bound by the federal requirements of preference unless the Congress were to impose this as a condition to approval of the compact or as a condition of federal investment. A compact agency would thus have considerably more latitude than a Basin agency established under federal statute in negotiating for the sale of hydroelectric power. The issue here is in part a matter of timing.

In the event that Delaware development is put under way by a federal statute, with hydro power contracts negotiated in accordance with the preference clause, and in the further event that these marketing policies are in effect for a number of years before the compact agency comes into existence, it will be difficult for the latter agency to upset what will be by that time an established marketing pattern.

Apart from preference, power marketing under authority of a compact agency will differ from marketing under federal statute in two particulars. First, the agency must secure a Federal Power Commission license. No difficulty should be encountered here since interstate public bodies are given priority. Second, the control of net power revenue and rate schedules under compact will be somewhat less restrictive than under federal statute. The terms of the compact presumably could authorize the setting of power rates at a point to produce a net revenue and permit the application of this revenue to other resource programs.

Contractual Relations for the Sale of Power

The realization of maximum value from Delaware hydro depends on the agreements that can be worked out among three parties: the Basin agency, private utilities operating in an integrated system, and public bodies and cooperatives. Under the marketing policy proposed here the agency would undertake to sell power on terms that would provide sufficient net revenue to strengthen its institutional position, and at the same time retain the flexibility required for any necessary alterations in long-run project purposes. This calls for reasonably stable contractual arrangements. The distributors of electric energy in the Valley power marketing area will expect the assurance provided by contracts with a duration of at least ten years, even though such contracts may contain provisos to permit re-negotiation of specific quantities and prices. SEPA and SWPA, for example, generally re-determine rates every five years.

There is no present shortage of transmission facilities in the Delaware Valley nor is such shortage likely to appear over the lifetime of Delaware projects, assuming that prevailing patterns of private power investment continue. It may be hoped that the new Basin agency will be able to negotiate satisfactory wheeling arrangements and so avoid any uneconomic investment in transmission facilities.

The institutional position of the Basin agency with respect to the control of water releases would undoubtedly be strengthened if the agency were to invest directly in the generators, penstocks, and other equipment necessary for power generation, and to contract for wholesale power at the bus bar. The alternative arrangement would be the sale of rights in falling water, as, for example, at Hoover Dam. This would require the purchaser to assume investment costs in generating equipment. If the control of water releases is to be retained by the agency, any contracts for the sale of falling water must necessarily be drawn to protect the use of water for other purposes and to permit flexibility over time.

In negotiating contracts for the sale of hydrolectric power, the Basin agency can expect to reach agreements that are mutually advantageous to all parties. The agency must seek to avoid an intensification of the latent conflicts between public and private power. The successful negotiation of the three-party agreements as described should go far to prevent this. The minimum price for power will be set by the cost assigned this project purpose; the maximum price will be determined by the system requirements of prospective purchasers and their alternative costs. Within this range there will be room for bargaining. Any net revenue above minimum assignable cost may be applied by the Basin agency to the financing of its continuing activities. The utilization of net power revenues in the general interests of Delaware water development may be expected to produce more significant contributions to the economic welfare of the Basin than if power were sold at minimum assignable cost.

A Basin agency will be in a position to lend support to the increased regionalization of the electric power industry. Power pooling, in combination with central electronic dispatching, now makes possible the production and distribution of electric energy at the least-cost combination available within a region as a whole at any one time. The interchange operating in and adjacent to the Valley is already performing with a high degree of effectiveness. It may be hoped that the power marketing policies of a Basin agency will make modest contributions to this kind of regional efficiency.

RECREATION

Three objectives are to be served by a water-based recreation program planned and conducted as a part of the development of the Delaware Valley. The first is to meet the present and emerging demands for additional recreational facilities. Population in the Delaware River Service Area is projected to increase by 8,400,000 between 1955 and 1980. Per capita personal incomes are expected to rise in the same period from $2,450 to $3,300.[9] With such large increases in population and income, it is reasonable to expect very rapid growth in the demand for recreational activities, including water-based recreation.

Increased interest in and expenditures for recreation are a nation-wide postwar phenomenon. For example, use of the national park system has increased by an estimated 8 per cent per year in the postwar period. The comparable figure for national forests is 10 per cent, and for TVA reservoirs 15 per cent annually.[10] Attendance at Corps reservoirs increased twenty-fold between 1946 and 1957. In the Delaware Valley existing recreational facilities are now inadequate to meet all demands. The National Park Service has reported deficiencies of non-urban land for intensive and extensive day use, particularly in the central metropolitan belt. New York and New Jersey have generally adequate land areas for recreation purposes, but many sites are unde-veloped.

There is an increasing awareness of the importance of recreation in and around the Delaware Valley. The governors of Pennsylvania and New Jersey have publicly supported an expanded recreation program for their states. The New Castle County (Delaware) Regional Planning Commission has been active in promoting additional facilities, as has the Welfare Council of Delaware. The New York Metropolitan Re-gional Council, through its Technical Committee on Recreation, plans to inventory all open-space facilities in its area. Other citizen and official groups have been active at both state and local levels.

A second objective for Delaware recreation undertakings is to fit them into a general program for water-resource development. If the goal of comprehensive development is to be attained, recreation values must be taken into account in planning future construction. Reservoir levels must be maintained to maximize recreational use consistent with other project purposes. Regional recreation programs must also be meshed organizationally with existing federal and state recreation agencies.

Third, recreation programs should be developed with a view to their general economic potential. Recreation is big business. The Federal Reserve Bank of Philadelphia has estimated that vacation activity is one of the Reserve District's top ten in importance, about equal to

[9] Office of Business Economics, U.S. Department of Commerce, *Economic Base Survey* (Washington, 1958), pp. 15-16.

[10] Resources for the Future, Inc., *Annual Report, 1957* (Washington, 1957), p. 40.

agriculture or textiles. Approximately $600,000,000 is spent annually by vacationers in the District; this includes outlays only within resort areas, without allowance for travel and other supplementary expenditures.[11] Furthermore, investment in reservoir recreation produces "acceleration" effects. It has been estimated that each dollar spent on shoreline development at TVA reservoirs leads to 10 dollars spent in the region on recreation investment. Since recreation development generates a substantial amount of economic activity, it may be possible to capture a part of the income from this activity to finance the recreation program itself. Recreation is a potential source of revenue, albeit a modest one, for a Basin agency.

Recreation programs are particularly difficult to evaluate as a part of multiple-purpose project planning and justification. In recent years federal water-resource agencies have set primary recreation benefits at $1.60 per visitor day, a figure arrived at by counting average expenditures for admissions and concessions within public recreation areas. This neglects the important intangible values that arise from reservoir-based recreation projects and probably produces an under-investment in recreation facilities. Some economists have suggested alternative approaches to the evaluation of recreation benefits and it may be that in the future techniques will be devised to reflect the benefits that are now omitted.[12] In the absence of satisfactory techniques, the evaluation and planning of recreation programs place a particularly heavy responsibility on the staff of a Basin agency. Lacking specific criteria, value judgments will necessarily abound, with no guide lines for reconciling the interests that are "pro-recreation" and those that are "con-recreation."

Federal Recreation Policy

As with other aspects of Delaware Valley water-resource development, the program and financial responsibilities of a Basin agency must be worked out in relation to the policies of the national government.

[11] "On Vacation," Federal Reserve Bank of Philadelphia, *Business Review*, April and May, 1958, pp. 3-5.

[12] See Marion Clawson, *Methods of Measuring the Demand for and Value of Outdoor Recreation* (Washington: Resources for the Future, Inc., 1959). For general discussion and suggestions specifically applicable to the California Feather River project see Andrew H. Trice and Samuel E. Wood, "Measurement of Recreation Benefits," *Land Economics*, XXXIV (August, 1958), pp. 195-207.

The following points, although not intended to be comprehensive of such policies, appear to be the most relevant for present programs.

First, federal interest in recreation is expanding. The 1958 session of Congress saw the enactment of the Outdoor Recreation Resources Review Act (P.L. 470, 85th Cong., 2d sess.), which provides for a nation-wide inventory and evaluation of outdoor recreation facilities and needs. A review commission established under the Act is to complete its study by 1961; this commission will undoubtedly propose additional federal involvement in recreation. The 1958 session also enacted a measure to strengthen fish and wildlife programs (P.L. 624, 85th Cong., 2d sess.).

Second, as things now stand, federal investment in recreation facilities at reservoirs constructed by national government agencies is limited. Recreation is treated as an incremental rather than as a primary project purpose, although provision of minimum basic facilities and of access to the project are deemed to be a part of general common cost. Any additional investment incurred to make recreation values available must be assumed by state or local governments. The exception to this is in areas that are determined to be of "national significance" for recreation purposes, but the criteria for this determination are regarded as restrictive by those favoring an expanded federal interest in recreation. However, federal water-resource agencies have been successful in securing congressional appropriations for recreation purposes at a number of specific projects that represent a modification of these restrictions. In practice federal agencies will not request authority to construct reservoirs that would be justified primarily on the basis of recreation.[13]

Third, it is accepted national policy that reservoir-based facilities shall be leased without charge to national, state, or local recreation agencies for administration. The lessee undertakes all capital and operating expenditures. This practice is followed by the Corps, the Bureau of Reclamation, and the Tennessee Valley Authority.

Fourth, as noted, where recreation is deemed to be of national significance, an area may be established and operated at federal expense. The National Park Service must initiate action to designate such an area; one is now under investigation at Tocks Island.

---

[13] This kind of situation has emerged at Tocks Island on the Delaware, where the National Park Service has estimated annual visitor days at a maximum of 5,000,000, equivalent to annual estimated benefits of approximately $8,000,000. The Corps of Engineers apparently feels that this is an "excessive" evaluation that should not be used as major justification for the project.

Price Policy for Recreation

State recreation agencies operating in the Valley establish charges for the use of their facilities at a level designed for maximum utilization to assure mass consumption of the recreation product. This pricing policy, characteristic of almost all state recreation services throughout the nation, requires substantial financial support from general fund appropriations. Operating revenues contribute only a minor fraction of current expenses and typically none of the necessary capital outlay. For the nation as a whole, the ratio of state park expenditures to revenue from operations is five to one. Of the four Basin states, New York and Delaware collect about 20 per cent of annual current and capital expenditures from operating revenue, Pennsylvania and New Jersey about 10 per cent.

Many recreation specialists insist that any departure from prevailing price policy will defeat the purpose of public recreation. They contend that higher pricing will restrict the use of facilities to middle and upper income groups, thus denying recreation to those who are most in need. On the other hand, it may be possible to adopt a different pricing policy, maximizing net recreation revenue while retaining mass patronage for some facilities. This would require what might be termed "differentiated-price recreation" and would contemplate recreation planning to provide a wide variety of activities and schedules of charges. For example, some areas around a reservoir might be leased on a long-term basis for boating clubs and marinas or for privately-operated hotels and motels. Other areas might be developed for public fee boating, other sites leased for private cabins. Depending on the physical possibilities at the reservoir, large areas might remain for parks, camp sights, swimming facilities, and playgrounds, and these could be operated as in the past on a minimum-fee basis. Some facilities could be rationed by means of surcharges on weekends and holidays.

Efforts have been made to explore recreation experience in a number of states to ascertain whether Delaware reservoir areas might be made financially self-sufficient by the adoption of such pricing. The most successful reservoir recreation program, from the standpoint of finance, is operated by the Muskingum Conservancy District in Ohio. Since 1946 recreation facilities in the District have been self-sufficient on both capital and operating accounts. The Cachuma Project in California, constructed by the Bureau of Reclamation and in operation since 1952, is now self-sufficient with respect to its current operating expenses and some revenue will eventually be applied to the retirement of capital costs.[14] The State of New Hampshire operated its entire state park system from 1952 to 1957 without general fund appropriations, covering all operating expenses from its operating income, including interest and amortization on a small issue of recreation bonds. The Recreation Division in that state, however, concluded that this experience ". . . necessitated an unfortunate degree of exploitation and commercialization and that fee increases have brought a lessening in park use." [15] In the last two fiscal years the Division has secured small operating and capital appropriations from general funds.

Experience elsewhere aside, price policies for Delaware Valley recreation facilities must necessarily be influenced by policies already in effect at alternative facilities and by existing patterns of taste and recreational habits. The Jersey coast is the major recreational attraction for citizens of the Valley. Inexpensive recreation there, together with low fees at existing state parks, will necessarily limit the level of charges for recreation facilities at new reservoirs.

It should be made the responsibility of the Delaware Basin agency to explore fully the revenue possibilities from recreation. As part of its responsibility in the Survey, the National Park Service undertook to prepare a master recreation plan for a number of specific reservoir sites. Once this plan is available it may be possible, with the help of a professional recreation consultant, to forecast recreation revenues with reasonable accuracy and to suggest modifications in the NPS plans to produce additional revenue.

The revenue goals for Delaware Valley recreation programs may be conceived as extending through a range of possibilities. The first goal would be to cover all current operating expenses out of operating income, but to find additional financing for the necessary capital funds for recreation investment (land for recreation areas, access roads, plant and equipment). A second goal would contemplate a bond issue to provide capital facilities for recreation, accompanied by a price policy adequate to meet current operating expenses plus interest and amortization. A third goal would extend beyond this to provide revenue that might cover a part of capital investment in reservoir lands and structures.

Judged by recreation experience elsewhere, the first revenue goal

[14] Correspondence with Paul W. Campbell, Supervisor, Division of Parks, Santa Barbara County, California.

[15] Forestry and Recreation Department, State of New Hampshire Recreation Division, *Biennial Report, 1955-56,* and correspondence with Russell B. Tobey, Director.

may be attainable even in the early years of project operation. At some later time the second revenue goal might be achieved. It would be unwise to anticipate that, at any time in the foreseeable future, recreation income will be sufficient to achieve the third goal.

Other Policy Issues

The possible establishment by the National Park Service of a recreation area of national significance at Tocks Island is probably the major policy issue which must be resolved in devising administrative patterns for reservoir recreation in the Valley. If the National Park Service finds that it is feasible and desirable to establish such an area and if this proposal ultimately is adopted by the Congress, financial responsibility at this site will, of course, be assumed by the national government. NPS will attempt to maximize the use of the facility with a policy of low user charges.

The development of Tocks Island by the National Park Service may, however, be detrimental to the efforts of the Basin agency to promote reservoir-based recreation for the Valley as a whole. Tocks Island affords the one site in the Valley that, if developed and administered in accordance with the price policy described above, might conceivably return substantial net revenue. Through federal development the Basin agency therefore would lose control over the most promising recreation facility in the Valley, and in addition would lose access to possible net revenue that might be employed for the development of other sites. Nevertheless, in view of the general uncertainty concerning the future of recreation revenue, it would appear at this time that the National Park Service should be urged to propose a national recreation area for Tocks Island. Federal funds would probably assure a more rapid realization of recreation potential at this reservoir than if the Basin agency were to undertake development from its own financial resources.

Apart from Tocks Island, the major policy decision which the new agency must face is this: should it both plan and administer recreation programs, or should it restrict its efforts to planning and coordination, leaving the administration of the areas to state and local recreation agencies? The pros and cons of this choice could be debated at length. On balance, however, it would appear that the Basin agency should follow federal precedent and negotiate contractual arrangements with state and county bodies, leaving to them responsibility for the actual conduct of programs. In its recreation planning the agency could explore the possibility of a differentiated price pattern to achieve the maximum of net revenue from a given facility. Another device worthy of examination is the lease-rental agreement now used in Pennsylvania for school construction. Following this precedent a state agency would agree to pay to the Basin agency an annual amount for the privilege of using a facility. The contracted annual payment would then serve as a financial base for a bond issue assumed by the regional agency, and the proceeds of the issue would be used to acquire the necessary recreation sites and capital facilities.

Land Acquisition

An effective program for the acquisition and control of land areas around reservoirs is an absolute prerequisite for the development of resource-based recreation programs. This requires the purchase of land necessary for the recreation areas themselves, together with space for access roads, and may extend to land use or zoning control in areas adjacent to recreation sites. The Basin agency, organized initially under federal statute, will encounter severe restrictions on land acquisition if required to operate within the scope of existing federal practice. Acquisition policy for federal projects is now governed by the joint Army-Interior agreement announced October 12, 1953. This policy provides that reservoir lands shall be taken in fee to the five-year flood line or to a point 300 feet horizontally from the edge of the full conservation pool (defined as the maximum water level exclusive of flood storage). Beyond this, easements are acquired to the level of the design or typical flood. This policy has been sharply criticized for its restrictive effect on recreation values, but there is no present indication that it will be changed in the immediate future.[16] Federal agencies may propose additional land acquisition for recreation and for fish and wildlife enhancement, but any such action involves a departure from standard practice. Unless general federal policy is altered soon, therefore, or unless special arrangements are made for the Delaware, a federal-interstate compact agency would be in a stronger position with respect to an effective land acquisition policy in the interest of recreation than an agency based on federal statute.

A comprehensive program for land acquisition and control is a hotly

---

[16] See Hearings before a Subcommittee of the Committee on Government Operations, *Army-Interior Reservoir Land Acquisition Policy*, House of Representatives, 85th Cong., 1st sess.; *Army-Interior Reservoir Land Acquisition Policy*, H. Res. 1185, 85th Cong., 1st sess., 1957.

disputed matter. In a mixed public-private economy land acquisition by government agencies is controversial simply because property is thereby removed from private ownership. These conflicts can be resolved in part, however, by the organization of public support for a broad program in and around reservoir areas. Several recent studies of land requirement policies in southeastern Pennsylvania give evidence of growing general demand for a long-range program to protect open spaces.

Abundant experience demonstrates that the construction of attractive reservoirs in populated areas gives rise to substantial increases in land values on property adjacent to the reservoir. Unless these increments are controlled or captured by careful planning, recreation values will inevitably suffer. Further, unless adequate land areas for recreation are acquired at the time of reservoir land acquisition, later purchases are possible only at sharply increased cost. Anticipatory land acquisition is of such importance that the states may be willing to appropriate funds specifically for this purpose, as Pennsylvania has done at Tocks Island. It would also be prudent for the Basin agency to urge the states to adopt comprehensive zoning regulations applicable to areas adjacent to reservoirs, in the interests of both use control and the limitation of increases in private land values.

OTHER REVENUE SOURCES

State Appropriations

The interests of the four Basin states in the Delaware Valley are substantial. The economic development of the Basin will redound to the economic welfare of these states as a whole: the level of economic activity will be increased, the income of the citizenry will be enhanced, and state tax bases will be enlarged. Material indirect and secondary benefits from Delaware Valley development may strengthen the positions of the states as governmental and economic units. The prospective realization of these important advantages from Delaware water-resource development, together with the exercise of substantial state authority and control over Basin programs, suggests the assumption of some fiscal responsibility.[17] There is a strong case in terms of regional interests for state appropriations to support a Delaware Basin agency

[17] For a discussion of water-resource development and state policy, both in general terms and in relation to California experience, see Central Valley Project Studies, U.S. Bureau of Reclamation, *Problems 10 to 13*, 1947, pp. 127-131.

both in its first phase, when it will be organized under federal statute, and in its second phase under a federal-interstate compact. As a matter of principle it could be argued that state fiscal responsibility and hence appropriations should be larger in the second phase than in the first. The need for appropriations, however, may diminish as water becomes more and more scarce and consequently increasingly valuable, and as revenue from the sale of industrial and municipal water grows over time.

Experience within the Delaware Valley suggests that the states will assume at least limited financial responsibility for the support of a Basin agency through general fund appropriations. In the second phase of organization these arrangements could be made a part of the compact, with commitments from the states on a semi-contractual basis. The Incodel proposal of 1949 called for such appropriations from all four Basin states. Three of the states adopted the proposal, thereby in effect accepting the principle of financial responsibility, and the fourth, Pennsylvania, rejected the plan only in part on financial grounds. In the intervening years the concern of the four states with water-resources management has continued and in some cases expanded. There is certainly no reason to conclude that state willingness to assume financial responsibility for Basin water-resource development is of smaller dimension now than a decade ago.

The amounts required for the annual operating budget of a Basin agency in its first years, as indicated in Chapter 10, are not startlingly large. If something between $500,000 and $1,000,000, exclusive of capital outlays, is accepted as a reasonable figure and if this amount is divided among the four states, the contribution from any one would not have serious impact on state financial structures.[18]

Federal Appropriations for Operating Purposes

It was proposed in Chapter 4 that the Corps of Engineers assume responsibility for construction in the initial phase of Basin organization. This implies that the federal government would make capital appro-

---

[18] The basis for dividing general financial responsibility among the four Basin states would, of course, be subject to negotiation and compromise. The general budget of the Interstate Commission on the Potomac River Basin is apportioned one-half on the basis of area and one-half on the basis of population. Incopot, *The Story of Water Pollution Control* (Washington, 1958), pp. 59-62. The proposed Northeastern Water Compact contains this same formula (Article VII-B).

priations to cover all or a portion of such costs. In the second organizational phase federal financial support for construction could be implemented by appropriations to the Basin agency. Non-federal capital responsibility would necessarily be assumed by the agency, but funds might be provided on loan from the federal government, or, if revenue prospects were secure, the Basin agency could raise capital by means of revenue bonds.

Similarly, a number of possibilities are available for the recognition and implementation of federal financial responsibility for operating programs. The national government might share with the states in the support of the Basin agency's annual operating budget. The preparation of comprehensive plans and surveys for water-resource development, as noted earlier, is customarily a federal responsibility. Funds for these purposes are appropriated directly to the Corps of Engineers, the Bureau of Reclamation, and the Soil Conservation Service. Admittedly there is little precedent for federal appropriations to a compact agency for water-resource planning; but on the other hand, the national government has a long-standing policy of encouraging state and local planning efforts. After the initial years of development, the Basin agency may stand more largely on its own financial feet. This may mean revenue bond financing, and in these circumstances federal appropriations for federal responsibilities, such as flood control, could be annualized and made payable to the regional agency. The annualized appropriation, in turn, could constitute a part of the support for revenue bond issues.

Charges and Taxes as General Revenue

A Basin agency would be very much strengthened in its ability to develop effectively the water resources of the Delaware Valley if it had access to a general source of revenue independent of state and congressional appropriations and independent of the revenue that may be derived from hydroelectric power and industrial and municipal water. Even if the amounts of such revenue were modest, say of the magnitude of $100,000 to $200,000 a year, this income would go far toward assuring organizational and program stability.

It has been traditional in this country, particularly at state and local levels, to collect considerable revenue on the basis of benefits received. State motor vehicle fees are customarily assessed on this basis. The states have authorized reclamation districts, flood control districts, recreation districts, sewer districts, and water districts, which charge in accordance with rough measurements of benefits accruing to property. Soil conservation districts are organized and at least partially financed on this basis, in a pattern of federal-state-local cooperation.

The economic basis for charges for water withdrawals is clear and persuasive. In the next decade or two water in the Delaware will move from its status as a relatively free good to a status of relative scarcity. Water rights will become more valuable. At the same time, this value will be enhanced by the activities of the Basin agency itself as it moves to regulate flows and protect the quantity and improve the quality of water. The legal basis for water charges is also clear. It is accepted that states may control and regulate the use of water either in their sovereign or in their proprietary capacities. The general taxing power, as an attribute of state sovereignty, permits the formation of special revenue districts. Also, water may be specifically allocated and charges imposed for its use.[19] There is ample precedent for financing water-resource development by charges on the beneficiaries of the program, under both riparian (eastern) and appropriation (western) water law. One of the most significant of all state water-resource enterprises—the Miami Conservancy District in Ohio—was organized to provide flood protection financed wholly by assessments against the beneficiaries of that protection.

There are two possible bases for the assessment of general charges to support water-resource development. The first of these rests on the concept of private benefit, the second on the concept of social cost. Either levy may be described as a tax or as a charge: the difference in description apparently is of no legal significance.

The first approach has been used widely in western states. The rationalization here is that an improvement in water supplies yields widespread indirect and secondary benefits over and above the charges per gallon or per acre-foot to direct beneficiaries. This approach calls for the formation of a water district through which a part of project costs is captured from commercial establishments and homeowners who are thought to be generally benefited. Collections are in proportion to assessed values as used for other property tax purposes. In California the basis for water district general taxes has been set at the value of land exclusive of improvements, although other bases have been

---

[19] For example, the Niagara Mohawk Power Company has paid annual charges for many years for the use of Niagara River water to the New York State Water Power and Control Commission. Legally this is a combined franchise tax, water-use charge, and payment for the value of downstream riparian rights.

considered and in some cases adopted.[20] Such districts are used both for irrigation from reservoirs and for ground water replenishment. In the East the water district is less widely used, although the Washington Suburban Sanitation Commission, organized in the State of Maryland, utilizes a general charge against all property to support the construction of flood control works, storm sewers, and sewage and water supply facilities.

An application of the private benefit concept is also recognized in New York State law to permit the organization of river regulating districts. These have access to real estate taxes on benefited property within the district to raise funds for the construction and maintenance of improvements. There are only two such districts in the state, although one, the Hudson River Regulating District, has successfully operated a major reservoir (Sacandaga) for low-flow augmentation for more than three decades.

There are no similar districts for water-resource development and control in the other three Basin states, but New Jersey and Pennsylvania provide for the organization of flood control districts to receive and disburse money from federal and state agencies. These districts have no independent taxing authority.

It would be possible to apply the benefit concept in the Delaware Basin by establishing one or more river improvement (or regulating) districts and financing a part of the cost of the control structures from levies on real property within these districts. Property assessments, however, are not closely related to the benefits that may be realized from Delaware development. Nor would this approach contribute to the long-run need for water conservation in the Valley. Payments based on property values would not encourage the users of water to control either the quantity used or the degree of pollution.

The second approach, which is cast in terms of social cost, has considerably greater appeal on grounds both of equity and of conservation. Under this plan the levy on each user would be determined by the impact of his use on water development. This might be called the "damage" or "social injury" concept. Charges would be based on the volume of withdrawals, on the quality of return flow, or on both. No effort would be made to measure the benefit of the water to the user. A relevant experience with this type of financing is the practice of some California water districts which impose charges for ground water replenishment. The charges are based on metered withdrawals, and

[20] Stephen C. Smith, "Problems in the Use of the Public District for Ground-Water Management," *Land Economics*, XXXII (August, 1956), pp. 259-269.

are used in combination with real property levies to finance capital and operating expenses.[21]

A general charge on water withdrawals would encourage the conservation of water.[22] Industrial firms would find it advantageous to install equipment for re-cycling and for treatment of effluents. Even a very low charge would tend to limit increases in gross water requirements, thus postponing the need for stringent water allocations or additional structures, or both. In the application of a charge for water withdrawals it is important to distinguish between water from reservoirs and water withdrawn directly from the river and its tributaries. Presumably all water from reservoirs will be sold at a price to reflect full cost, including fees or charges for support of the generalized activities of the Basin agency. A charge for withdrawals of stream water would be aimed at the riparian user, and, in particular, the industrial and municipal user.

Unfortunately, data are not now available on water use in the Valley which would permit the drafting of an equitable schedule of charges for water withdrawals based on the social cost or damage concept. Some industrial users, notably steam-electric plants, make very large withdrawals but return the water to the river unchanged except for temperature increases; these users might appropriately be exempt from a withdrawal charge based on a concept of social cost. Other firms, such as chemicals and pulp and paper, may discharge a high volume of pollutants and might thus be appropriately subject to charge. A careful measurement of the costs imposed by these differing degrees of industrial use cannot be devised now and may, indeed, be difficult to devise at any time in the near future.

In spite of the foregoing technical difficulties in drafting a schedule for water withdrawal charges, it may be desirable to establish very early in Delaware Valley development a firm authority to permit such charges to be imposed. The best way to establish this is to institute, from the outset of the Basin agency's existence, a permit system, applied first to stream water and perhaps extended later to other surface and ground waters, probably with an exemption for small

[21] Howard W. Crooke, *Financing Ground Water Replenishment by Acre Foot Charge for Water Extracted* (Santa Ana, California: Orange County Water District, 1958).

[22] There is very little discussion of water withdrawal charges in the literature. One economist has suggested that a use tax might be practicable for streams and that rebates could be used to encourage conservation and pollution abatement. Jerome W. Milliman, "Commonality, the Price System, and Use of Water Supplies," *Southern Economic Journal*, XXII (April, 1956), pp. 426-437.

users. A minimum charge could be made for the permit, whose initial purpose would be informational. Each permit holder would be required to provide for his operation the kind of information on river water use that is now lacking—data on gross withdrawals, re-use, and quality and quantity of return flow. This information could serve as a basis for drawing a schedule of charges for application over time. The level of such charges must, of course, be kept low for the immediate future. The economic development of the Delaware Valley will not be promoted by a pattern of water-use charges that places the Basin at a competitive disadvantage with other eastern river basins in terms of attractiveness to industry. On the other hand, industrial water users will be major beneficiaries of Delaware River improvements, and equity requires that these beneficiaries pay at least a part of the costs of such improvements.

CONCLUSIONS

1. The Basin states should contribute to the support of the Delaware Valley agency out of appropriated funds, particularly in the first decade of operations.

2. The national government may be expected to provide capital and operating funds for navigation and flood control, to continue data-gathering activities, and possibly to provide annual appropriations to the Basin agency for plans and surveys. In addition, the national government has a number of grant-in-aid programs for water-related activities; the regional agency should coordinate and promote these programs for Valley governments that are eligible to participate.

3. The national government is moving toward expanded responsibility for low-flow augmentation with a part of the benefits financed on a non-reimbursable basis. The Basin agency should assume responsibility for the measurement, assessment, and collection of reimbursable levies from the beneficiaries of such low-flow control. The agency's role for this purpose might be that of investigator and negotiator.

4. Industrial and municipal water supply is critically significant for the economic development of the Valley, but this area is not susceptible of precise analysis at this time. Research to date, including studies that have been sponsored by the Delaware Valley Project, indicates that no major revenue can be expected from industrial and municipal water until some time after 1980.

5. The national government will provide capital funds to construct water supply storage in anticipation of early need. The Basin agency

should encourage such construction where needed and undertake
negotiations with water distribution agencies to assure that such investment will eventually be reimbursed to the national government. It is
reasonable to anticipate that by the turn of the century revenue from
water will be substantial, that investment in water supply storage will
be on a self-liquidating basis, and that sale of water will provide some
net revenue for the support of other water resource programs.

6. In the first years of development, revenue from the sale of hydroelectric power could be the most significant source of income for a new
Basin agency.

7. The hydro power potential of the Delaware, which is a small
proportion of the total regional public and private power needs, should
be developed for peaking purposes, its most efficient use in the
circumstances which prevail in the Valley. The Basin agency, organized under federal statute, will probably be required to market power
under established preference policies for public bodies and cooperatives, although it would be possible to seek an exception to established
policy to permit a partnership arrangement with private utilities. If
preference is required and is not to interfere with the efficient utilization of hydro power for peaking, it will be necessary for the Basin
agency to negotiate wheeling and firming contracts with private
utilities, and particularly with those now party to the Pennsylvania-
New Jersey-Maryland inter-connection.

8. If the sale of hydro power is to provide net revenue for the
regional water-resource program, it will be necessary to seek a change
in federal law to permit the establishment of wholesale power rates at
levels above minimum assignable cost.

9. It is not realistic to expect that reservoir-based recreation programs will be immediately self-sustaining, let alone productive of net
revenue. Every effort should be made, however, to explore the possibilities for differentiated-price recreation in an attempt to increase
revenue potential.

10. The Basin agency must retain responsibility for planning for
recreation based on the reservoirs, but should negotiate agreements
with state and local bodies for program administration. The National
Park Service should be encouraged to establish a national recreation
area at Tocks Island.

11. There are possibilities of revenue from general charges on water
use. The legal and economic bases for such charges are reasonably
firm, but there are many technical details to be considered in drawing

up a schedule. It would be desirable to impose a fee under a permit system, with an exemption to small users, from the Basin agency's beginning, and to introduce user charges only after further data and experience are available.

Part IV: American Experience in River Basin Administration

CHAPTER 12

American Experience: An Introduction

So FAR in this study, water-resources administration has been considered in terms of the substance and processes, organizational considerations, and issues underlying the concept. In Part IV this bundle of concepts, programs, and practices called "water-resources administration" or, in the present context, "basin administration," will be viewed whole, at the geographic place of impact. Several comprehensive studies have been made of parts of the American experience in river basin administration. In the following sketches of action in a few selected basins, there has been no intention to duplicate earlier studies; instead emphasis has been laid on those aspects of the national experience that may have special significance for particular river basins. How have theories been translated into action and how has public policy been forged from techniques, ideas, and attitudes? Examination of individual basins is one way—it may, indeed, be the best way—of analyzing the action and interaction of the politics, economics, and administration of water.

IS THE DELAWARE BASIN UNIQUE?

The point has been made that each river basin is different as to natural features, social, economic, and governmental structures, and popular attitudes and predilections. At the same time, one may readily observe that geographic location strongly affects the character of any basin, including of course the Delaware; and it is easy to illustrate the direct dependence of the Delaware Valley on ideas and activities commonly connected with other river basins or with the nation generally. Important features of the Delaware Basin—that is, those

227

which give it whatever special character it possesses—may be depicted by a series of propositions:

1. New York City's Catskill aqueducts provide one of the four or five major inter-basin diversions in the United States, and it is quite possible that other works will transfer water between neighboring watersheds during the next fifty years.[1] Therefore, the physical principle of hydrologic unity does not have to be accepted as a limiting factor on the future of this area.

2. There is time to plan and build to provide for all the uses of as much water as engineering and economic techniques are capable of providing. There is no overpowering crisis (flood, famine, depression) today that is compelling precipitate action toward ill-considered, unbalanced, and unwise construction along the Delaware.[2]

3. Water development clearly is not *the* key to economic growth in this humid eastern area, hence other broad social and economic considerations will need to be taken into account if the maximum economic potential of the Basin is to be realized. Serious shortages of good water may appear by around 1980, for the supply is becoming progressively less generous. Undoubtedly, development will be planned and construction begun before any crisis appears.

4. No permanent priorities for water use could be set by governmental authorities in this Basin or Service Area. In this as in other basins there would be changing uses through changing times. Water escaping in spring floods today will be needed for domestic and industrial uses tomorrow, and perhaps for agricultural use the day after. What is available for hydro generation now may be employed for irrigation or dilution of pollutants by 1980 or 1990. The idea of a 50-foot navigation channel to Trenton may succumb to Philadelphia or Northeastern New Jersey domestic supply needs in the future.

5. Inter-agency and inter-governmental conflicts have not crystallized to the point where they are an immovable block to rational development in the Delaware Basin. In particular, there is no major division of geographic responsibility between federal agencies in the Delaware as in the Missouri basin. There is no dry land-wet land dichotomy in

[1] See Gilbert F. White, "A Perspective of River Basin Development," *Law and Contemporary Problems*, XXII (Spring, 1957), p. 186. New diversions into or out of the Delaware Valley have been suggested in terms of water from the Susquehanna, a New Jersey ship canal, and so on.

[2] See Norman Wengert, "The Politics of River Basin Development," *Law and Contemporary Problems*, XXII (Spring, 1957), pp. 260 ff.; and Henry C. Hart, "Crisis, Community, and Consent," *ibid*. pp. 512 ff.

this eastern Basin, with its accompanying intransigence in relationships.

6. It is obvious that existing governmental organization in all its complexity is inadequate and unequal to the performance of those water-related functions indicated as desirable for the near future. There is no single source of unified water policy, even in the broadest terms, nor is there an agency charged either with basin-wide administrative responsibilities or with the task of coordinating existing agencies.

Singly or in varying combinations these conditions occur elsewhere; in the combination suggested here they typify the Delaware. They provide reference points by which to compare this eastern River Basin with others, and by which to appraise experience in general in the light of Delaware Basin needs. The best thinking about water administration and the best practical experience must be joined with the uniqueness of the Delaware to arrive at solutions to its emerging problems.

Evolution of Water Administration Ideas and Techniques

The story of the development of water management ideas and techniques resembles the history of modern man's discovery, adaptation, and use of knowledge in many fields.[3] A brief review of the story as Americans know it will set the stage for treatment of some of the existing river basin programs. The Delaware will inevitably be developed in the context of that history with ideas and techniques examined or tested elsewhere.

Man has employed engineering means to alter natural distribution of water for longer than recorded history. Remains of canals, dams, and irrigation and flood control works built millennia before Christ have been discovered in the Near East. In modern times, the realization of advanced methods for water-use management has been made possible slowly by the perfection of scientific and engineering techniques. The actual implementation of ideas, however, has lagged far behind development of useful techniques, for the translation of intellectual endeavor into plans and thence into reality is a time-consuming process. Furthermore, under democratic conditions public acquiescence must come before techniques can be applied, and public acceptance of governmental planning for water has been slow to materialize in

[3] See generally United Nations Department of Economic and Social Affairs, "Integrated River Basin Development."

America. Only in the late nineteenth century did the idea that water control structures might serve more than one purpose gain first a hearing, then gradual acceptance.[4] After that point the unfolding of modern water development practices followed at a pace limited chiefly by what was politically possible.

The Leading Ideas

There are five principal ideas that seem to encompass the current conceptualization of river basin development.[5] First among these is the multiple-purpose storage project, a concept that first came close to realization in the Boulder Canyon Project only 30 years ago. Most engineers aver that the theory of the big multiple-purpose project remains unperfected today, a consideration that basically conditions the realization of the remaining four concepts.

Basin-wide development is the second major concept. This is the idea that a system of works can be geared together to maximize use of all the water in an entire basin. The Miami Conservancy District was one of the earliest examples of American development for a whole basin, but only a single purpose received emphasis in that Ohio valley. Multiple-purpose planning and development for entire basins was in progress in the Tennessee, Missouri, Columbia, Central of California, and other major basins in 1959, but in no case was utilization complete nor were all the important problems solved. The Tennessee Valley Authority's work comes closer to fitting this ideal than does that in any other basin today.

Comprehensive regional development, the third concept, represents an even more general attempt to formulate the connections between water development and the maximization of all the other factors that go to make up general economic growth. Wherever water is used more efficiently, other direct and indirect benefits result therefrom. The TVA's operations are again the best demonstration of this fact, although multiple-purpose projects or basin-wide developments have been undertaken in many watersheds. The many complex economic and social components that result in general economic change, however, await sounder theories and better techniques of analysis than now exist before their nature and their interrelationships can be fully comprehended.

Articulated land and water programs and unified administration, the

---

[4] Gilbert F. White, *op. cit.*, is the best brief treatment of the history of basin development. The classification of ideas adopted here is White's.

[5] *Ibid.*, pp. 160-179.

fourth and fifth concepts, are logical accompaniments of the first three ideas. They represent attempts to theorize about the administration of the first three concepts. Examples of efforts to articulate land and water programs are found in the field committees of the Interior Department, the inter-agency committees in the Missouri, Columbia, and Pacific Southwest basins, and again the TVA. Efforts to implement this concept bring to light the inter-bureau conflicts and rivalries of the national administration, the problems of fitting state and national programs together, the big dam versus little dam controversy, and others. The continuing discussion of articulation reflects the theme running throughout this study: that water is not a clear-cut basis for organization, and that water and land are so blended as on occasion to defy placement in separate programmatic cells. The fifth concept, that of unified administration, represents an attempt to circumvent the imperfect nature of water as an organizing principle and to blend land and water problems by consigning both to a single agency for administration. The precise span of control of such an agency defies statement even in theory, and in those cases where unified administration has been essayed the meaning of unification has had to be defined through years of practice and trial and error.

The worth of the multiple-purpose project has been proved many times over, and the limited experience with basin-wide programs seems to indicate that concept is valid. To varying degrees, however, the theories of comprehensive regional development, articulated land and water programs, and unified administration remain to be worked out and applied. All five are dealt with at length in other parts of this study and will not be elaborated further here. Throughout the study these terms are used in a broad sense, as ideals at which planners, policy makers, and engineers should aim.

Application of the concepts has gone slowly, awaiting first of all the evolution of basic scientific and engineering tools sufficient to the task. A number of examples will illustrate this point. First, water and related data satisfactory in form and quantity have been collected very slowly, and much more must be done in the field of data collection and interpretation.

One of the difficulties in preparing an effective, organized defense against the oncoming deficiency of the supply is that knowledge of our water resources is so inadequate for the task. Basin studies of the occurrence and limits of our water resources on a broad scale are being undertaken by the federal government and by several state agencies, but for the most part these data collecting programs lack an adequate interpretive counterpart. There is a large accumulation of hydrologic data, much of which is scattered and incomplete but which, if assembled and applied more effectively to our water problems by competent hydrologists, would greatly increase in usefulness.[6]

Ground water is a subject on which data are very sparse. The continuous growth of possibilities is evidenced, however, by the fact that new data and new uses of data are being originated all the time. There is increasingly wider adoption of machine data-processing methods in connection with water problems. New procedures, like that for "water balance bookkeeping," offer great promise for empirical use.[7] Innovation continues in hydroelectric energy theory and practice where, for example, pumped-storage techniques are under constant study.[8] More and more efficient earth-moving equipment makes possible now types of dams that once could not have been built. The Bureau of Reclamation and the Corps of Engineers, chief dam-building agencies in the national government, have large permanent research staffs and laboratory facilities.

Early Applications

Virtually all of these concepts have been clarified if not created in this century, and attempts to convert the ideas into actualities have come close on their heels. Many single-purpose reservoirs were built before 1900, both by private persons and by governments.[9] The Corps of Engineers gradually developed interest in flood control works, and

[6] Jack B. Graham, "Preface," in Jack B. Graham and Meredith F. Burrill, *Water for Industry*, p. v.

[7] See Douglas B. Carter, "The Average Water Balance of the Delaware Basin," and T. E. A. van Hylckama, "Modification of the Water Balance Approach for Basins within the Delaware Valley," *Publications in Climatology*, XI, No. 3 (Centerton, N. J.: Drexel Institute of Technology Laboratory of Climatology, 1958).

[8] The Rhône River experienced one of the earliest applications of the idea of using rent from hydro power to offset other costs for projects. United Nations Department of Economic and Social Affairs, *op. cit.*, p. 3.

[9] Nathan O. Thomas and G. Earl Harbeck, Jr., "Reservoirs in the United States," Geological Survey Water-Supply Paper 1360-A (Washington, 1956), pp. 1-10. A dam built in 1738 at Massabesic Lake, New Hampshire, to power a gristmill and sawmill may have been the first substantial American effort. Many dams were built in the East in the early 1800's to supply canal water. French Lake, California, in 1859 was perhaps the first large irrigation reservoir. Flood control dams have been chiefly twentieth century phenomena. The first hydroelectric station began operation in 1882 at Appleton, Wisconsin.

that interest rapidly heightened after the creation in 1879 of the Mississippi River Commission.[10] The Flood Control Act of 1936 marked the extension of Corps concern in flood control to all the United States. The Reclamation Act of 1902 brought the national government into western irrigation construction on a large scale. Federal investment has grown each year under the direction of the Corps and the Bureau, but until 1928 efforts were concentrated on single-purpose structures which occasionally had other minor purposes.

In 1928 the multiple-purpose idea finally was adopted by Congress on a large scale in the Boulder Canyon Project Act. The great Hoover Dam was dedicated to these purposes:

> Controlling the floods, improving navigation and regulating the flow of the Colorado River, providing for storage and for the delivery of the stored waters thereof for reclamation of public lands and other beneficial uses exclusively within the United States, and for the generation of electrical energy as a means of making the project herein authorized a self-supporting and financially solvent undertaking. . . .[11]

The four purposes have been carried out in the dam completed by the Bureau of Reclamation.[12] It remains one of the world's largest dams, with a storage capacity of 32,300,000 acre feet and ultimate generating capacity of 1,300,000 kw. All costs but $25,000,000 allocated to flood control will be repaid from sale of power and water and from payment of generating charges. Generating, transforming, and switching facilities are operated by the City of Los Angeles and Southern California Edison Company under supervision of a Director of Power appointed by the Secretary of the Interior.

Governmental spending in depression years and after World War II gave a tremendous impetus to planning and building water control structures. By 1956 there were about 476 dams with two or more purposes in the United States, of which 21 had usable reservoir capacities of 2 million acre feet or more and were definitely multiple-purpose in character.[13] All 21 were constructed by the Bureau, Corps,

[10] Luna B. Leopold and Thomas Maddock, Jr., *op. cit.*, pp. 97 ff.

[11] 45 Stat. L. 1057.

[12] U.S. Bureau of Reclamation, *Dams and Control Works*, 3rd ed. (Washington, 1954), pp. 33-46. See, also, ———, *Reclamation Project Data* (Washington, 1948), pp. 37-43.

[13] Nathan O. Thomas and G. Earl Harbeck, Jr., *op. cit.*, p. 9. Lake Murray, South Carolina, is the largest privately-owned reservoir (1.6 million acre feet); Quabbin Reservoir, Massachusetts, is the largest reservoir devoted to municipal purposes (1.28 million acre feet).

or TVA. Twelve of the 21 have been completed since 1946, a fact that emphasizes the recent trend to large, multiple-purpose dams.

Hoover Dam was planned as a part, if a very significant part, of a multiple-purpose system of dams being built in the Colorado Basin.[14] Major dams already have been constructed in the upper basin. Davis, Parker, and Imperial Dams and other works are finished downstream, and they will soon be augmented by Glen Canyon Dam on the Lower Colorado. Thus multiple-purpose Hoover Dam is being worked into a basin-wide system, on a legal foundation provided by federal law, two interstate compacts, many court decisions, and myriad contracts and administrative arrangements.

All the 21 great multiple-purpose dams mentioned above either are undergoing the same transformation or were from their inception viewed as parts of systems of control structures. This is the case with the main-stem Missouri structures, Bonneville and Grand Coulee on the Columbia, and Norris and Kentucky on the Tennessee, for examples.

Ohio's Miami was the first important river on which basin-wide development was affected completely for a single purpose.[15] It is one of the best examples in America of single-purpose, basin-wide development. A 1913 flood devastated Dayton and the Miami River Valley, took the lives of four hundred people, and brought about the passage by the Ohio legislature (in 1914) of the Ohio Conservancy Act.[16] On the basis of this Act the Miami Conservancy District (MCD) was created under the supervision of a Board of Directors of three appointed by a ten-judge Conservancy Court. Acceptance of the concept of unified administration thus accompanied adoption of a basin-wide program for the Miami. Since that time five "dry" detention dams and many channel and local improvement works have been built on the River, all in accordance with an official plan approved in 1916.[17]

The Conservancy District has paid the entire cost of the flood control structures. Bonds amounting to $34,000,000 have been retired on schedule by means of levies on property owners and political subdivisions.

[14] See Paul L. Kleinsorge, *The Boulder Canyon Project* (Stanford: Stanford University Press, 1941), pp. 230 ff.

[15] See "The Story of the Miami Conservancy District" (Dayton: Miami Conservancy District, n.d.); and Arthur E. Morgan, *The Miami Conservancy District* (New York: McGraw-Hill Book Co., 1951). The Miami River drains 3,672 square miles above Hamilton, Ohio.

[16] *Ohio Revised Code*, Title LXI, Chap. 6101.

[17] Arthur E. Morgan, *op. cit.*, Chap. VIII. The benefit-cost ratio was better than two to one.

The levies were based upon damages caused by the 1913 flood and were approved by the Conservancy Court. In addition, a maintenance tax based on the original appraisal of benefits is employed, and its proceeds approach $500,000 annually. By 1956 expenditures, including bond retirement and maintenance, totalled more than $41,000,000. These figures and the works they represent are sources of local pride. They reveal why the MCD is considered by many to be the best example of local initiative in the whole field of American water management. MCD's accomplishments contrast sharply with those by the same state's Muskingum Watershed Conservancy District, where financing has come primarily from the national government.

Despite its overriding emphasis on flood control, the MCD has gradually experienced limited involvement in other related uses. Over 3,000 acres of dry reservoir sites are, during safe periods, heavily used for recreation purposes. Largely via the depression programs of the National Park Service, CCC, and WPA there have been added shelters, trails, fireplaces, and other improvements. Maintenance of these facilities is financed from the flood control levies. MCD charges no admission fees, although the Conservancy Court presumably could approve that course of action. Most of the recreation areas are near metropolitan Dayton, and their use will certainly increase. In this way land and water uses are beginning to undergo modest articulation on the Miami River.

Population and industrial growth brought gradual recognition of water supply problems in the Miami Valley after World War II. In 1953 industrial representatives and the MCD pressed for action, and the Conservancy Court approved formation of a Water Conservation Subdistrict, financed through private contributions but staffed by MCD personnel. A consulting engineering firm was commissioned to investigate the water supply situation. The resulting report in effect concluded that:

1. the idea of providing low water regulation storage on the Miami was sound;
2. future needs will make such facilities necessary;
3. but the two best sites would require dams costing $20,000,000, while benefits provable to the Conservancy Court under the terms of the Conservancy Act would amount only to some $7,000,000.

Two possible courses of action were to seek amendment of the state law to allow for financing anticipated construction for projected needs, or to turn to the federal government for funds. As of 1958 nothing had been done.

The significant point is that managers of a basin scheme which originally was single-purpose are now having other purposes forced on their attention. In a manner parallel with the adaptation of multiple-purpose Hoover Dam to basin-wide development plans, this basin-wide flood control organization is being compelled to turn to consideration of multiple purposes. Both examples illustrate the impact of changing conditions and the expanding economy on narrowly conceived water projects. Pressures for using water in new ways are manifest even in basins where the original planning was reasonably bold and imaginative in scope—the Columbia, Tennessee, and Missouri.

In this chapter, early applications of two of the principal concepts of modern water management have been examined: the multiple-purpose project and basin-wide development. In the remainder of Part IV, the conjunction of the two ideas in selected river basins will be examined. Further, the tendency toward the logical extension of the two toward the other three leading ideas—comprehensive regional development, articulated land and water programs, and unified administration—will be illustrated in those basins: four intrastate basins, the Tennessee, and the Missouri.

CHAPTER 13

Intrastate Basin Developments

IN the years since the creation of the Miami Conservancy District other intrastate rivers have experienced interesting applications of the water management concepts suggested in Chapter 12. As the human and physical geography of these basins have differed, so have the concepts varied in application. It is the purpose in this chapter to examine some selected intrastate experiences. The basin developments to be described concern the Grand River (Oklahoma), the Muskingum River (Ohio), certain Central and Southern Florida streams, and the Lower Colorado River (Texas). Emphasis is placed on the last, which represents the most complete elaboration of the leading water-administration ideas in any intrastate basin. Notwithstanding that these streams are intrastate while the Delaware is interstate, there are elements in the histories to be related here that are relevant to the Delaware.

GRAND RIVER DAM AUTHORITY

The Grand (Neosho) River of Oklahoma provides an early example of more than single-purpose development in which a state-created authority played an important role. The Grand is a tributary of the Arkansas River and drains a little of Kansas and Missouri in addition to a large part of rural eastern Oklahoma: its watershed totals 10,298 square miles. No disaster hastened its development. Instead, the policy of depression spending led to the establishment in 1935 of the Grand River Dam Authority (GRDA), a non-profit corporation for developing the resources of the Grand River and its tributaries in Oklahoma. GRDA drew up a plan and four years later succeeded in getting PWA funds to build Pensacola Dam, one of three recommended by it and

237

by the Chief of Engineers, for flood control and power purposes.[1] The PWA granted outright 45 per cent of the cost of the project and loaned GRDA 55 per cent to be secured by revenue bonds of the Authority. The Dam was completed in 1940 for about $27,000,000, and the next year it was taken over and managed by the federal Southwestern Power Authority for power only for the duration of World War II. In 1946 control of Pensacola and its Lake of the Cherokees reservoir was returned to GRDA. The Corps of Engineers the same year began construction downstream of Fort Gibson Dam, the second of the three reservoirs originally recommended for the Basin. This dam was dedicated in 1953.

Pensacola Dam serves primarily power and secondarily flood control purposes. It contains about 1,898,000 acre feet of storage, of which only 245,000 acre feet are now available for flood control. Flood control storage at Pensacola is directed by the Corps through GRDA personnel, and is coordinated with flood control storage at Fort Gibson. GRDA has absolute control of power generation and sales, and it manages the power pool without reference to the Fort Gibson power operation by the Corps of Engineers. Pensacola has an installed capacity of 90,000 kw supplemented by a 45,000 kw steam plant. Power from Fort Gibson is marketed by the Southwestern Power Authority along with power from other Corps dams nearby.

By GRDA policy, preference in power sales is given to public bodies, while retail sales are made to industrial customers and surplus power is sold to utilities. The only revenues available to the Authority come from sales of power and sales of up to 100,000,000 gallons of water per day for municipal, industrial, and irrigation uses. GRDA has yet to develop other uses. Permits are issued for commercial recreation facilities on the Lake of the Cherokees and its 1,300 miles of shoreline. The Oklahoma State Park Board has established a few recreation facilities on that shoreline, but public use is otherwise free and uncontrolled.

A third Grand River dam at Markham Ferry is authorized for GRDA construction,[2] but until 1959 funds had not been made available. Flood

---

[1] H. Doc. 107, 76th Cong., 1st sess. On the Grand River generally, see *Hearings before a Sub-Committee, Markham Ferry Project, Grand River, Oklahoma,* U.S. Senate, 81st Cong., 2nd sess. (Washington, 1950). Senator Elmer Thomas expressed the motive of backers of the 1937 bill authorizing money for Pensacola: ". . . in those days in Congress, we were looking for places to spend money" (p. 22).

[2] P.L. 476, 83rd Cong., 2nd sess., 1954.

control funds in the amount of $6,500,000 have been held up in Congress pending resolution of several technical and legal questions. The Authority argues that it should have been allowed to manage the Fort Gibson power operation.[3] GRDA itself has been unable to market bonds for its portion of Markham Ferry costs. Only after renegotiation of power sales did the Authority successfully manage repayment of its Pensacola issue. The reputation consequent on this uncertain beginning has been hard to escape. Further, a long dry period has affected power generation at Pensacola and hence returns on the investment. All in all, the history of the GRDA is far from reassuring.

True multiple-purpose, basin-wide development has not come to the Grand River. Two of three projected dams serve several purposes, but their operation is not unified. Recreation and other purposes remain neglected, while shoreline activities on the major reservoir continue uncontrolled. Investment in Pensacola was federal, but management rests almost entirely in a state agency. Other than appointment of the GRDA board by the Governor with senatorial consent and general legislative oversight, the Authority has absolute independence from state control.[4] Wherever one looks in the Grand Basin, the lack of successful application of sound principles of basin development is evident.

MUSKINGUM WATERSHED CONSERVANCY DISTRICT

The Ohio Conservancy Act was the framework for establishment of the Muskingum Watershed Conservancy District (MWCD), as it was for the Miami District.[5] A long series of floods devastated the Muskingum Valley before 1933, including the 1913 flood that brought the citizen action in the Miami Valley described in Chapter 12. Fewer lives and less property were lost in the Muskingum because it was less heavily populated.[6] Zanesville, the traditional damage center, is far

[3] Basic to this question is the problem of the status of the Grand River. If it is an intrastate stream, the state would have good claim to jurisdiction over Fort Gibson Dam; but if it is either an interstate or a navigable stream, jurisdiction would rest with the federal government. This issue had not been resolved in 1959.

[4] Letter from Q. B. Boydstun, General Counsel, GRDA, Aug. 7, 1958.

[5] See Ohio Forestry Association, Inc., "Ohio's Conservancy Districts" (Columbus, 1956, mimeographed). In 1956, 26 districts had been organized but 4 of these had been dissolved. The Miami and Muskingum districts, however, are outstanding. See also Allen I. Pretzman, "History and Purposes of the Scioto-Sandusky Conservancy District" (mimeographed, n.d.).

[6] The Muskingum drains 8,038 square miles, which gives it a watershed more than twice the size of the Miami Basin.

smaller than Dayton, and a privately-supported study after the 1913 flood indicated the financial impracticability of flood protection for Zanesville alone. Only after much discussion, the onset of the depression, the 1930 drought, a 1930 multiple-purpose study of the basin by the Ohio Department of Public Works, and expression of interest by the Corps of Engineers and various New Deal agencies did action commence on the Muskingum.[7]

MWCD was formed in 1933, as a locally-oriented center of the attention aroused by the history of floods and the interest of the Ohio Department of Public Works, the Corps, and the PWA. The court order creating it conceived the District's purposes as basin-wide and many-sided, and one result was a 1937 amendment of the Conservancy Act to make it much more comprehensive in nature.[8] MWCD has not, however, lived up either to this original multiple-purpose emphasis or to the promise of local initiative and control that was implicit in its inception.

A brief financial summary will make the point. Originally MWCD was committed to raising $6,000,000 through property taxes; $6,000,000 was to be paid by the State of Ohio for various purposes; and $20,000,-000 was to come from the national government for building flood control structures. A combination, however, of the effects of the depression, local reluctance to pay MWCD taxes, and the increasing federal assumption of flood control responsibilities prevented realization of that plan. By one recent authoritative estimate, of the $50,000,000 ultimate cost, the national government paid 83 per cent, the state 14 per cent, and the local beneficiaries 3 per cent.[9]

From the first, then, dam building and operation in the Muskingum Basin were in the hands of the Corps of Engineers, and today the Corps manages the 14 reservoirs in the Valley which assist in flood control on the Ohio River itself.[10] Navigation, irrigation, pollution

---

[7] References include Lyle E. Craine, *The Muskingum Watershed Conservancy District: An Appraisal of a Watershed Management Agency* (unpublished doctoral dissertation, University of Michigan, 1956) and "The Muskingum Watershed Conservancy District: A Study of Local Control," *Law and Contemporary Problems,* XXII (Summer, 1957), pp. 378-404; William G. Hoyt and Walter B. Langbein, *Floods* (Princeton: Princeton University Press, 1955), pp. 228-232; and Muskingum Watershed Conservancy District, "Muskingum Country" (New Philadelphia, n.d.).

[8] Lyle E. Craine, *The Muskingum Watershed Conservancy District: An Appraisal of a Watershed Management Agency,* pp. 92-4.

[9] William G. Hoyt and Walter B. Langbein, *op. cit.,* p. 232.

[10] Most of the water supply in the area comes from wells which probably depend upon the main stream for supply. Cambridge, Ohio, gets some water directly from the River.

abatement, and power development have never been pursued. Management of recreation at 10 of the reservoirs is the chief concern of MWCD,[11] which also carries on forestry and farming operations on some of the 60,000 acres of land it controls. Income in recent years has come from these sources:[12]

Forestry operations	21%
Park operations	18
Cottage rentals, leases, concessions	31
Non-forest land use (farm lands and mineral rights)	17
State of Ohio (fees for control of fish and wildlife management)	13
Total	100%

The last item is astonishing: the state pays the MWCD for the use of lands and waters in which the District has almost no investment.[13] About 39 per cent of annual expenditures go to recreation, 24 per cent to forestry, and the rest to assorted other purposes (7 per cent to pay local property taxes).

The District was created and is governed under the act of 1914 mentioned earlier in connection with the Miami.[14] The law provides that a prescribed number of citizens residing in any county of a watershed may petition for establishment of a conservancy district. On receipt of such a petition a conservancy court, consisting of one judge of the court of common pleas of each county in the drainage basin, is convened. The conservancy court then takes a series of carefully defined steps to create the district requested, and names a board of directors of three members which thereupon assumes responsibility for the affairs of the new district. The board operates through an executive officer called, in the case of the Muskingum District, the Executive Secretary-Treasurer.

The District today is a recreation agency with a few land management functions. State and federal resource agencies carry on their regular operations in the basin with pleasant but minimal relations with MWCD. "What started out to be a local project has become

---

[11] Attendance in recent years has averaged about 3,000,000 visitor days. Both the Corps of Engineers and the State of Ohio manage other small recreation areas in the Muskingum Watershed.

[12] Muskingum Watershed Conservancy District, *op. cit.*, p. 26.

[13] See Lyle E. Craine, *The Muskingum Watershed Conservancy District: An Appraisal of a Watershed Management Agency*, p. 268.

[14] *Ohio Revised Code*, Title LXI, Chap. 6101.

almost wholly a federal project." [15] The investment has been mostly federal, and flood control, the chief water function, is run by the Corps of Engineers. Some general economic development may be attributed to these water activities in the Muskingum Valley. Only a little progress has been made, however, toward applying any of the five leading concepts of water management.

CENTRAL AND SOUTHERN FLORIDA FLOOD CONTROL DISTRICT

Working relationships between the national government and the State of Florida are perhaps the most relevant aspects of administration of a multiple-purpose program covering more than 15,000 square miles in 17 counties on the peninsula.[16] Schemes to drain the Everglades for agricultural uses pre-date the Civil War, and from 1907 to 1938 the Everglades Drainage District, a state agency, spent $18,000,000 on drainage efforts. On the basis of a cooperative data-gathering program begun in 1932, the District Engineer of the Corps of Engineers, after the disastrous 1947 flood, prepared a water control plan. Two months later the Governor approved the plan for Florida, and it was quickly passed by Congress as part of the Flood Control Act of 1948. The lack of later congressional support for project appropriations is often attributed to the failure in 1948 to develop a strong base of support and understanding for the project in Congress and in the nation.[17]

The plan was broadly conceived. Hydroelectric power generation was the only major water purpose not mentioned—the flat Florida terrain makes that impossible. The Corps of Engineers was to construct levees, improve channels, create three large water storage reservoirs, increase the storage capacity of Lake Okeechobee, and build pumping stations.[18] Local interests were to supplement these works with small drainage projects.

[15] Lyle E. Craine, *The Muskingum Watershed Conservancy District: An Appraisal of a Watershed Management Agency,* p. 188.

[16] John M. DeGrove, *The Central and Southern Florida Flood Control Project* (unpublished doctoral dissertation, University of North Carolina, 1958); ———, *Approaches to Water Resource Development in Central and Southern Florida, 1845-1947* (Gainesville: University of Florida Public Administration Clearing Service, 1958).

[17] See, for example, L. Boyd Finch, "The Florida Swamp That Swallows Your Money," *Harpers* (February, 1959), pp. 77-82. Mr. Finch is violently opposed to the project on grounds, among others, that ". . . its chief beneficiaries are a few large landowners." The plan is described in H. Doc. 643, 80th Cong., 2d sess.

[18] Estimated benefit-cost ratio was 2.05:1, but it has doubtless increased as Florida's urbanized area has grown.

The Central and Southern Florida Flood Control District was created in 1949 as the state's agency for work on the total plan. The District, which has the status of a corporation, is governed by a five-man Board of Directors appointed by the Governor. The Board in turn appoints a Chief Administrative Officer. Reports are made by the Board to the State Board of Conservation, an ex officio body chaired by the Governor. Through the power to appoint these officials, the different Governors in the succeeding ten years have controlled district activities closely.

The District has chosen to emphasize three principal tasks. (1) It represents the total project in Congress and with the Corps. Relationships with the Corps have ranged from good to bad, for the District officials have frequently been very aggressive. Generally, in the Congress the District has not been able to promote sufficient annual appropriations to keep the project on schedule. (2) It coordinates the work of other federal and state agencies as it affects the project. Some federal water-related programs and programs of at least nine state agencies have been successfully channeled through the District. But in the coordination of recreation, small watershed development, and fish and wildlife programs the District has not been at all effective. These activities remain today largely outside its influence. (3) It encourages local governments and private interests to support its programs and to build a secondary system of on-the-farm drainage works. A 1950 program of emergency works undertaken directly by the District was dropped with Governor Leroy Collins' election in 1955. Before that year, however, $800,000 was spent in what opponents charged was "pork-barrel" construction.

Florida's share of project costs has come from two sources: a one-mill tax on District property and annual appropriations from the state. The tax suffers from the fact that three predominantly urban counties must pay 90 per cent of the total, while the project directly affects rural areas for the most part. Beginning in 1951, the Legislature planned to appropriate $3,250,000 biennially until the completion of the project in twenty years. The reluctance of Congress to provide the federal share of costs has slowed up construction by the Corps, however, so that a large state surplus has built up. Consequently, state legislative skepticism has grown and state contributions have been cut back. When a substantial federal appropriation was at last obtained, the situation was abruptly reversed; for then the absence of matching state funds limited the expenditure of federal monies. In 1957, eight years after creation of the District, only 15 per cent of the project had been completed, although Florida officials at first hoped it would be finished in ten years.

Here, then, is a multiple-purpose program, perhaps based as closely as is possible in Florida on watershed lines. Administration is but partly unified. The impact of the enterprise on Florida's economy has been a constant preoccupation, especially in the minds of many officials in that booming state. Prosperity has made it possible for state funds ordinarily to be offered faster than congressional enthusiasm has allowed matching them. Congress has never been strong in its support of the project, nor has it had much confidence in Corps participation there. It is clear that the case for significant federal action in Florida marshland development has not been made, although local interests have been both strong and possessed of ample development money.

LOWER COLORADO RIVER AUTHORITY

The Colorado River of Texas (the "Lower Colorado") is the second longest stream in the United States lying within the confines of a single state. Originating near the New Mexico border, it flows across Texas 600 miles in a southeasterly direction to the Gulf of Mexico. The river pivots on Austin, the capital of the State, which lies almost exactly at its midway point. It drops nearly 4,000 feet from its headwaters to its mouth, most of it upstream of Austin, whose elevation is about 500 feet. Above that city the drainage basin is hilly and broken and dry; below, it levels off into good farming country. The Colorado Valley is preponderantly rural; industry is just beginning to make its influence felt, and that principally in the vicinity of Austin.

Early Efforts to Control the River

The Colorado has been known for two centuries as a moody stream, one day virtually dry, the next a raging torrent. The extremes for this century occurred in the drought year of 1918, when the flow at Austin fell to 13 cubic feet per second, and the flood year of 1935, when the flow at that city reached a high of 481,000 cubic feet per second. Old-timers used to be able to tell on what tributary watershed heavy rain had fallen by the color and silt content of the downstream flow at flood time. The river's notoriously erratic behavior early led to efforts to bring it under a measure of control by dam. There were as many as a dozen such efforts—"schemes" might be a better word for some of them—but only two or three assumed serious proportions. In 1893, the City of Austin completed construction of ". . . the greatest over-flow dam ever built on a large and torrential stream." The dam lasted until 1900, when it gave way with a resulting loss of 47 lives and property damage estimated at nearly $5,000,000. Efforts to rebuild the dam resulted in an impasse when the city refused to accept the work done by its contractor. Meanwhile the river, oblivious of the wrangle, continued its normal way: in 1915, another great flood took 32 lives and caused extensive property losses.

Meanwhile, too, there was considerable private activity, with dam sites being acquired for a hundred miles up-river from Austin and with three or four serious efforts at construction being undertaken. The most pretentious development was that proposed by Midwest Utilities (In-sull), which announced a plan for a series of dams. Construction actu-ally began on one, which was almost 50 per cent completed when the Insull empire collapsed. The depression ensured that there would be no further work for the time being.[19]

By 1932, then, all significant development activity on the river had stopped. It was clear that the resources devoted to the task to that point had been wholly insufficient. Further, the conviction was widespread that private enterprise was unequal to the challenge posed by the river. There was a growing feeling that the development of the Colorado was an undertaking calling for important public support.

Establishment of the LCRA

Inasmuch as the Colorado is an intrastate stream, the advocates of public action placed chief reliance in the Texas Legislature. The in-strument chosen was the conservation and reclamation district, with which the State had had some experience. A bill to establish a Colo-rado River Authority, based on the district concept, was introduced in the Legislature in 1933 but failed of passage. A second similar bill and yet a third, proposed early in 1934, likewise failed of adoption. A fourth bill, introduced in the fall of 1934, benefited from removal of several obstacles which had blocked favorable action before. Approved by both houses and signed by the Governor, it became effective early in 1935.

Chief among the factors which combined to bring about passage of the act were these: (1) the generally recognized need for control of the river; (2) the repeated failure of past efforts to meet the need, and

[19] Walter E. Long, *Flood to Faucet* (Austin: privately printed, 1956), contains a useful historical account of activity on the Colorado.

specifically the failure of private enterprise to mount an effective development program; (3) the presence of a half-finished dam which presumably could be acquired at a bargain; (4) stagnant economic conditions, which a construction program would help to ameliorate; (5) the prospective availability of federal aid, both loans and grants on the one hand and work-relief labor on the other; (6) the interest expressed by President Roosevelt in such enterprises, tangibly manifested only months before in his vigorous support of federal legislation creating the Tennessee Valley Authority; and (7) the presence in Congress of two politically influential representatives of Colorado Valley districts. These were Congressman J. P. Buchanan, Chairman of the House Committee on Appropriations, and Congressman J. J. Mansfield, Chairman of the House Committee on Rivers and Harbors. It would be difficult to overemphasize their contributions to the development of the Colorado.

The Lower Colorado River Authority, created by the Texas Legislature's Act of 1934, is a conservation and reclamation district. It is also a public corporation with the rights and privileges appertaining to such a body, including specifically the right of eminent domain and the power to borrow money, accept grants, and issue revenue bonds. It was denied the power to levy taxes or to pledge the credit of the State. The territorial extent of the agency is variable: for some purposes, it includes the lower ten counties through which the river passes, which comprise the district; for others, the entire watershed; and for others still (notably the distribution and sale of electric power), an area limited only by the phrase ". . . within or without the boundaries of the district." [20]

The governing body of the LCRA is a Board of Directors, which consists of twelve persons appointed by the Governor with senatorial consent. The Board serves for six-year overlapping terms, four directors being appointed every two years. The agency's chief administrative officer is a general manager, who is appointed by the Board of Directors for a term set by that body. As his title indicates, the general manager serves the Authority as its chief executive, within the framework of policy determinations made by the Board. [21]

[20] The standard reference on the LCRA is Comer Clay, "The Lower Colorado River Authority," in Emmette S. Redford, *Public Administration and Policy Formation* (Austin: University of Texas Press, 1956). This is a careful study of the Authority; it provides the basis for much of the summary analysis that follows.
[21] Comer Clay, *op. cit.*, pp. 211-213.

The mission of LCRA, as defined by the Act of 1934, includes the following major purposes:

1. "To control, store and preserve, within the boundaries of the District, the waters of the Colorado River and its tributaries for any useful purpose, and to use, distribute and sell the same, within the boundaries of the District, for any such purpose . . . ";

2. specifically, to control or aid in controlling floods;

3. "To develop and generate water power and electric energy within the boundaries of the District and to distribute and sell water power and electric energy, within or without the boundaries of the District";

4. to protect the watershed area through promotion of sound forestry and soil conservation practices.[22]

In the pursuit of this comprehensive mission, LCRA has acquired or built six dams. The structure farthest downstream lies within the limits of the City of Austin, that farthest upstream is about 116 miles away. The six make full capital of the almost 600 foot fall in the 150 miles upstream from Austin. They permit the Authority to serve well the river control function, for all are integrated into a single system and operated as a unit. Each dam contains hydroelectric power generators; but since navigation is confined to pleasure craft, none has a lock. The dams and reservoirs constitute the core of the Authority's facilities although there are certain auxiliary properties, notably more than 1,000 miles of high voltage transmission lines and a headquarters building near Austin.[23]

To finance acquisition and construction of its properties, the LCRA resorted to several sources. First, it received a number of loans and grants from federal agencies, chief among them the Public Works Administration, which granted the agency more than $8,000,000 and loaned over $13,500,000; the Bureau of Reclamation, which spent more than $23,300,000 on the project, most of it for the construction of the biggest dam (which it turned over to the LCRA on condition that the agency repay it for its power investment); the Reconstruction Finance Corporation, which loaned the Authority somewhat more than $20,000,-000; and the Works Progress Administration, which contributed more than half a million dollars for reservoir land clearance. For self-financing, the Act of 1934 authorized the LCRA to issue revenue bonds

[22] *Ibid.*, p. 209. See also Lower Colorado River Authority, *LCRA* (Austin, 1954), unpaged.

[23] Comer Clay, *op. cit.*, p. 217 ff; Lower Colorado River Authority, *op. cit.*, *passim.*

in an amount not to exceed $10,000,000, a limit subsequently raised to $50,000,000. The agency has used this authorization to issue bonds in the amount of somewhat less than $21,000,000 for constructing two dams, and further in the amount of $27,000,000 for re-funding bonds outstanding. To climax its financing program, the State Legislature appropriated $15,000, of which the agency expended $14,982.51. This represents the State's total investment in the project. As of June 30, 1955, the Authority had an accumulated surplus of more than $10,000,-000.[24] Three years later, an independent audit reported its assets at $71,135,677.97,[25] although as early as 1954 the agency claimed properties with an estimated replacement value of $150,000,000.[26]

Program

The program mounted by the LCRA in pursuance of its legislative mission hinges on river regulation. This means, first of all, flood control. Effective control of floods depends essentially upon accurate and timely records and adequate detention facilities. The data on rainfall and river reaction are recorded by 143 rainfall gauges scattered throughout the watershed and by 12 river gauges strategically placed. The key detention structure is Mansfield Dam, which reserves for flood control 33 feet of storage space capable of holding 830,000 acre-feet of water. From 1900 to 1938, the river took a toll of 99 lives and caused economic losses estimated at more than $2,000,000 per year; since 1938, there have been no lives lost and virtually no property damage. During the great floods of the spring of 1957, the system contained without damage *five separate floods,* two of which, without control, would have peaked at 500,000 cubic feet per second at Austin.[27] (It will be recalled that the most destructive flood of this century, that of 1935, reached a flow of 481,000 cubic feet per second at that city.)

Another aspect of river control concerns low flow augmentation. As noted elsewhere, the drought year of 1918 produced a low flow of 13 cubic feet per second, or about 8,400,000 gallons per day, at Austin. With the LCRA dams in operation, the average minimum flow is some-

[24] Comer Clay, *op. cit.,* pp. 224-226.

[25] Arthur Young and Company, *Lower Colorado River Authority, Financial Statements* (June 30, 1958).

[26] Lower Colorado River Authority, *op. cit.*

[27] Lower Colorado River Authority, "Summary of Floods on Colorado River, April 19, 1957-May 24, 1957" (Austin, mimeographed).

what less than 1,000 cubic feet per second, or 646,000,000 gallons per day. That such a notable augmentation of the minimum flow has important consequences for those who depend on the river goes without saying. There is, in the first place, the matter of water supply, both municipal and industrial. Chief among the municipal users is the City of Austin, though a number of smaller communities also depend on the river. The stream, however, as regulated, could supply the needs of the ten largest cities of Texas. Second, the rice growers of the lower part of the valley have doubled the number of acres irrigated in the last several years under the stimulus of a guaranteed supply of water. Third, although the visionary scheme of making Austin an important river port has been abandoned, the regulation of the river has revived interest in navigation in its lower portion.

The Act of 1934 specifically recognized the production and sale of power as a primary function of the LCRA. Generators at the six dams are capable of producing 230,000 kilowatts of hydroelectric power. In addition, the Authority has leased a steam plant which produces 60,000 kilowatts; and it purchases the entire output of a series of small hydro plants on the nearby Guadalupe River which produce 10,000 kilowatts. The system's total production capacity is, therefore, 300,000 kilowatts. This power it markets throughout an area of 31,000 square miles in central Texas. It sells electricity wholesale to 32 municipalities and 11 rural electric cooperatives, and retail in three cities which have preferred not to operate power distribution systems. Finally, it sells direct to a number of major industries, and to several privately owned utility companies (the latter mostly for peaking purposes). The Authority reports a marked increase in the consumption of electrical power throughout its territory, and at the same time a considerable reduction in rates. The sale of power produces 97 per cent of the Authority's total annual revenue. Apart from its activities in producing and marketing electricity, it acts as the coordinator for the transmission of power throughout the State. This last obligation was undertaken at the request of the private utility companies.

The LCRA has moved into the conservation field with an exploratory but currently expanding program. First, it appointed an experienced agricultural expert to serve as its director of conservation. Second, it established a number of "example" farms, through which it seeks to demonstrate good agricultural practice through technical assistance to selected individual farmers. Third, it purchased a considerable amount of machinery which it makes available to farmers for conservation work on a cost-of-operation basis. Fourth, it built and equipped a soil testing laboratory, which is operated by a junior college in the lower part of the Valley. These activities add up to a modest program which nevertheless is gathering momentum. The Authority has not yet gone into the field of forestry, excepting in connection with its farm conservation program.

Recreation, though not featured as a basic program, has followed naturally in the wake of reservoir construction and operation. The Authority has made available through lease or grant a number of park sites and other recreational areas. The State Parks Board is the principal operating agency in the Valley. There are now a dozen major public parks along the reservoirs, and they attract increasing thousands of campers, boating enthusiasts, and fishermen. Both public and private bodies have collaborated in a spirited campaign to advertise Central Texas' "Highland Lakes," which have become the center of an active and growing tourist industry.[28]

Conclusion

The accomplishments of the Lower Colorado River Authority have been substantial. The control of the river has resulted in large benefits through banishment of flood damages and through the guarantee of adequate water for municipal and industrial use and for irrigation. The power program palpably is a highly successful undertaking. Nevertheless, there are those who aver that the agency has pursued an overly cautious course, thus failing to realize its full program potential. Its officers reply that they have not been timid but only practical. The Authority has steered a sound middle course, they maintain; for it has carried forward successfully the progressive program placed in its hands by law without incurring the animosity of established interests.

Apart from its program achievements, the LCRA is to be remembered in the present context for a number of distinguishing features. First, it is a state agency with jurisdiction over an intrastate stream. Second, it utilizes the techniques of multiple-purpose basinwide development, though pursuing neither concept to a logical extreme. Third, in employing the device of a citizen Board of Directors (whose members are paid only a nominal fee for attending meetings) together with a full-time general manager appointed by the Board and paid a generous salary, the Authority recognizes basic principles of sound administrative organization. Fourth, the agency has powers com-

[28] Comer Clay, *op. cit.,* pp. 226-234, describes the program of the agency; so likewise does the Lower Colorado River Authority, *LCRA.*

mensurate with its responsibilities, notably the right of eminent domain and the power to issue revenue bonds. Fifth, the history of the agency constitutes a rare lesson in financial management, detailing as it does the story of a vigorous and highly solvent enterprise which was put together from a variety of sources by a public agency at a total cost to the State of less than $15,000. Sixth and finally, study of the LCRA induces reflection once more on the role of circumstance, not to say chance, in public affairs. The agency enjoyed a number of advantages in unusual combination in its early days; with them, it still experienced some difficulty in getting under way, without them it is doubtful whether it would have made the grade.

SUMMARY

Many other intrastate basins might have been chosen for description in this chapter: in the East, the Santee-Cooper and related streams (South Carolina) and the area covered by the Massachusetts Metropolitan District Commission; in the West, the much-studied Central Valley of California, the Middle Rio Grande Conservancy District, and Nebraska's public power and irrigation districts. By and large, however, the same kinds of problems and features would have been discovered as have appeared from the four examples used.

Chief among the lessons to be learned from these accounts are the following:

1. Intrastate basin development normally has been initiated more or less directly as the result of crisis, usually either flood or depression. Deliberate action in anticipation of need is a rare occurrence in this field.

2. Federal money commonly has played a central role in the development of intrastate streams. Only in the Florida case has substantial state capital been provided. In the 1930's federal funds came from the ad hoc spending agencies; more recently they have come through outright construction by the Corps or the Bureau of Reclamation.

3. In three of the four cases examined, partial or complete control of federally-financed structures has been relinquished to state agencies. This finding is of great potential significance to the future of the Delaware.

4. Legal and organizational bases have varied, but commonly a state agency or special district has represented the states in intrastate basin development. The experiences related here indicate that there is no consensus in practice regarding organizational form.

5. In the Grand and Florida instances conflicts between the two levels of government continue to disrupt the progress of development, although in neither case is the disruption necessarily unhealthy in view of uncertainties as to the wisdom of policies at both levels. Satisfactory operating arrangements among the governments involved, and more especially between the principal state organism and the federal agencies active in the field, appear difficult of consummation.

6. In no case has comprehensive basin development approached full realization, for one reason because such development has failed to command aggressive leadership. Fragmentation of management between purposes or between dams and other structures typifies three of the four basins. The LCRA comes closest to multiple-purpose, basin-wide, unified management, and it falls short in certain respects. It will prove useful to examine two interstate streams for more elaborate attempts to bring about river basin development.

CHAPTER 14

Interstate Basin Experience

INASMUCH as most of the nation's major rivers flow across state boundaries, it is not strange that much of the history of basin development has revolved about interstate arrangements. One thinks at once of the Colorado, the Columbia, and the Missouri in the West, and of the Tennessee, the Ohio, the Delaware, the Connecticut, and perhaps the Potomac in the East. The principal organizational devices for action or for coordination of activities on interstate streams, as we have noted elsewhere, are the federal public corporation, the basin inter-agency committee, and the interstate compact agency. The Tennessee, with its Valley authority, provides the sole illustration of the first; the Missouri is one of the best-known of the inter-agency basins; the Delaware has had considerable experience, though not notably successful experience, in interstate compact negotiation. The Tennessee and the Missouri will be examined here; the Delaware will be reserved for separate treatment. Much has been written both about the Tennessee and the TVA and about the Missouri and the efforts at basin organization there; this summary will attempt nothing more ambitious than a pointing-up of the salient organizational features of each basin, along with the major lessons to be learned from Tennessee and Missouri experience.

THE TENNESSEE: BASIN DEVELOPMENT THROUGH FEDERAL ACTION

Interest in improving the Tennessee River for navigation goes back to 1824, but it was not until the time of World War I that the United States government became directly concerned with the River's development. At that time the government built a munitions plant on the

River at Muscle Shoals, Alabama, and, in connection with that enterprise, two small steam-electric plants and a dam (Wilson) across the
River. These structures were not completed in time for service during
the war, and shortly after the end of hostilities they were declared
surplus. The problem of what to do with the properties, and more particularly of how to salvage some part of the government's investment
(which totalled somewhat more than $100,000,000), elicited a number
of proposed solutions during the next fifteen years. Senator George
Norris of Nebraska took an active interest in the issue, espousing early
the cause of public development. A series of bills introduced into
Congress by Norris failed of adoption, either through lack of support in
that body or through Presidential veto; but in 1933 a combination of
circumstances produced an environment in which Senator Norris' proposal found favor. In the spring of that year Congress passed and on
May 18 President Roosevelt signed into law the Tennessee Valley
Authority Act.[1]

Some Features of the TVA

The agency created by the act has a number of features which are
worthy of note in the present context. First, the TVA is a federal organ,
created by an act passed by the Congress. It is not connected in any
way with any other federal department or agency, but enjoys substantial administrative independence—subject always, of course, to
control by the President and Congress. It is governed by a Board of
Directors of three members, appointed by the President with senatorial
confirmation for overlapping terms of nine years. The Board in turn
appoints a General Manager who, serving without term, operates as
administrative head of the agency under general policy direction by
the appointing body.

Second, the position of substantial independence occupied by the
TVA is abetted by the fact that it is a government corporation, which
means, among other things, that it may sue and be sued and may acquire and dispose of property with substantial freedom. The TVA also
enjoys more independence of action than most federal agencies with
respect to such matters as personnel, policy decisions regarding expenditures, and disposition of revenues. In so far as the agency's special
position is defined by the Act of 1933, it is neither peculiar to nor
necessarily inherent in its status as a government corporation, although

[1] 48 Stat. L. 58 (1933), 16 U.S.C. Sec. 831 (1952).

that status unquestionably contributes to its substantial autonomy.[2]

Third, while the TVA is a federal organ, it is also a regional agency. This is noteworthy for two reasons. First, concentration on the region has enabled TVA personnel to develop a technical competence with respect to regional problems not found in other river basins. Second, it is extremely important that the TVA maintains its headquarters in the Tennessee Valley, and that it emphasizes its regional rather than its Washington orientation. The agency maintains a small Washington office, and its top executives of course journey to that city when the occasion requires. But the Act of 1933 places emphasis on *regional* development, and TVA's officials have recognized and have sought to implement that emphasis from the beginning. It is significant that the people of the Valley regard the TVA as a local agency, and its employees as friends and neighbors. The evidence of this sense of regional identification is to be found on every hand.

Finally, the Act of 1933 identified the new agency's central mission as that of bringing about the integrated development of the natural resources of the Tennessee Valley. The mission is defined in a sweeping grant of powers and in unmistakable terms: it is elaborated in the statute for all who may read to see. That the statutory grant was not made in vain is to be seen from such phrases as ". . . an experimental program in regional development" and ". . . the unified development of all the resources of the region" which recur in the public statements of the agency's responsible officers. It is to be seen more explicitly in the program pursued by TVA, which until the last few years gave an important place to regional resources development.

Here, then, are TVA's distinguishing features: it is a federal agency which assumes the form of a government corporation, and it is at the same time a regional agency with broad powers for the integrated development of water and resources related to water. It has been called, with good reason, a regional department of natural resources.

Methods of Work

Other characteristic features of the TVA are found in its methods of work, of which three are singled out for mention here. First, and

---

[2] Joseph C. Swidler, formerly General Counsel of the TVA, has analyzed the significance of corporate status for the Authority in an article titled "Legal Foundations," in Roscoe C. Martin (ed.), *TVA: The First Twenty Years* (University, Alabama, and Knoxville, Tennessee: The University of Alabama Press and The University of Tennessee Press, 1956), pp. 16-34.

because of its pioneering nature most significant, is the multiple-purpose, fully integrated approach which the agency brought to the River and its problems. TVA was charged with three principal responsibilities with regard to the River as such. These were the control of floods, the improvement of navigation, and the utilization of surplus power. These indeed are characteristic primary responsibilities which have inhered in most efforts at river basin development. Before TVA a few rivers had been developed for special purposes, as the Miami for flood control; moreover, there were a few (though in 1933 not many) individual multiple-purpose projects, like the Hoover Dam on the Colorado. But nowhere had a whole river valley been developed through application of the multiple-purpose principle. The TVA undertook to employ the technique of multiple-purpose treatment not on one project alone but throughout the Valley, whose integrated development thus became a hallmark of the new agency.

A second important work method of the TVA is to be found in the system of cooperative administration which it has fostered. In the beginning, the agency might have established its own operating organization throughout the whole of the broad programmatic field entrusted to it; for it had the undoubted legal power to do so, and it had both the external support and the internal leadership such a course would have required. The first Chairman of the Board of Directors held the view, indeed, that the agency should proceed at once with the business of establishing its own program organization. Contrary counsel prevailed, however, and the Board decided instead to work primarily through the region's existing administrative organization in those areas where such a procedure was feasible.[3] By way of implementing its decision, the TVA entered into manifold negotiations with state and local governments active in the region looking toward the effectuation of cooperative arrangements for administration. The end result of these discussions is found in the complicated network of agreements entered into between the Tennessee Valley Authority and a wide variety of governmental units. These agreements cover all programmatic areas, and they involve such agencies as state departments of health, agricul-

---

[3] Those favorable to TVA point to this decision as evidence of the grass-roots approach adopted by the agency. Others see in it a reflection of political expediency. Thus an observer, commenting recently on the subject, suggested that "TVA, as an invading agency, was intelligent enough to recognize its need to make friends in the region and so reduce the fears and antagonisms of agencies and persons threatened with supercession."

ture, commerce, forestry, and natural resources; state water resources boards, planning boards, and geological surveys; cities and counties (health departments, planning boards, public works departments, parks departments, library departments); and local electric cooperatives. They give ample evidence of TVA's intent to seek the collaboration of the Valley's governments in the discharge of its responsibilities, and of the willingness of those governments to accept the challenge.

Third among TVA's methods of work is the propensity of its officers to think, talk, and act in terms appropriate to democratic administration, which may be said to be marked by two basic features. The first is internal to the organization; it concerns such matters as the spirit in which action is taken, interpersonal relations among officers themselves and between officers and employees, and staff morale. The spirit of an organization is not susceptible of exact measurement, though to a practised eye and ear its tone is unmistakable. The following testimony by an experienced observer is therefore relevant:

> The greatest thing about TVA is . . . morale. Never in the United States or abroad have I encountered anything more striking than the faith its men have in their work.[4]

The external evidences of democratic administration are found in an organization's responsibility—in the question, in the case of the TVA, whether the agency is responsive to Presidential authority, and whether Congress maintains the ultimate control essential to the preservation of democracy. The President demonstrated the vitality of his authority by removing TVA's first Board Chairman, and he exhibits it further through his continuing close relations with the agency and through constant assertion of the policy leadership of his office. One who has witnessed the progress of a TVA bill, appropriation or otherwise, through Congress will be slow to believe that that body has sacrificed any significant part of its final control.

The procedural goals which TVA has set for itself are well summarized in the following statement by a former Chairman of the agency's Board of Directors:

> Those responsibly involved like to regard the TVA as a method of thinking about regional problems, of organizing for regional action, of making government more accessible to people and of bringing the people into a more vital association with their government, of enlisting

[4] John Gunther, *The Story of TVA* (New York: Harper and Brothers, 1951), p. 8.

the energies of all in the processes of planning and governing for the welfare of the greater number.[5]

Men's judgments will vary as to the success the agency has encountered in achieving these goals, but the evidence of good progress is substantial.

Program

The way in which a government agency works is, of course, only part of its story, albeit in a democracy a fundamental part. Equally important for the evaluation of a public enterprise are considerations of program. The program of the Tennessee Valley Authority is elaborated with some care (although with considerable flexibility as well) in the Act of 1933. A basic responsibility placed on the new agency is control of the River to the end that danger from floods may be minimized. The TVA has proceeded about the discharge of this duty by building or acquiring control over 31 dams, of which 9 are on the main stem, 22 on tributary streams. Of these, the agency acquired one (Wilson) from the federal government and 10 (either outright or for purposes of management) from private industry; the remaining 20 it constructed itself. For flood control purposes, all dams are integrated into a single unit under the management of the River Control Branch of the Division of Water Control Planning, Office of Engineering. So effectively has the system operated that there has not been a major flood on the River since it went into effect. The greatest flood of record occurred in 1867, when steamboats are said to have plowed through the streets of Chattanooga. The second greatest flood came in 1957— or would have come but for TVA's control system. As it was, operations proceeded routinely, destruction was negligible, and damage averted at Chattanooga was estimated at $66,000,000. Thus was the greatest flood in 90 years contained, and thus did the TVA system of river control pass its severest test.[6]

Even 31 dams, synchronized into one grand system, cannot eliminate all floods; for on the one hand some minor watersheds are beyond the limits of the big dams' control areas, while on the other the continued practice of building on flood plains makes more and more property subject to damage by floods. With regard to the first problem, TVA from its beginning has recognized the significance for flood control of land and forest treatment in the upper watersheds, and for years has

---

[5] Gordon R. Clapp, "The Meaning of TVA," in Roscoe C. Martin (ed.), *TVA: The First Twenty Years*, p. 15.

[6] Tennessee Valley Authority, *Annual Report* (Knoxville, 1957), pp. 10-16.

collaborated in demonstration small-watershed projects. With respect to the second, it has encouraged and has entered into agreements with a number of local governments looking to flood-plain zoning.[7] In these ways does the agency seek to broaden its already successful river control program into a comprehensive program for flood damage reduction throughout the Tennessee Valley.

As the second primary leg of the river development tripod, the Act of 1933 directed the TVA to dredge and equip with appropriate facilities a 9-foot navigation channel from the mouth of the Tennessee (at Paducah, Kentucky) to Knoxville, Tennessee, 650 miles away by river. This objective has now been achieved, with TVA's nine mainstem high dams providing a series of tranquil lakes between the two cities. "Appropriate facilities" include a series of locks which make possible continuous traffic. Further, there are almost 300 more miles of navigable water, as much as a third of it 9 feet deep, in embayments and in the tributary streams. The maintenance of these almost 1,000 miles of navigable channels depends in no small part on the minimum flows made possible by the system of river control. During the war, the TVA constructed 4 public service terminals along the river; subsequently, when traffic warranted, private concerns took over the operation of these terminals. Additionally, more than 75 private terminals have been built and placed in operation. The facilities for navigation, then, have been constructed, as the law required.

River traffic has responded to this invitation in a manner exceeding all expectations. Repeatedly traffic engineers have seen their estimates far outstripped, with raw materials inbound and finished products outbound taking the place of the short-haul, low-value cargoes of earlier days. In 1957, commercial freight traffic on the river totaled almost 13,000,000 tons and more than 2,000,000,000 ton-miles; the costs of operating the waterway were approximately $4,000,000, and the savings to shippers were estimated at $21,500,000.[8] The steady increase in traffic reflects the rapid growth of industry along the river, which in turn harks back to the provisions of the Act of 1933 emphasizing the development of natural resources.[9]

The law contained, as the third leg of the primary program tripod,

[7] Tennessee Valley Authority, *A Program for Reducing the National Flood Damage Potential* (Knoxville: September, 1958, mimeographed).

[8] Tennessee Valley Authority, *TVA, 1958: Twenty-fifth Anniversary Year* (Washington, 1959), p. 5.

[9] Tennessee Valley Authority, *River Traffic and Industrial Growth* (Knoxville, May, 1959).

a forthright directive to the Tennessee Valley Authority to produce and market power, recognizing always the primary claim to water use of river control and navigation. Among the government properties at Muscle Shoals which fell to the TVA were Wilson Dam, with its facilities for hydroelectric generation, and two small steam-electric plants. TVA was therefore in the electric utility business from the beginning, and with both hydro and steam facilities. Its preoccupation was such, however, that it concentrated on hydroelectric power production (as an adjunct of its expanding river control system) for a number of years. Only with the onset of the war, with its large new demands for electricity for defense plants located in the region (including notably the Oak Ridge and Paducah plants of the Atomic Energy Commission) did the TVA go intensively into the construction of steam-electric plants. The generating system now includes the 31 hydroelectric plants on the Tennessee and its tributaries, 5 hydroelectric plants on the Cumberland River, 8 steam-electric plants built by the TVA (including the largest known steam-electric plant in the world), and 7 small acquired steam-electric plants. The total installed capacity is more than 10,200,-000 kilowatts. In 1958 the system generated almost 61,000,000,000 kilowatt-hours of electricity, of which somewhat less than one-third was produced by the hydroelectric plants. Federal agencies (including again the Atomic Energy Commission) purchased 52 per cent of all kilowatt-hours sold; the remainder was divided among some two dozen industries, served direct because of their size, and 150 local municipal and cooperative retail distributing systems.[10]

The power program is by all odds the most vigorously disputed of all TVA's varied activities. It is not to be expected that a controversy which has raged for a quarter of a century will be dissipated here, yet some general comments may add modestly to understanding of the program. First, the power program was mandated by Congress: it rests squarely on the Act of 1933, which was both broad and explicit in its directives regarding the production and distribution of power. Second, the process by which the TVA became so largely a public utility was a logical one, with each step following the one preceding in a natural sequence, and with the requirements growing from World War II providing the principal stimulus. Third, by the criteria normally employed, the power program has been highly successful: power consumption in the Tennessee Valley has increased remarkably, electricity rates have gone down dramatically, and TVA payments are ahead of

[10] Tennessee Valley Authority, *TVA, 1958: Twenty-fifth Anniversary Year*, pp. 46-60.

the schedule set by Congress for liquidation of the federal government's power investment in the Valley. Fourth, while the TVA does not pay taxes in the usual sense of the term, it does make payments to states and counties in lieu of taxes. The governments of the Valley seem well satisfied with this system, which in 1959 produced revenues of $5,900,000.[11] Fifth, TVA's activities in producing and marketing electric power have contributed measurably to the agency's success in developing the Valley and so furthering ". . . the economic and social well-being of the people living in (the) river basin." [12] Sixth, the power program has been kept in the perspective provided by the law, which required ". . . the maximum generation of electric power consistent with flood control and navigation. . . ." [13] The power program undoubtedly has served an important purpose in the development of the Tennessee Valley; in another basin—in that of Delaware, for example—power would have nothing approaching the same impact.

A fourth important program activity stipulated by the Act of 1933 called for operation by the TVA of the fertilizer-munition plant at Muscle Shoals. From this directive has grown an active research and experimentation program for testing and developing new fertilizer materials. From it, too, has developed an extensive program for demonstrating the value of such fertilizer materials under controlled use, a program in which, in 1958, 3,600 farmers in 29 states participated. There were 71 cooperatives and private firms located in 31 states which took part in the distributor demonstration program, designed to get experimental fertilizers into the hands of farmers.[14] The Agricultural Extension Service and a number of state agricultural colleges participate in these programs, which have helped to improve fertilizers while reducing prices substantially, and so to increase agricultural production at lower costs. The fertilizer industry, originally suspicious lest the TVA undermine established practices, has experienced a change of heart and is now an enthusiastic supporter of the whole program.

In forestry as in agriculture, the TVA has limited its activities largely to demonstration, service, and assistance. Rejecting an early proposal that it acquire a vast acreage and turn it to public forests, the agency decided to devote its efforts to the improvement of forest practices by private owners. To that end, its foresters have operated nurseries from

---

[11] Tennessee Valley Authority, *TVA Power and Taxes* (Knoxville, 1959), p. 6.
[12] 48 Stat. L. 69 (1933), 16 U.S.C. Sec. 831v (1952).
[13] *Ibid.*
[14] Tennessee Valley Authority, *TVA, 1958: Twenty-fifth Anniversary Year*, p. 5. The program is described in some detail in pp. 61-81.

which hundreds of millions of seedlings have been supplied for the reforestation of thousands of acres; inaugurated and pursued a forest inventory which, though far from complete, has already proved its utility; and cooperated actively with state and private foresters both in research projects and in such practical areas as the prevention and control of forest fires and the extension of sound forest management practices. The improvement of the forest stand and the resultant growth of finished wood products industries in the Valley are direct consequences of improved forest practices, to which TVA's Division of Forestry Relations has made substantial contributions.

Of a number of significant collateral program activities, two, recreation and health, are worthy of brief mention. With respect to the former, there has been a spectacular increase, largely in water-related recreational activities, particularly in the last fifteen years. Fishing and boating in particular have come into their own on the "Great Lakes of the South." Pursuing its established practice, the TVA operates no recreational enterprises, though it lends continuing aid and encouragement to both public and private recreational bodies. With regard to health, TVA officials have cooperated with state and local officers to such effect that, to choose a single illustration, there has not been a single case of malaria in years traceable to the river—and this in a region where that disease is endemic and previously was widespread.

Progress toward the integrated development of the natural resources of the Tennessee Valley, and in particular toward bringing the River under control for the amelioration of floods, the improvement of navigation, and the production of power, palpably has been great since 1933. The measurement of regional growth and the objective identification of causes therefor are difficult undertakings at best. Some, perhaps much, of this progress would have come about in any event with the passing of time. For all that, the Tennessee Valley Authority has served the region notably as planner, stimulator, and facilitator, and in the case of flood control, navigation, and power, as developer direct. Most observers, and in particular most local leaders who know the agency at first-hand, are willing to allow the TVA substantial credit for its contribution to the quite considerable economic growth which the Valley has experienced in the last quarter-century.

Appraisal

In evaluating the Tennessee Valley Authority, it is well to begin with reference to a step which the TVA *did not take.* The Act of 1933 led some to fear that the newly created agency might move into the region and establish itself as a super-state. Note has been made of a contrary decision by the Board of Directors, which elected to act through existing governments in so far as possible rather than to build an elaborate operating organization of its own.

Two results, both significant for the TVA program, followed immediately. The state and local governments of the Tennessee Valley as a general rule were not notably vigorous or effective in the thirties: programs in important areas were ill-supported or even, in some instances, non-existent, while the basic tools of administration frequently were rudimentary and the practice sometimes primitive. Yet it was to these governments that the TVA by deliberate choice entrusted fundamental responsibilities in some of its important program fields. It is wholly unlikely that, in the early years at least, the results which followed were as good as the TVA could have obtained through use of its own personnel. Further, it has been argued that the TVA sacrificed something of precision in program definition and something of vigor in execution through its reliance on existing governments and agencies with long-standing, traditional program commitments.[15] Few of TVA's new partners, it has been surmised, knew or cared much about the economic and social development of the Valley; and in any case, the argument goes, the piecemeal pursuit of local activities did not add up to a significant regional program, even when government was vigorous and administration sound.

A contrary view insists that the method of operation chosen by the TVA has strengthened and lent added validity to the federal system. This result has followed first from the growth of a vigorous regional awareness on the part of both citizens and public officials of the Valley, and second from the improvement of state and local government in the region. For one thing, the fact that public decisions are made close at home and that the people participate actively in the affairs of government has led to a quickened sense of civic responsibility.[16] For another, with success in important program areas largely dependent upon the quality of the existing machinery of administration, the Board of Directors set about to help strengthen the governments of the Valley. The systematic pursuit of this policy contributed to the invigorated administrative agencies and the many new or expanded pro-

[15] Philip Selznick has argued this point persuasively in his *TVA and the Grass Roots* (Berkeley: University of California Press, 1949).

[16] For a lively development of this theme, see David E. Lilienthal, *TVA: Democracy on the March* (New York and London: Harper and Brothers, 1944).

grams to be seen in such fields as forestry, health, commerce, agriculture, recreation, and planning. Nor are these developments limited to any particular level of government or any geographical area, for state and local governments alike throughout the River Basin have benefited from TVA collaboration. That the responsible officers of the region's governments are sensible of this contribution to the federal system is indicated by the results of a poll of the Valley states' governors made by the *Knoxville News-Sentinel* in 1952. The consensus of the governors, as reported by that newspaper, follows:

> The governors deny the two charges most frequently made against the TVA . . . that such a federal agency is a "super-state" which violates States' Rights, and that it robs the states of tax revenues. They also testify unanimously to the co-operative spirit of the agency and its avoidance of high-handed methods and agree that the rights and interest of the states . . . have been strengthened by TVA's operations.[17]

A lively sense of movement, of alertness, of awareness of large events is essential to the vigorous practice of federalism, which profits measurably from collaboration among governments. A second major contribution made by the TVA to the federal system is found in its stimulation of intergovernmental relations in the Valley. This follows in part from its very presence, for the TVA, in providing a means for bringing the resources of the national government directly to bear on regional problems, serves naturally as an exhilarator of intergovernmental communication and cooperation. But more than this the agency, mindful of the importance of such cooperation for the success of a number of its programs, pursues a deliberate policy both of encouraging and of taking an active part in intergovernmental arrangements. A principal result of this policy is that the state and local governments have become accustomed to common action, so that the negotiation of general agreement seems a quite normal procedure. The continuing concern of the states in a field in which the TVA has a lively interest is indicated by a recently completed interstate compact on pollution, to which the seven Valley states are parties.

It is only fair to observe that the enthusiasm of the governments of the region for the TVA is not shared universally by the federal departments and agencies.[18] The TVA professes to welcome, and certainly

[17] *Knoxville News-Sentinel,* June 29, 1952.

[18] See Roscoe C. Martin, *From Forest to Front Page* (University, Alabama: The University of Alabama Press, 1956), especially pp. 9-12, for an account of a wrangle which developed in 1951 between the United States Forest Service and TVA's Division of Forestry Relations.

does not openly oppose, the pursuit of active programs in the Valley by other federal bodies. In practice, however, its vigorous representation of the federal interest in regional problems tends to preëmpt the field, so that other federal agencies, for example the Soil Conservation Service and the Forest Service, find the region somewhat cool to their operations. Here in truth lies a fundamental problem for the river basin organization. In any given valley a number of federal agencies will have active programs under way. The agencies are of long standing and possess great going-concern strength, and they are understandably loyal to their programs as set forth in law and enshrined in tradition. It is not strange that the TVA has encountered the agency defensiveness which is well-nigh universal and which in varying degree characterizes every river basin in the country. This problem will be examined with greater care in connection with the Missouri.

It remains to comment briefly on the subject of the Tennessee Valley Authority and political viability. The TVA is well and favorably known abroad, as is evidenced both by the number of foreign visitors (now approaching 3,000 a year) who come to the Valley, and by the river basin developments on other continents which rely upon TVA experience and draw upon TVA personnel. The agency's high reputation in other lands is matched by the respect which it commands in the Tennessee Valley, where it has few critics and almost no public detractors. On the contrary, most public officials, in so far as their views are known—and many are quite vocal on the subject—are staunch supporters of the TVA, as are most of the region's newspapers.

Outside the Valley there is continued powerful resistance to the concept of regional development as exemplified by the TVA. This is found in such manifestations as an outspoken interest group opposition, full-page advertisements in national journals attacking the TVA, a widely unfavorable press, a vocal group of critics in Congress, and a national Administration which does not view the TVA idea with favor. Notwithstanding this formidable combination arrayed against the TVA, a series of events of recent years have proved the agency's staying power. First among these may be mentioned the proposal made by the Second Hoover Commission's Task Force on Water Resources and Power that the TVA, in effect, be liquidated, that its "miscellaneous activities" be transferred to "other appropriate Federal and State agencies," and that its power facilities be disposed of to "non-federal interests." [19] This recommendation excited so little interest that it may be said to have been ignored. Second, there was the Administration-

[19] *Task Force Report,* pp. 323-324.

backed Dixon-Yates proposal, under which a power plant would have been constructed by a private group to furnish electricity to the City of Memphis, previously a customer of TVA. The defeat of Dixon-Yates can be interpreted only as a triumph for the TVA and its supporters. Third may be cited the act, passed by Congress after spirited battle running through several sessions, authorizing the TVA to issue revenue bonds to finance the construction of new steam-electric facilities.[20] Here again was a significant victory for the TVA, this time a positive one. Perhaps more than any other one event this measure signalized the coming-of-age of the Tennessee Valley Authority. That it will be subjected to attack again in the future is certain, but that it will be able to contain its opposition and move on to new achievements appears less doubtful now than in the recent past.

THE MISSOURI: AN "INTER-AGENCY" BASIN

The case for developing Missouri Basin water resources (as for most major basins) may be depicted in terms of potential contribution to national economic growth, defence needs, conservation goals, or the lives of individuals in the Basin. So well has it been argued that development now is over half finished and it is estimated that $5,500,000,000 will be spent before existing authorized plans are completed. Few persons contest the need for intensive governmental activities in this Basin; the methods, however, have been subject to constant criticism. The history of Missouri development thus far is a classic case of the unsuccessful search for unity in diversity, and of the conflict between function and area. In that history there are points relevant to future development of eastern rivers, points dealing with inter-agency coordination, with attitudes toward valley authorities and interstate compacts, with changing water uses, and with techniques of river control.

More than forty times the area of the Delaware Basin, the Missouri has widely variable climatic conditions. Population is relatively sparse and agriculture is widespread. In public debate as well as for many legal and administrative purposes, this Basin has been considered as divided into an eastern wet half and a western dry half. Industry is confined largely to urban centers downstream. Agriculture predominates upstream. More obviously than in the East, water is life in this vast area.

[20] The TVA self-financing act, passed in the spring of 1959, was signed into law by the President as P.L. 137, 86th Cong. 1st sess.

Pick-Sloan Development

With nineteenth century human settlement, economically justifiable water developments sprang up all across the Basin. By the end of World War II large federal investments in such projects were being managed by the major water-resource organizations—the Bureau of Reclamation to the west and the Corps of Engineers to the east, roughly, of the 98th meridian. Both had attracted strong local political support. In terms of both physical works and water politics, the Missouri Basin was bipolar by 1944.

A combination of renewed attention to domestic economic issues, fear of a postwar slump, and flood ravages in 1943 created the atmosphere which led to passage of the Flood Control Act of 1944. The Act embodied the Pick-Sloan Plan—in reality one plan emphasizing irrigation and power for the Bureau in the upstream dry areas and another emphasizing flood control and navigation for the Corps along the main stem. General Lewis A. Pick of the Corps and W. G. Sloan of the Bureau brought their separate schemes to Congress where five committees aired the subject for more than a year. Unwilling to challenge the political and bureaucratic strength of either agency and unable to surmount the technical obstacles to formulating an alternative, integrated plan, Congress had the two agencies join their plans with few modifications and called the result the Pick-Sloan Plan. Enormous federal investments by these two agencies and smaller participation by other federal bureaus (the over-all total was over $1,250,000,000) were thus authorized in a document that contained many internal inconsistencies. For example, there was no agreement about the volume of flows in the main River, nor were uniform methods of cost allocation adopted.

The logic of comprehensive planning demanded that incidental work by state governments and other federal agencies be parts of the Pick-Sloan Plan. The relevant Interior agencies—Geological Survey, National Park and Fish and Wildlife Services, and Bureaus of Reclamation, Mines, Indian Affairs, and Land Management—were appropriated funds for operations under the plan in a single budgetary item. The Department tried to unify Basin supervision of these bureaus by establishing at Billings (Montana) a Field Committee of ranking field officials. It should be noted that these Interior bureaus contribute not only to Reclamation projects but also to Corps projects. Other federal agencies quickly joined in the expanded work in the Basin.

Among these were the Federal Power Commission, the Public Health Service, and the Departments of Agriculture, Commerce, and Labor.

Four states were concerned enough with the Pick-Sloan plan to be represented at the organization of the Missouri Basin Inter-Agency Committee in 1945, and within a few years all ten states within the Basin were MBIAC members. (Seven states have half or more of their territory within the Basin: Nebraska, South Dakota, Montana, Wyoming, North Dakota, Missouri, and Kansas. Iowa has 31 per cent, Colorado 29 per cent, and Minnesota 2 per cent.)

The Department of Agriculture in 1949, as a supplement to Pick-Sloan, recommended for long-term agricultural investment in the Basin a "Missouri River Basin Agricultural Program." [21] About $3,000,000,000 were to be provided by the federal government, while states and local governments and farmers were to contribute over $5,000,000,000! This program never received Congressional approval, although many of the measures it encompassed are today being carried out under the authority of soil conservation legislation, including the Small Watersheds Act of 1954.

Missouri Basin water developments originated in an atmosphere of inter-agency rivalry and have continued to the present day in that same atmosphere. To be sure, numerous forces and interests have striven for truly unified development. The basic legal authority, however, remains the Flood Control Act of 1944, and the leading federal agencies, the Bureau of Reclamation and the Corps of Engineers, receive startlingly similar appropriations from Congress year after year. All other federal and state activities depend mostly on the dams, canals, and levees these two erect.

Measures proposed in the original plan were more than half finished in 1958. By that time 27 major dams and reservoirs had been erected. This total included four of the six very large reservoirs planned on the main stem (the figure includes Fort Peck Dam, which was actually completed as to flood control features before 1944). New irrigation units by 1958 provided full water supply to 222,717 acres of land. Eight hydroelectric power plants had been installed and were to produce nearly 5,000,000,000 kwh annually. Eighteen local flood protection works were done; twelve more were under construction. Navigation and bank stabilization measures were 85 per cent finished from Omaha to the mouth and 46 per cent from Sioux City to Omaha. Many other less spectacular or expensive programs were completed or well under way by the Department of Agriculture, Fish and Wildlife

[21] H. Doc. 373, 81st Cong., 1st sess., 1949.

Service, National Park Service, and other federal and state agencies.[22]
A great deal of money is spent each year. Illustrative 1959 budget
figures are:[23]

Federal Agencies		*States*	
Interior	$ 95,657,000	Missouri	$7,795,000
Corps	103,130,000	Kansas	6,730,634
HEW	7,889,800	Colorado	5,902,000
Agriculture	4,933,800	Nebraska	4,754,900
		North Dakota	4,622,738

Not all this money is being devoted to work in the Basin within the
terms of the revised Act of 1944, and this is especially true of that
reported by the states. Furthermore, just how well all of these pieces
fit together and how unified is the development of Basin water resources remained subjects of controversy in 1959.

Inter-Agency Relations

That federal agencies and states have reached an administrative
modus vivendi is symbolized by the Missouri Basin Inter-Agency
Committee (MBIAC). Established by action of the Federal Inter-
Agency River Basin Committee in 1945, MBIAC at first had four
federal members. They were joined by four of the governors on the
Missouri River States Committee, which had been created in 1941 to
try to unify state interests in water resources development. By 1958,
MBIAC had seven federal organizations and ten states as its constituents. Its purpose was declared to be ". . . the coordination of
. . . policies, programs and activities . . . in the field of water and
related land resource investigation, planning, construction, operation,
and maintenance. . . ." A subcommittee has described its operations
thus:

> As a committee, it has never been granted, nor has it sought, the
> power to make policy decisions. Through voluntary action, it has cleared
> thinking, crystallized opinions, broadened understanding, and charted
> the way for coordinated purpose and achievement.

[22] Programming Subcommittee, Missouri Basin Inter-Agency Committee, "Missouri River Basin Development Program and the Missouri Basin Inter-Agency Committee," Appendix B, *Minutes of the One Hundredth Meeting of the Missouri Basin
Inter-Agency Committee* (May 15, 1958), pp. B-23 and B-24.

[23] Missouri Basin Inter-Agency Committee, *Annual Report on Programming, Fiscal
Years 1958-1960* (May, 1958), p. 2.

Possibly the greatest proof of the effectiveness of the committee's manner of operation is the fact that never in its history has an opinion deadlock forced the passing of a question to higher authority, yet State Governments, organizations, and private groups have modified construction plans through appeals to the MBIAC forum.[24]

"Coordination" has been sought through MBIAC's acting as a forum where virtually everyone interested in Basin problems may voice his opinions. Conflict has been rare, for one important reason because specific operating decisions have been avoided.

Despite its lack of legal basis or power, MBIAC has some accomplishments to its credit. For example, in 1951 the Committee approved a *Report on the Adequacy of Flows in the Missouri River.* The debate over the quantity of water available in the Basin was resolved by finding that there was enough water, up- and downstream, for the express purpose of Basin development.

The 1951 *Report* has served as a basis for many operations by member agencies, notably the regulation of the five main-stem dams and reservoirs. The Corps has legal responsibility for the system, but in nominal practice its management is a cooperative endeavor. The responsible official, the Omaha Division Engineer, manipulates the dams through a Reservoir Regulating Section. He and the Section are advised by a Coordinating Committee of seven federal agency representatives and nine state water engineers (Minnesota has not joined). This control system is described more thoroughly below.

Coordination has also brought agreements for division of operating authority like that on the Kansas River, where two multiple-purpose reservoirs have been built by the Corps and eight by Reclamation.

> Regardless of which agency actually built the facility or operates it, the Corps of Engineers is responsible for all flood-control operation and the Bureau of Reclamation is responsible for all irrigation operation. By agreement . . . , the elevation of the water surface in a reservoir determines which agency has primary control in ordering reservoir releases. If the reservoir level is between the . . . elevations allocated to irrigation, the regulation is the responsibility of the Bureau. . . . If it is between the elevations allocated to flood control, the regulation is the responsibility of the Corps. . . . In all cases, the same personnel operate the control gates, but orders for releases may originate with either the Corps or the Bureau. The Federal agencies, however, operate under the control of State water laws and thus require the assistance of State water administrators.[25]

[24] Programming Subcommittee, MBIAC, *op. cit.*, p. B-10.
[25] *Ibid.*, pp. B-13 and B-14.

Even without an MBIAC, such a practical arrangement probably would have been made.

Governor Phil Donnelly of Missouri in 1948 stated a judgment not unlike those other officials have made: the MBIAC has created a "close working relation between Federal agencies . . . [between] various States and between State agencies and Federal agencies. It has solved some of the most intricate and difficult problems of State-Federal relationships." [26] What problems Governor Donnelly had in mind is not clear, but several governors have used the MBIAC quarterly meeting to make policy pronouncements, an activity federal representatives usually find it hard to engage in.

In the Basin there are many unstructured contacts between working officials, by which oral and written agreements continually are effected. The chief means for coordination, permanent but extra-legal, is the MBIAC. It provides (1) interstate and inter-agency communication by inspection trips, circulars, study projects; (2) quarterly meetings for discussion of state and agency work; and (3) dissemination of annual and other reports. Some problems of integrating operations have been overcome by direct inter-agency negotiation or by the MBIAC. Central issues of gearing together plans and operations based on different laws, work habits, and traditions remain unsettled.

It is most difficult to evaluate "coordination," but the over-all situation on the Missouri may be summed up in a few words. Federal and state governments are investing enormous amounts of capital in great water control structures and in numerous related programs all over the Basin. Two federal bureaus in separate departments carry the bulk of the load, although five or more other federal agencies and ten state governments participate. Directing all these efforts is the responsibility of no one below the levels of the President or Bureau of the Budget. Commenting on the MBIAC in this situation, Henry C. Hart has observed that "The Inter-Agency Committee [has] taught its political lesson of the interdependence of water plans in a drainage basin so well that its administrative impotence [has begun] to show." [27]

Dissatisfaction with Missouri Development

The vigor of criticisms levelled at the Basin "programs" and the enthusiasm of proponents of change have waxed and waned since 1944.

[26] MBIAC, *Minutes of the Twenty-Eighth Meeting,* December 9, 1948, p. 1.
[27] Henry C. Hart, *The Dark Missouri,* p. 199.

Through the years the idea of establishing an authority (MVA) cast in the Tennessee Valley Authority mold has frequently reappeared. The *St. Louis Post-Dispatch,* the Farmers' Union, the CIO, and Senator James E. Murray have been among its backers. Their pleas for an MVA and the bills they have introduced in Congress to create it have been warded off, however, to the delight of the *Kansas City Star-Times;* high officials in the Corps, the Bureau, and other federal agencies; numerous governors; private groups organized behind federal bureaus; and a heterogeneous mass of anti-TVA and anti-authority people.

A second line of attack has hit the bipolar nature of national water administration and that of the Missouri Basin especially. The First Hoover Commission recommended uniting Corps and Bureau in a new bureau in the Department of the Interior, after their Natural Resources Task Force reported:

> Analysis of [the Pick-Sloan Plan] reveals the fact that it contains many projects which previously had been subjected to devastating criticism by one or the other agency. The 'compromise' consisted for the most part in a division of projects, each agency agreeing to forego the privilege of criticizing projects assigned by the agreement to the other. The result is in no sense an integrated development plan for the Basin, and there is serious question in this case whether agreement between the two agencies is not more costly to the public than disagreement. . . .[28]

The general suggestion that the two bureaus be united is an old one, and has of course been taken up by other critics in recent years. The 1950 President's Water Resources Policy Commission and the 1952 Missouri Basin Survey Commission echoed the criticism and emphasized the detrimental effects of having two bureaus on the same job in the same valley.

A third important proposal for reform has been that of strengthening the states' role in water development by means of an interstate compact. At the request of the Missouri River States Committee, the Council of State Governments in 1953 sponsored a draft of a "Missouri River Basin Compact." The draft called for a Missouri Basin Commission composed of state and federal representatives to replace the MBIAC and to carry out three functions: (1) promote coordination,

---

[28] U. S. House of Representatives, 81st Cong., 1st sess., H. Doc. 122, "Department of the Interior," 1949, p. 30.

(2) provide "effective participation" by states and national government, and (3) "utilize established governmental agencies in the construction of facilities and in the operation of programs." [29] It was emphasized that the commission was to plan, recommend, and review agency proposals, but that it was "not intended to displace existing agencies—it is not an 'authority' and may not engage in construction or other direct operations." For more than two years the compact idea was pressed in the Basin and in Washington. Henry C. Hart points out that the compact draft was a fairly weak assertion of state authority, and concludes that the discussions about the draft "made it clearer that the states cannot gain any legal right to wield any of the federal constitutional powers." [30]

In September of 1955, the Missouri River States Committee voted to ". . . shelve any action pertaining to a compact and [not to] renew their efforts to secure passage of a Missouri River Compact by Congress." [31] This campaign was dropped because of satisfaction by the governors with the status quo, because of fear of alienating Corps and Bureau officials and powerful private backers, and because of the achievements of the MBIAC. There were, doubtless, other reasons.

The Missouri Basin Survey Commission, appointed by President Truman, in 1953 tried to breed a hybrid. It called for creation by federal law of a five-member Missouri Basin Commission to be appointed by the President with the consent of the Senate. Among its proposed functions were directing and coordinating activities of all federal agencies involved in Basin resource development, preparing comprehensive plans incorporating present plans, studying, preparing a "basin budget," and exercising "central control of river operations." [32] The plain intent was to give the Commission planning powers that would to some extent enable it to direct the work of all bureaus active in the Basin. The states were to be allowed to assent to its operating within their boundaries. Financial arrangements were to remain essentially unchanged. Presented to the incoming Eisenhower administration, this idea was fated to die as the product of a lame duck body. The 1952 floods on the Missouri meanwhile had seemed to prove the worth of the Pick-Sloan Plan and of administrative arrangements under

[29] "Revised Draft Missouri River Basin Compact" (Chicago: Council of State Governments, January 1953), p. 1.
[30] Henry C. Hart, *The Dark Missouri*, pp. 205-6.
[31] Missouri River States Committee, *Minutes*, September 7, 1955.
[32] Missouri Basin Survey Commission, *Missouri: Land and Water*, pp. 264-7.

that plan. Consequently the idea received little or no support in Congress, and no action was taken.

Senator Thomas C. Hennings, inspired by his service with the Missouri Basin Survey Commission, since 1955 has urged enactment of his prescription for water management in the Basin. His plan calls for alteration of the Commission's 1953 proposals to include a slightly stronger voice for state governments. The 1957 draft proposed a Missouri Basin Commission appointed by the President to operate in much the same fashion as the one outlined by the Survey Commission. An additional body, the Missouri River Compact Board, was to be created subsequently by compact. In general, the Compact Board, was to review and approve or disapprove programs formulated by the Commission, to promote supplemental water agreements, and generally to encourage cooperation in water matters among the states and between the states and the federal government.[33] Little congressional support has as yet rallied to Senator Hennings' proposal,[34] which, however, re-emphasizes the widespread dissatisfaction in the Basin with present administrative devices.

Changing Uses

Dissatisfaction about both administration and substance of the Basin programs in recent months has come to light in congressional hearings.[35] Public power interests in Montana, North Dakota, and South Dakota persuaded their state legislatures in 1957 to memorialize Congress on the operation of the five main stem reservoirs. Their major contention was that water-use priorities laid down in the Flood Control Act of 1944 were being violated by the Corps. Their attack, however, was clearly on the status quo in the Basin, and thus against the entire system then in operation. The O'Mahoney-Millikin Amendment to the 1944 Act read:

> The use for navigation in connection with the operation and maintenance of such works herein authorized for construction of water aris-

[33] S. 1107, 85th Cong., 1st sess., 1957. The 1959 version of this, S. 1636, 86th Cong., 1st sess., drops the Compact Board and adds a "Governors' Advisory Committee."

[34] See also the Missouri Basin Organization proposed by Henry Hart, *The Dark Missouri*, Chap. 10.

[35] U.S. Senate, 85th Cong., 1st sess., *Missouri Basin Water Problems*, Joint Hearings before the Committee on Interior and Insular Affairs and the Committee on Public Works, Part I, May 1-3, 1957. Similar hearings were going on in February, 1959.

ing in States lying wholly or partly west of the 98th meridian, shall be only such use as does not conflict with any beneficial consumptive use, present or future, in States lying wholly or partly west of the 98th meridian, of such waters for domestic, municipal, stock water, irrigation, mining, or industrial purposes.[36]

Public power spokesmen said this amendment was intended to give a priority to hydroelectric power generation over navigation downstream. They pointed out that since hydroelectric power, under the latest allocation of cost estimates, is slated to repay over 88 per cent of total project reimbursable costs, it is only fair that a preferred position be given to releases for power in comparison with those for navigation. Further charges, directed at the Bureau of Reclamation, maintained that its policies were inimical to public power interests.

In reply, Corps representatives and other officials have pointed out that recent drought years on the Missouri have prevented optimum operation of the main-stem reservoirs. They further denied that hydroelectric power was accorded a higher priority than navigation at any point in the negotiations leading up to the Flood Control Act of 1944 or in the law itself.

The dispute continued in 1959. The emergence of a strong demand for further public power emphasizes the changing uses of water in the Missouri Basin. It should not be surprising that a 15-year-old law and the priorities stated therein should come under attack as the population of the Basin increases and as industrialization proceeds even in upstream areas. As in any basin, for example the Delaware, settlements of water priorities cannot be expected to satisfy all users forever.

> In a sense, water requirements are ever in a state of flux, and there is often need for reappraisal or readjustment to meet changing needs or to assure that original concepts are still valid in light of more recent knowledge and development. . . .
> . . . twenty years ago, water for storage for municipal, industrial, and recreational needs seemed almost incidental when compared with flood control and agriculture requirements in the Basin. Not so today. Undoubtedly continued growth in these requirements will in turn require future adjustments in present and past concepts of water development. . . .[37]

[36] See 58 Stat. L. 889 ff.
[37] Programming Subcommittee, MBIAC, *op. cit.*, pp. B-16 and B-17.

Summary

The Missouri and the Columbia Basins are the major instances where the inter-agency approach to handling water resources has been tested. Many maintain that the approach has "worked" on the Missouri, but there are serious doubts whether it has worked well or economically or has served the best interests of the Basin and the nation, almost regardless of how those interests are defined. As a minimum criticism it must be said that the Missouri Basin story illustrates some of the basic weaknesses of inter-agency administration in the field of water.

Three more general conclusions may be drawn from the Missouri experience. First, attitudes toward both the valley authority and the interstate compact and their adaptability to water development problems have been generally unfavorable in the Missouri Basin. Therein lies a general warning for proponents of those devices in the Missouri and in other basins as well. Second, the general proposition that major water uses or demands may and probably will change through time is supported by the Missouri Basin story. Such changes can be expected in any sizable basin. Finally, the techniques of control of the main-stem dams on this river appear to be worth serious consideration in setting up the control system on any other river where a series of multiple-purpose dams are to be built. Some valuable experience in this type of operation is being stored up there.

CHAPTER 15

Travail on the Delaware

A CHAPTER that would deal in full with the history of the Delaware River—even if confined to the use of the waters of the Delaware by man—would be of interminable length. The first use of the River for navigation can be traced to 1609 when Henry Hudson in his *Half Moon* poked into the mouth of the Delaware before sailing north to discover the river to which he gave his name. Water power was being developed on the Brandywine at Great Falls by the late seventeenth century, and by the time of the Revolution its water-powered mills had made the Brandywine area a colonial center for the production of flour, gunpowder, textiles, and paper. The first municipal water works in the United States to employ steam engines for pumping was built at Bethlehem in 1764 in the watershed of the Lehigh River. The early history of the Delaware is absorbing but it is not directly relevant to the present account, which must emphasize current water-use problems and their immediate antecedents. This story will focus perforce on the various plans for the use of the waters of the Delaware River and their impact upon water quality. It can be dated readily from the 1920's, when the City of New York first reached into the Delaware watershed for water for its expanding population.

NEW YORK CITY AND DELAWARE WATER

It is not necessary to discuss in detail the ways by which New York City was supplied with water in the past. The story has been told elsewhere, and in any case does not directly affect the Delaware since the sources first developed were located in the Hudson-Mohawk Valley. By the mid-1920's, however, the city was approaching full use of its available water resources. In 1926 the (City) Board of Water

Supply estimated that by 1935 consumption of water would match supply and that additional sources would then be required.[1]

The city had not waited until this critical moment to seek a new water source. In 1921 the Board of Water Supply was instructed to investigate additional sources beyond the existing Catskill System. Five alternatives were seriously considered, and each of the first four was rejected in turn. By elimination this left only the fifth proposal, which called for construction of reservoirs in Delaware, Ulster, and Sullivan counties to draw water for the first time from the headwaters of the Delaware River. The technical problems were not insoluble, and the Chief Engineer of the Board of Water Supply ultimately produced a plan to develop a supply of 600 mgd of water from Delaware River-Rondout Creek Reservoirs at an estimated cost of $272,587,000. But there were objections from the counties where the reservoirs would be built; moreover, and more seriously, since the Delaware is an interstate stream, litigation with other states might be involved.[2]

Inconclusive negotiations with Pennsylvania and New Jersey concerning the use of the Delaware had been conducted fifteen years before. These were now resumed, and in 1923 the legislatures of the three states appointed commissioners to write an interstate compact. A draft was prepared and reported unanimously in 1925, dividing the flows above Port Jervis in thirds among the states, and the waters arising between Port Jervis and Philadelphia half and half between Pennsylvania and New Jersey. New York State ratified at once, but the agreement was sharply criticized in the other two states and no legislative action was taken. Instead, commissioners met again and in 1927 a new second draft was referred to the states for approval. This version did not seek to allocate all of the waters of the Delaware, but established limited allocations of 600 mgd for New York and New Jersey and of 900 mgd for Pennsylvania. New York's legislature again ratified promptly, but Pennsylvania and New Jersey once more failed to act. It would appear that Pennsylvania was never reconciled to the apportionment proposed, but its legislature let New Jersey take the lead in opposition. New Jersey's objections were various—in particular the reduction in

[1] New York City Board of Estimate, *Journal of Proceedings*, V (June 30-Oct. 26, 1926), p. 6483.

[2] New York City Board of Water Supply, *Minutes*, 1927, p. 140; *idem., Annual Report*, 1927, p. 5. The story of New York City's quest for water is told in Roscoe C. Martin, *Water for New York* (Syracuse: Syracuse University Press, 1960), Chapter V.

minimum flow requirements in the second compact was criticized—but a subsequent report of the New York Joint Legislative Commission on Interstate Cooperation suggested that New Jersey hoped to drive a better bargain by waiting until New York City was desperate for water.[3]

Following the failure of the first compact and in the face of the fact that negotiations were being resumed, the New York Board of Water Supply determined to advance an alternative solution to New York City's water problem; and in October of 1926 presented a plan for the utilization of the east-side Hudson tributaries. Clearly described as a second-best to the Delaware proposal, it was estimated to provide 500 mgd of water at a cost of $347,934,000. A bill to authorize the project was introduced into the 1927 New York legislative session and passed by the Senate, but died in committee in the Assembly. In the interim the second compact had been drafted, and the Board of Water Supply decided to withdraw the Hudson proposal and substitute that for the Delaware.[4]

In quick sequence the Delaware plan was endorsed by the Merchants Association of New York, the Brooklyn Chamber of Commerce, the Bronx Board of Trade, and the New York City League of Women Voters. Inevitably representatives from the areas to be inundated protested, but that substantial support also existed in those areas was suggested by the fact that the necessary legislation was introduced into the 1928 legislature by Senator Wicks of Ulster County and

[3] *Report of Joint Legislative Committee on Interstate Cooperation,* 1938, No. 90 in New York State Legislative Documents, pp. 83-88. More detailed accounts of the negotiations will be found in Maynard Hufschmidt, *The Supreme Court and Interstate Water Problems: The Delaware Basin Example* (Cambridge, Mass., mimeographed, 1958), pp. 21-25; and in Corps of Engineers, "308 Report," *op. cit.,* pp. 89-91. The texts of the two proposed compacts are reprinted in the U.S. Department of the Interior, *Documents on the Use and Control of the Waters of Interstate and International Streams,* pp. 324-353. The political obstacles that prevented ratification of these compacts by the downstream states are briefly discussed by Duane Minard, legal counsel for New Jersey in the subsequent Supreme Court case, in "The Norris and Mansfield Bills from the Viewpoint of the Lawyer," *Toward Unity: A Series of Addresses Presented at the Second Annual Regional Conference of the Interstate Commission on the Delaware River Basin* (Philadelphia, 1937), pp. 51-52.

[4] New York City Board of Water Supply, *Annual Report,* 1927, p. 104; New York City Board of Estimate, *Journal of Proceedings, 1926,* V (June 30-Oct. 26), p. 6483; *idem,* 1927, p. 811; *New York Times,* Dec. 1, 1926, p. 29; New York State Senate, *Journal,* 1927, p. 1111; New York State Assembly, *Journal,* 1927, index.

Assemblyman Loomis of Delaware. The Board of Estimate approved, the legislature followed suit, and the New York State Water Power and Control Commission added its consent.[5]

The Board of Water Supply may have hoped for a time that the development might proceed under interstate agreement; when the second compact failed of ratification, however, the Board determined to go it alone. Even before the permit authorizing construction was issued by the New York State Water Power and Control Commission, New Jersey petitioned the United States Supreme Court to enjoin the city and state from proceeding with the plan. Pennsylvania asked and received permission to intervene and a Special Master was designated to take evidence. Following his report and argument by the parties the Court reached its decision, and on May 25, 1931, a little over two years after the complaint was filed, the cause was determined.

The opinion of the Court was delivered by Justice Oliver Wendell Holmes.[6] New York had proposed to build storage reservoirs that would divert an ultimate 600 mgd for water supply. The waters stored would consist of the excess over a stipulated "ordinary flow," and during the summer months when the natural flows fell below this minimum New York proposed to release water and augment downstream flows. The decision of the Court followed the recommendation of the Master in accepting the major part of the New York plan.

New York thus was permitted to divert water out of the Delaware Basin, though because the diversion would result in some damage to recreation and to the oyster industry in the lower Delaware, the Court set a limit of 440 mgd. In order to expand the benefits of the New York plan in augmenting downstream flows, a revised formula was developed based not on rainfall over the watersheds feeding the city reservoirs, but upon actual water in the River. The effect was to provide for low-flow augmentation releases when drought affected the River even if flows were normal or above on the tributaries developed by the city. And to protect downstream communities from an increase in pollution from diminished stream flow, New York State was ordered to assure the treatment of sewage from Port Jervis, New York.

The Court's decision stipulated that jurisdiction over the case would

[5] New York City Board of Water Supply, *Minutes*, 1927, pp. 140, 178; Board of Estimate, *Journal of Proceedings*, 1928, pp. 19-21; *New York Times*, Feb. 2, 1928, p. 2; March 2, 1928, p. 18; and March 25, 1928, II, p. 2; New York Senate, *Journal*, 1928, pp. 985-86; New York Assembly, *Journal*, 1928, pp. 1767-68.

[6] *New Jersey v. New York and the City of New York*, 283 U.S. 336 (1931). The decision is discussed in detail in Hufschmidt, *The Supreme Court*, pp. 25-43.

be retained by the Supreme Court and that any of the party states might reopen the case if future circumstances should suggest the desirability of modification. New York City was granted the greater part of its requested allocation, therefore, but without any guarantee as to the future.

The "308 Report"

The draft compacts of the 1920's had spoken in terms of a comprehensive development of the water resources of the Delaware, enumerating the values to be attributed to domestic and industrial water supply, sanitation, hydroelectric power, and navigation. Indeed the 1925 compact had specifically provided that "Every . . . development shall be so planned and the works shall be so constructed as to bring about the greatest practicable conservation and use of the waters . . . on which it is located," and had directed the tri-state Delaware River commission established by the compact to "proceed with a study and investigation looking toward a complete and comprehensive development of all the water resources of the drainage area of the Delaware River. . . ." [7]

Despite these professed intentions, the consequence of the Supreme Court decision was to authorize a development of the upper Delaware designed primarily for water supply, with incidental benefits from low-flow augmentation but without regard to the other values attainable through over-all planning. The first step toward preparation of a comprehensive plan of the kind referred to in the 1925 draft compact was taken not by the interstate commission there proposed but by a federal agency, the Corps of Engineers, with the publication in 1934 of the "308 Report" on the Delaware River. [8]

This study went beyond the ordinary format of the "308" to consider water supply needs in view of the special character of the Delaware River. It attempted to provide an integrated plan for the development of the River, balancing the various uses of water. Its influence is suggested by the fact that substantial parts of its recommendations have been incorporated in each subsequent report on the Delaware. The principal conclusions reached by the Corps report were that: (1)

[7] U.S. Department of Interior, *Documents,* Article III in both compacts; see also Articles V and XX.

[8] This was one of the series of such reports authorized by the Rivers and Harbors Act of 1927 and enumerated in H. Doc. 308, 69th Cong., 1st sess. (1927). The report for the Delaware was published as H. Doc. 179, 73d Cong., 2d sess.

development of the Delaware and Lehigh Rivers for navigation above Trenton was not justified at the time; (2) flood damage was not sufficient to justify any federal flood control works; (3) development of the Delaware River for generation of hydroelectric power was feasible (a group of power sites, capable of unit operation at a profit, was identified); but (4) the most efficient use of the waters of the River would be for a combined development for water supply and power which would provide incidental benefits in flood control and regulated minimum flows.[9]

The effect of the Corps' findings was to dispel the prospect of early action in the two fields, navigation and flood control, in which federal programs were then operative. So far as the immediate future of Delaware development was concerned, the most significant conclusions of the report were found in the last two sentences: "Federal participation in any present or prospective project above Trenton does not appear justifiable. Future water supply and power developments within the Delaware watershed should be coordinated, supervised, or controlled by an interstate agency." And this recommendation of the district engineer (Philadelphia) was concurred in successively by the division engineer, the Board of Engineers for Rivers and Harbors, and the Chief of Engineers.[10]

THE INTERSTATE COMMISSION ON THE DELAWARE RIVER BASIN: 1936-1948

At the time of the Corps report there was no interstate agency capable of assuming the responsibility referred to in its findings. As it happened, however, an agency capable of filling this role, at least in part, was created within the two years following. This was the Interstate Commission on the Delaware River Basin, or Incodel. Incodel did not take the form, contemplated in the draft compacts of the 1920's, of a commission based upon interstate compact; instead it was created by parallel legislation among the states and has operated from the beginning on the principle of voluntary interstate cooperation.

Interestingly enough in view of its subsequent history, the initiative

---

[9] "308 Report," pp. 73-76, 116-119.

[10] Ibid., pp. 5-6, 6-7, and 33. The two sentences quoted are here interchanged from the original report for clarity.

for the creation of the Interstate Commission on the Delaware River Basin came in substantial part from the federal government. The National Resources Committee helped to finance the agency's staff through its first three years, and a 1938 report of the New York Joint Legislative Committee on Interstate Cooperation described the Water Resources Committee of the NRC as "working shoulder to shoulder" with Incodel.[11] The second principal motivating force for the creation of Incodel was the nationwide interstate cooperation movement of the period, which was encouraged by the Council of State Governments. The first step toward institutionalizing interstate cooperation was taken with the establishment of a Commission on Interstate Cooperation in each state. New Jersey was the first state in the union to create such a commission, acting in March, 1935. Two other Delaware states, New York and Pennsylvania, followed suit in April and May to become second and third respectively.

It was the subcommittee on stream pollution of the Pennsylvania Commission on Interstate Cooperation that took the first step toward regional cooperation concerning the Delaware. The subcommittee invited representatives of the New Jersey and New York Commissions, the Corps of Engineers, the Public Health Service, the National Resources Committee, and local agencies to a meeting held April 3, 1936. Those attending determined to establish a coordinating unit to integrate the work of the Commissions, the Council of State Governments, the state planning boards, and the National Resources Committee, in so far as it affected the Delaware River. This coordinating unit was called the Interstate Commission on the Delaware River Basin. Delaware, which did not have a commission on interstate cooperation, was invited to participate informally; it did not establish a commission until 1939.[12] In view of Incodel's central position in the development of the Delaware during the ensuing decade, the events of that period can most conveniently be analyzed in terms of the actions taken by Incodel and its reactions to the developmental projects of other agencies.

[11] *Report of Joint Legislative Committee on Interstate Cooperation, 1938*, p. 93; see also pp. 93-98; Maynard Hufschmidt, *The Interstate Commission on the Delaware River Basin: A Study of Its Role as a Planning Agency Engaged in the Political Process*, pp. 7-13; and David W. Robinson, "Voluntary Regionalism in the Control of Water Resources," *The Annals*, 207 (Jan., 1940), pp. 116-123.

[12] Authorization for participation in the work of Incodel will be found in New Jersey, *Laws*, 1936, p. 32; Pennsylvania, *Laws*, 1937, p. 109; New York, *Laws*, 1939, p. 1409; and Delaware, *Laws*, 1939, p. 432.

Pollution Control

Some uncertainty attended the question of the proper functions of the new agency. The Committee on the Quantity of Water, composed of the state water engineers and established by Incodel to prepare a formula for resolving interstate disputes over allocations of water, insisted that a comprehensive plan for Delaware development was a necessary first step. The Commission leadership, however, decided to proceed at once to the solution of immediate, specific problems, and so rebuffed the Committee on Quantity.[13] What the first of these specific problems would be was foreshadowed by the original source of the proposal to create Incodel in the subcommittee on stream pollution of the Pennsylvania Commission. That the new agency was quick to ratify the predisposition of its sponsor is indicated by a 1940 publication which reported that "From 1936 through 1939, Incodel has devoted a major portion of its time and resources to the critical problem of water pollution control."[14]

Along with the Committee on Quantity, Incodel had set up a Committee on the Quality of Water with a membership from the departments of health in the four states. After some months of negotiations, this committee prepared a reciprocal agreement on pollution control. The agreement classified the waters of the River and its tributaries in four categories or zones based on use, and prescribed standards of treatment for each. The agreement was promptly adopted by the department of health in each of the four states.[15] The document also asserted that each state "agrees to enact adequate legislation if necessary." Using a panel of attorneys, Incodel from the agreement prepared a draft of a uniform pollution control bill, which was then sponsored in each of the four state legislatures by legislative members of Incodel. Approval came at once in New Jersey and New York at the 1939 sessions, and Delaware's Legislature approved the measure in 1941. In the Pennsylvania Legislature, however, the reciprocal agreement was strongly opposed.

Tighter pollution control legislation necessarily struck at two types

[13] The long-continued controversy over whether Incodel should prepare a comprehensive plan for the Delaware or not is reported in detail in Hufschmidt, *Incodel,* pp. 20-42. Hufschmidt portrays the decision reached as a disastrous "wrong turn" in the organization's history.

[14] Incodel, *Planned Progress in Pollution Control,* Series B, No. 3 (January, 1940).

[15] Incodel, *Water Pollution,* Series B, No. 1 (November, 1938). The text is included in Department of the Interior, *Documents on the Use and Control of the Waters of Interstate and International Streams,* previously cited, at pp. 354-59.

of offenders: municipalities that were providing insufficient or no treatment for sewage dumped into the river, and industrial firms whose use of water served to pollute it. Incodel concentrated its attention upon the former type of pollution, minimizing the importance of immediate action with regard to industrial wastes. In 1940 an Incodel publication announced that the Commission ". . . maintained the view that adequate municipal sewage collection and treatment facilities must be secured before the industrial waste problem can be vigorously attacked." [16] A formal Incodel resolution of October 24, 1941, repeated this assertion, arguing that first priority should be placed on compelling Philadelphia to meet its responsibilities regarding sewage disposal and that industrial pollution should not be dealt with until later.

The City of Philadelphia possessed the distinction of being the most serious offender among the municipal polluters. Estimates were that in 1940 half the untreated domestic sewage dumped into the Delaware was contributed by Philadelphia and its sister city of Camden, and that Philadelphia was discharging about 80 per cent of its sewage into the river without any treatment. Philadelphia had been under pressure by the state government to clean up the river since 1905, but World War I, the depression, and World War II each in turn served as reasons for not acting.[17]

Notwithstanding this background, the principal opposition to the Incodel pollution control bill in the Pennsylvania Legislature came from industrial opponents rather than from municipalities. Little dissent was apparent in the House of Representatives where the measure passed 117 to 12, but it never emerged from the Senate Committee on State Government. Ellwood Turner, Incodel chairman and a member of the Pennsylvania House, attributed its defeat to ". . . the ignorance of small officials holding positions in big business." [18] Incodel tried again in the 1941 session. This time the bill passed the House unanimously and was passed on first reading in the Senate. The Garden Club Federation of Pennsylvania, the Pennsylvania Roadside Council, the Philadelphia Maritime Exchange, and the Philadelphia Bourse sent communications to the Legislature in its support. But after the

[16] Incodel, *Planned Progress*, p. 1.

[17] Incodel, *Water Pollution Abatement in the Delaware River Basin with Special Reference to the City of Philadelphia: A Symposium* (Philadelphia, 1941), provides extensive information on the depressing history of Philadelphia's struggles with its sewage problem.

[18] *New York Times*, May 21, 1939, p. 34; cf. June 10, 1939, p. 19.

first reading the bill was recommitted to the Committee on Public Health, from which it never emerged; and the "industrial lobby" was credited with another victory. No bill was presented to the 1943 session, but in 1945 Incodel offered its plan again. In the meantime the political atmosphere of the state had altered: the administration of Governor Edward Martin was committed to a clean streams program, and the measure passed unanimously through both houses.

Without waiting for final approval of the reciprocal agreement, Incodel had pushed ahead with its pollution control program. In cooperation with the Interstate Commission, the Sanitary Water Board of Pennsylvania succeeded in securing the agreement of the Philadelphia City government to act on its sewage problem. Across the River the New Jersey State Board of Health served anti-pollution orders on Camden, Gloucester, Beverly, and the Borough of Riverton. Although the material shortages produced by World War II delayed compliance by the municipalities, construction commenced immediately after the war. With victory on both sides of the River, Incodel regarded this, its principal task, as completed, and began to point with pride to results accomplished instead of planning further action. The 1958 Incodel *Annual Report* highlighted the organization's career and asserted:

> . . . water pollution is no longer the number one problem it was a short two decades ago. . . . Incodel wishes to congratulate the citizens of the Basin on the virtual accomplishment of the stream pollution abatement program . . .
>
> Incodel's basin-wide pollution program, according to a recent nationwide survey made by the U.S. Public Health Service, has progressed further and faster than any comparable program in the whole country. At the present time virtually all major sources of pollution are under control. . . .
>
> Today, in 1958, virtually every municipality, industry, and institution in all four of the Delaware River Valley states has met, or is fully prepared to meet, its responsibility in complying with the requirements and standards of Incodel's comprehensive basin-wide pollution abatement program.[19]

Schuylkill River Restoration

The reciprocal agreement affected primarily pollution on the main stem of the Delaware; a separate Incodel program was concerned

[19] Incodel, *Annual Report*, 1958, pp. 2, 13, 17.

with cleaning up the Schuylkill River, long badly polluted by culm deposits washed down from the anthracite mining operations in the upper reaches of the stream. There was some question as to whether the Schuylkill, an intrastate stream, was properly within Incodel's jurisdiction, but a 1941 business meeting decided that the federal-state-local interrelationships involved and the consequences for the other Delaware states justified it in taking up the matter.

A plan for cleaning up the river had been prepared by the Corps of Engineers in 1939; Incodel's contribution therefore was principally one of encouraging action. In 1943 it advanced its own proposals for implementing the Corps recommendations: the coal companies would construct facilities to prevent further pollution; the state would fine those who failed; and Pennsylvania and the federal government co-operatively would dredge the river of the existing deposits of culm. Appropriate legislation was introduced into the 1945 session of the Pennsylvania Legislature and, despite some opposition from the coal industry, was passed by the same body that approved the reciprocal agreement on pollution. In the Congress, at Incodel's request, the Corps of Engineers was instructed to restudy the Schuylkill problem and a subsequent report recommended federal participation in the cooperative program.[20] The Congress approved and the Schuylkill River Restoration Project was written into the Rivers and Harbors Act of 1946.

Reciprocal Diversion Laws

Second in importance only to pollution control in the original Incodel program was the development of a formula to determine water allocations among the states and to prevent further quarrels over diversions. Mindful of the failure of past compact attempts, the Incodel leadership determined to approach the problem through the device of reciprocal legislation; and the Committee on Quantity, composed of the state water engineers, was delegated the task of finding a basis for agreement. The first reaction of the committee was to argue that a comprehensive plan for Delaware development was an essential prerequisite to any allocations, but Incodel rejected this plea and di-

[20] H. Doc. 529, 79th Cong., 2d sess. A description of the physical features of the project and texts of several of the relevant documents will be found in Final Report of the Schuylkill River Project Engineers, *The Schuylkill River Desilting Project*, July 1, 1951.

rected the committee to develop a generalized statement of the conditions under which diversions might be made.

While the Committee on Quantity was still deliberating, a proposal was advanced by Governor A. Harry Moore of New Jersey to secure a diversion from the River for his state without attention to any such formula. In a message to the New Jersey Legislature he proposed that the Delaware and Raritan Canal be used to carry 150 mgd of water from the Delaware River as a permanent diversion out of the Basin, and that an additional 50 mgd be awarded to Trenton and southern Jersey within the Basin. A few weeks later the Incodel staff responded with a report concluding that the effects of a diversion would be adverse in the absence of any provisions for compensating releases when the flow at Trenton fell below the 3,400 cfs (cubic feet per second) fixed by the Supreme Court decree. A 1940 report to the New Jersey Legislature on the Governor's plan incorporated Incodel's suggestion of a compensating reservoir on a Delaware tributary, but no further action was ever taken.

The general formula ultimately developed by the Committee on Quantity paralleled that advanced for modification of New Jersey's diversion project. Water could be taken out of the stream for diversion elsewhere only at times of high flow; storage reservoirs must be provided and compensating releases must be made at times of low flow to maintain prescribed minima. The formula was similar to that used by the Supreme Court, but the minima stipulated were higher. This formula was incorporated in draft legislation which was submitted to the three state legislatures. (Since any diversion by Delaware could have only an intrastate effect, that state was not included.) Ratifications followed promptly: New York and Pennsylvania approved in 1943 and New Jersey in 1944. A deletion in the New York State version, however, appeared to have the effect of requiring Supreme Court approval of any future diversion, and Incodel sought to obtain a clarification of meaning from the Court. Before such a clarification could be had, however, and indeed before the formula became effective in any actual instance of diversion, the laws were superseded by the Incodel-proposed compact of 1951.

Hydroelectric Power on the Delaware

In these three instances Incodel was in the position of the proposing agency. It did not, however, always play this role. Particularly in regard to proposals to develop hydroelectric power on the Delaware,

Incodel was found in a posture of opposition to plans advanced by others. No objection was made to the long-existent Lake Wallenpaupack system of Pennsylvania Power and Light on the Lackawaxen River, constructed in the 1920's, or to the Mongaup River development of Rockland Light and Power on another Delaware tributary. Incodel considered, however, that more serious problems were raised by power development on the main stem of the river.[21]

The "308 Report" of the Corps of Engineers had discussed the possibility of hydroelectric power generation favorably and in detail. The report had concluded that a hydro project on the Delaware was feasible, but recommended against federal development. In the first years of Incodel's existence some voices were raised in favor of that agency's entering the power field, but with its decision not to become an operating agency the question became moot. Instead, the power issue was raised during the thirties in two other ways: an application in 1935 by the Electric Power Company of New Jersey to the Federal Power Commission for a license to develop hydroelectric power at dams at Tocks Island, Belvidere, and Chestnut Hill;[22] and a resolution of the House Committee on Rivers and Harbors in 1939 directing the Corps of Engineers to restudy the "308 Report" with respect to the "advisability of constructing dams in the vicinity of Tocks Island, Belvidere, and Chestnut Hill for the development of hydroelectric power; for improving the existing navigation facilities on the river below; and for other beneficial effects, including possible sources of public water supplies that can be made available by said dams."

Public hearings were held on both proposals. Opposition came in both cases from three principal sources. First, the private electric companies already operating in the area insisted they had no use for such power and were prepared to meet the needs of the region for twenty to thirty years without hydro plants. Second, representatives of the coal industry argued that the plan would throw miners out of work by replacing steam-generating power plants with hydro power. Third, various interests, but particularly governments anticipating future water supply needs, objected to committing Delaware water to a use for power that might later preclude other uses.[23]

With all three criticisms Incodel associated itself, adding as a special objection to the second plan that the federal government should be

[21] Incodel, *Report on the Utilization of the Delaware*, pp. 15, 17.
[22] FPC Project No. 1305, filed February 16, 1935.
[23] *The Philadelphia Inquirer*, April 23, 1935, p. 5, summarizes the testimony at the public hearing on the application by the Electric Power Company of New Jersey.

kept out of the Delaware and a federal regional power authority thus prevented. Compared with this opposition the proponents of the hydro power project were badly outnumbered. The Electric Power Company not unnaturally asserted its feasibility, and the proposed public power plan was endorsed by a handful of organizations, chiefly labor unions (though the railroad unions joined with the United Mine Workers of America in opposition). Given the balance of forces the outcome was hardly surprising. The Electric Power Company's application was rejected first and then, in 1939, the district engineer advised against a further survey.

A renewed application by the Electric Power Company after the war for a license for Delaware power development reawakened Incodel's concern; and the 1948 Incodel Annual Report contained a statement by Orus J. Matthews, a Pennsylvania member, describing the application for an FPC permit as a "dangerous proposal." Matthews, the Secretary of the Pennsylvania Department of Commerce, wrote:

> Such construction, if authorized, would seriously jeopardize the interests of the States in the use of the Delaware. It is imperative that New York, New Jersey, and Pennsylvania, at the earliest opportunity, declare by reciprocal legislation or compact their intention of preserving to themselves the exclusive authority to build and operate such dams and reservoirs on the Delaware and its tributaries as they may jointly determine, after adequate study, to be necessary or advisable in order to meet the estimated prospective water supply requirements of their respective political subdivisions.[24]

Nevertheless, in the succeeding years additional applications for FPC licenses were made by the Electric Power Company and by a second concern, the Delaware River Development Corporation, and in June of 1951 the Federal Power Commission granted a preliminary permit to the latter company to study the sites at Tocks Island, Belvidere, and Chestnut Hill. This preliminary permit was renewed for one-year intervals to the statutory limit of three years and expired June 30, 1954. Following the hurricane floods of 1955 the Delaware River Development Corporation filed once more with the FPC for a preliminary permit, but the application was withdrawn "without prejudice" on August 15, 1957.[25]

[24] Incodel, *Annual Report,* 1948. Cf. Incodel, *Multiple Purpose Reservoirs on the Delaware River,* September 12, 1948.

[25] See discussion in minutes of second meeting of Delaware River Basin Survey Coordinating Committee, Bethlehem, Pa., August 15-16, 1957, p. 3. Two additional

New Jersey Cross-State Ship Canal

Incodel had been opposed to federal action to develop hydroelectric power, and in alliance with politically powerful forces it had succeeded in blocking a weakly supported proposal to this end. In the plan for a New Jersey ship canal to link New York Bay and the Delaware River Incodel was again in opposition, but this time encountered as adversary one of the most powerful interest groups in the water resources field, the Atlantic Deeper Waterways Association. The Association was organized in 1907 for the purpose of securing legislative authorization and appropriations for an intracoastal waterway. To this purpose a coalition was created, consisting of shippers, contractors, and civic organizations interested in port development, which collectively was capable of generating enormous pressure for action. By the 1930's only one link in the system remained to be constructed, the ship canal which by crossing New Jersey would provide a protected water route from the Port of New York to the Port of Philadelphia.[26]

The omission was not for want of trying. The Association had secured surveys and resurveys of the canal in 1909, 1913, 1920, 1930, 1934, and 1936, but each report had been unfavorable. A resolution of the Senate Committee on Commerce in December of 1936 directed still another restudy. This time the result was favorable: in August of 1942 the Chief of Engineers submitted a recommendation for the Cross-Jersey Canal. The justification for the shift in the Corps' position rested on a recalculation of capital costs on a lower interest rate and an increased estimate of the value of the canal for national defense. Early in the 1943 session of the 78th Congress a bill to authorize construction of the canal was introduced by Representative John McCormack of Massachusetts, the House Majority Leader.

In the hearings on the McCormack bill the Atlantic Deeper Waterways Association, whose president, J. Hampton Moore, was a former Congressman from Pennsylvania and former mayor of Philadelphia,

---

power projects during this period involved the use of Delaware water through the Delaware system of the New York City water supply. The Central Hudson Gas and Electric Corporation develops 25,000 kw from the fall of water through the tunnel from Neversink Reservoir to Rondout Reservoir, while Rockland Light and Power develops 15,000 kw at the lower end of the tunnel from Pepacton Reservoir to Rondout. See *New York Times*, July 4, 1951. The Federal Power Commission disavowed jurisdiction over the two projects by referring to the Supreme Court decision in *New Jersey* v. *New York et al.* Cases DI-181 and DI-194.

[26] See Arthur Maass, *Muddy Waters*, pp. 41-43.

appeared as principal proponent. A parade of witnesses came from up and down the coast—representatives of port authorities, of shippers, of manufacturers interested in low cost transportation, and so forth. Interestingly enough, the only break in the front of port authorities mobilized by the Atlantic Deeper Waterways Association came in the area directly affected. The Port of New York Authority testified against the project in 1943, while the Philadelphia Chamber of Commerce, the Philadelphia Port of Trade, and the Port of Philadelphia Ocean Traffic Bureau had voiced their opposition in a public hearing at Philadelphia in July of 1937.[27] Opposition to the canal likewise was expressed by the railroads serving the ports of New York City and Philadelphia.

Leadership in the fight against the project was taken by the State of New Jersey, supported by a number of civic organizations and municipalities in the State. In part the challenge to the canal rested on an analysis of its economics and a denial of its military utility, but the argument relied principally on the alleged damage the canal would do to the land and water resources of the State. Dredging the canal might affect the underground water supply. Employing the waters of the Raritan River would prevent their later use for industrial and municipal water supply. Augmentation of canal water from the Delaware might produce dangerous salt water intrusion in the lower river. Some of the State's best farmland would be taken for the canal. Incodel supported these arguments, emphasizing its concern over a major diversion of water from the primary use of water supply.

Despite this opposition, however, the Committee on Rivers and Harbors voted to report the bill favorably on a straight party-line vote of 14 to 8, a tribute presumably to the influence of both House Majority Leader McCormack and the Atlantic Deeper Waterways Association. The force of the decision was destroyed when three months later the same committee instructed the Corps of Engineers to review its report ". . . with a view to determining whether any change in the plans for the water supply is advisable." With this directive further action on the authorization bill was abandoned and the New Jersey Water Policy Commission—and Incodel—claimed victory.[28]

---

[27] House of Representatives Committee on Rivers and Harbors, *Hearings on H. Res. 1880*, 78th Cong., 1st sess. The proceedings of the earlier hearing are summarized in the New Jersey Department of Economic Development report, *The Proposed New Jersey Canal.*

[28] New Jersey Water Policy Commission, *New Jersey Ship Canal: Effect upon Potable Waters;* Incodel, *Annual Report,* 1948, pp. 22-23.

Other incidents might be recorded from the history of Delaware development to highlight Incodel's activities during the first decade of its existence; but these five episodes, major events of the years 1936-1946, are sufficient to indicate both the position taken by Incodel on water-resource issues and its substantial success in securing acquiescence in its views. Incodel's general position may be summarized in three basic principles:

1. The first use of the waters of the Delaware River is for water supply; any competing uses that might impair such use should be prevented.

2. To maximize the value of the Delaware for water supply and for other purposes, the primary need is to improve the quality of its water by a sustained attack on pollution, especially by municipalities.

3. Programs for pollution and for water supply—and hence for the Delaware River generally—are peculiarly the province of state action. Federal aid may be solicited, particularly for its established function of flood protection, but federal control of the Delaware must be avoided at all costs.

In terms of these tenets Incodel policy was entirely consistent. Moreover, it was highly successful as well. Pollution control was becoming a fact by 1946, to the amazement of those who had thought the port of Philadelphia would never cease to smell. While the reciprocal diversion laws had not worked out precisely as intended, no conflicts had as yet developed among the states over water allocation; and Incodel had headed off the principal threat, posed by New Jersey, of unilateral withdrawals. The Lehigh and Lackawaxen flood control projects, supported by Incodel, had been authorized by Congress and funds had been obtained for the Schuylkill River, while the New Jersey ship canal and the hydro power proposal had been rejected. Incodel had been only one force among many in the latter cases, but the fact that it was on the winning side indicated, at a minimum, that its goals were widely shared in the Valley.

Indeed, Incodel's principal problem appeared to lie in its very success. It had accomplished the original goals it had set for itself and, though it could speak with pride of things done, it was ominously silent with respect to things to come. A glance at the (very thin) 1947 Annual Report suggests the difficulty. The report describes the pollution program as accomplished and promises to "keep the wheels in motion" (page 11). It claims credit for the instructions by New Jersey and Pennsylvania to the Delaware River Joint Commission to prepare a port program and offers its cooperation "to the fullest possible limit" (page 12). And so forth. Its specific programs are all accomplished rather than prospective, an unusual position for an agency and one giving little reason for optimism regarding the future.

THE INCODEL PLAN FOR BASIN DEVELOPMENT

The 1948 Report, however, signalized a departure. The statement of Orus Matthews contained in this document has already been cited. His suggestion (that the states of New Jersey, New York, and Pennsylvania should, "after adequate study," consider the joint construction and operation of dams and reservoirs on the Delaware) presaged a change in the long-standing preference of Incodel for parallel state legislation and against the preparation of a comprehensive plan for the River.[29] It is difficult to determine with precision the reasons for Incodel's shift in attitude. In his study of Incodel, Maynard Hufschmidt suggests it may have been "plain luck, not crystal gazing," that caused the Commission to begin talk of a joint water supply project just before the severe drought hit New York City in the summer of 1949. It is not impossible that the change in direction was partially related to the shift in Incodel leadership with the death of Ellwood Turner and the selection of Francis Pitkin as the new chairman. But from the chronology of events it would appear that the most important factor was the impending decision of New York City to return to the Delaware in search of additional water supplies.

Interestingly enough, this decision was taken before the City had yet begun to withdraw water from the River in accordance with its original authorization. Construction of the three reservoirs authorized by the Court had been delayed first by the depression and then by the war, but by 1947 it was already obvious to the Board of Water Supply that the three reservoirs, when completed, would not fulfill New York City's requirements. Under authorization from the Board of Estimate in December, 1947, the Board of Water Supply restudied the possible water sources and in the fall of 1949 produced a recommendation for an additional reservoir, at Cannonsville on the west branch of the Delaware.[30] On January 26, 1950, the Board of Estimate

[29] Compare Matthews' statement with, for example, Incodel's *Second Progress Report, Regarding a Study of Multiple Purpose Development in the Delaware River Basin* (December 16, 1941).

[30] Compilation of studies to December 1, 1949, leading to recommendation of Third Stage of Delaware Water Supply Project, to Board of Consultants by Cannonsville, Division Engineer (typewritten report).

gave its approval and the Cannonsville plans were submitted to the New York State Water Power and Control Commission for final approval.

It is inconceivable that the Incodel staff members were unaware of these developments and their probable outcome. Simultaneously with New York's restudy, Incodel had proceeded with its own program. Following up the suggestion made in its 1948 Report, Incodel asked the 1949 sessions of the legislatures of New York, New Jersey, and Pennsylvania for funds to conduct studies preparatory to a comprehensive, Basin-wide plan of development. No funds were asked from Delaware, but appropriations of $70,000 each were obtained from the other three states. Rather than attempt to build up a staff of its own to conduct the survey, Incodel contracted with two engineering firms, Malcolm Pirnie Engineers and Albright and Friel, Inc., to prepare a plan.

After a preliminary report January 20, 1950, the two firms presented their final recommendations August 17, 1950, proposing a series of structures to be built in stages. Scheduled for immediate construction were three major dams: Cannonsville, a diversion dam at Barryville on the main stem, and Godeffroy on the lower Neversink and Basher Kill. An alternative was also offered: the construction of these three dams plus Wallpack Bend, a dam substituted for the original Tocks Island in a 1946 review of the "308 Report" by the Corps of Engineers. For construction in the second stage the report recommended two additional reservoirs at Fish's Eddy and Flat Brook, plus Wallpack Bend if not previously constructed. Principal benefits of the plan were water supply (465 mgd to New York City and northern New Jersey in the first stage) and stream flow regulation (a minimum flow at Trenton of 4,800 cfs if Wallpack Bend were included). An incidental product of the project would be the generation of hydroelectric power with an installed capacity of 56,130 kw.[31]

Incodel approved and adopted the recommendations of the report "in principle" at its annual meeting September 11, 1950. The report had also proposed in general terms the creation of a commission by interstate compact that would construct and operate these facilities. The Incodel leaders, with past failures in mind, at first were dubious of the compact approach, but with the active encouragement of Governor Driscoll of New Jersey they decided to take positive action. A committee was established with representation from the attorneys general of the four Valley states to draft such a compact, and Fred-

[31] Incodel, *Report on the Utilization of the Delaware.*

erick Zimmermann and Mitchell Wendell, consultants to the Council of State Governments, were engaged to assist in its preparation. A first weak draft was scrapped in favor of a revised and relatively strong compact which called for a commission that would include Delaware as well as the three states that sponsored the study. It was this compact proposal, adopting in principle the engineers' plan for the Delaware but not authorizing construction, that Incodel presented to the four states for action on January 15, 1951.[32]

CRITICISMS OF THE PLAN

As might have been expected, the plan drew vigorous opposition as well as widespread support. On its face, it was subject to attack on two major fronts: first, its physical features laid it open to criticism; and second, its proposal for an interstate compact was viewed with disfavor by some. As the campaign for adoption developed, eight individual issues came to the fore.

Opposition to Cannonsville

The classic objection to any water development plan has come from those whose lands are to be inundated by a particular project. In the case of the Incodel proposal the most vigorous opposition centered on the Cannonsville site. Municipalities, local governments, civic organizations, individual farmers, and businessmen in Delaware County protested that Cannonsville Reservoir, with others already built, would inundate the best farm land in the county, drive farmers from their homes, destroy the prosperous dairy industry, and transform the county into a land of lakes without an adequate tax base to meet the costs of government. Echoes of these complaints came from sportsmen's groups objecting to the destruction of fishing and hunting areas.

Resistance at Wallpack Bend

Less vociferous in their objections, but likewise opposed to the inundation of their property, were the residents of the area within the Wallpack Bend reservoir site. Chiefly affected was Pike County in

[32] Incodel, *Report Filed with Governors and Legislatures of Pennsylvania, New York, New Jersey and Delaware*, January 15, 1951. See also Hufschmidt, *The Supreme Court*, pp. 50-51.

Pennsylvania; lands would be flooded also on the New Jersey side of the River but this produced less complaint. The compact did not in itself authorize construction of a dam at Wallpack Bend, which was listed as an alternate in any case, but since it was scheduled for eventual construction, resistance to it was converted into opposition to the entire plan.

The Issue of Comprehensiveness

One of the criticisms of the Incodel plan was that it was not sufficiently comprehensive, in particular in its failure to give due consideration to the power potential of the basin.[33] An interesting feature of this avenue of attack was that it operated largely without publicity. An article by Ralph W. Page in the *Philadelphia Bulletin* on October 10, 1950, shortly after the Incodel report was made public, complained that it provided water releases only "for two specific purposes" and ignored flood control, navigation, fish and wildlife, power, pollution, and irrigation. This is, however, about the only public survivor of this line of criticism. As a result the proponents of the plan minimized the importance of this kind of opposition; many indeed were altogether unaware of it.[34] Yet it would appear that some persons at least, concerned with this aspect of the problem, exercised a behind-the-scenes influence against the Incodel plan. By their expression of doubts as to the quality of the plan of development, they served both to neutralize some "liberal-minded" political figures who might otherwise have supported the proposal, and to reinforce the opposition of others with their own reasons for doubting its worth.[35]

The Issue of Anti-Federal Bias

Connected closely with this criticism was the accusation that the Incodel approach unnecessarily rejected the possibility of federal cooperation in Delaware development. The anti-federal bias of many of Incodel's supporters was obvious; a favorable article in the *Saturday*

[33] Norman Wengert, *Natural Resources and the Political Struggle* (Garden City, N.Y.: Doubleday, 1955), pp. 48-49, makes this criticism.

[34] This conclusion rests upon interviews and extensive correspondence with the members of Incodel at the time, who were most generous with their assistance.

[35] This judgment is based upon examination of a confidential file of correspondence of one of the persons opposed to the plan. A detailed analysis of the weight to be accorded this type of opposition would require a more elaborate investigation of the private correspondence of the parties to the dispute.

Evening Post, for example, "Look What They're Doing to the Delaware," was subtitled: "This is one river the Federal project planners didn't get to first. An alliance of four sovereign states, with the aid of some engineering magic, is going to dam it, divert it, and store its waters—with no help from Uncle Sam needed." [36] Incodel did not itself foreclose the possibility of federal financial aid in the project. At the Commission's request Senator Hendrickson of New Jersey presented a resolution to the Senate Committee on Public Works early in 1950, asking the Corps of Engineers to review previous reports on the Delaware in the light of Incodel's report ". . . with the view of determining the extent and magnitude of the benefits which are in the national interest, of the water project recommended in the report of the Interstate Commission on the Delaware River Basin." [37] The wording was changed to conform to standard usage before adoption by the Committee, but the Corps understood it to require a report as to whether a federal contribution to the Incodel project was justifiable. A request for federal funds to support an interstate project was not, however, the kind of national-state cooperation envisaged by its advocates. It is noteworthy that Mayor Joseph Clark, silent during the controversy over the Incodel plan, later testified to his belief that the Incodel proposal was faulty in that it "was not sufficiently comprehensive in scope" and paid insufficient attention to the need for federal action.[38]

Hudson versus Delaware Water for New York City

One of the principal arguments used against the Cannonsville aspect of the plan rested on the conviction that New York City should obtain

[36] Sidney Shalett, "Look What They're Doing to the Delaware," *Saturday Evening Post,* September 30, 1950. The extent of Incodel's responsibility for the viewpoint expressed in Shalett's article was discussed in the testimony of Francis Pitkin before the House Committee on Government Operations, *Commission on the Organization of the Executive Branch of the Government* (*Water Resources and Power Report*), Part 1, Mt. Pocono, Pa., 84th Cong., 1st sess., pp. 95, 104-109. On the views of the Incodel group at the time, cf. Malcolm Pirnie, "Objectives of a National Water Policy," *Journal of the American Water Works Association,* XLIII (June, 1951), p. 409.

[37] Statement of Francis Pitkin, *Public Hearing on the Delaware River and Its Tributaries Held in Monroe County Court House, Stroudsburg, Pennsylvania* (Office of Philadelphia District Engineer, January, 1956).

[38] Testimony of Mayor Joseph S. Clark of Philadelphia, *Mt. Pocono Hearings,* pp. 23-24. Cf. his position as stated in the Corps of Engineers *Philadelphia Hearings,* pp. 21-26, and in his address to the 1957 Incodel Annual Meeting, "A Look Towards the Future of the Delaware River Basin," September 18, 1957.

its water from the Hudson River. A plan for a Hudson River water supply prepared by Lawrence T. Beck was endorsed by Delaware County interests as a protective move, and by the Citizens Budget Commission of New York City, in the belief it would be more economical. The Hudson River plan received additional support when, in a slightly different form, it was endorsed by an engineering subcommittee of the Mayor's Committee on Management Survey.[39] The Board of Water Supply, however, strongly opposed the use of Hudson water. This opposition was based partly upon a different estimate of cost—the Board insisted that the Hudson River source would be more expensive than the Delaware supply—and partly upon the polluted character of the Hudson. In the end the latter view prevailed, though not by such a margin as would warrant complete confidence in the outcome.

Pocono versus Delaware Water for Philadelphia

A somewhat similar problem involved the water supply of the City of Philadelphia. Many and varied solutions had been proposed over the years to the problem of improving that city's water supply. The Incodel plan did not itself propose a solution, but its adoption would guarantee that one of the alternatives involving use of a Delaware River water supply would be chosen.[40] The most strongly supported alternative proposal that would be thus precluded was the scheme of the Lehigh Coal and Navigation Company for a Pocono water supply for Philadelphia. This plan, which had been persistently but unsuccessfully advanced by the Company, involved the sale of Lehigh's water rights in the Lehigh River, held since 1822, to the city. Its advocates, principally the Lehigh Coal and Navigation Company itself, accordingly had ample reason to oppose the Incodel plan.

[39] Engineering Panel on Water Supply, *Future Water Sources of the City of New York* (July, 1951).

[40] Incodel, *Report on the Utilization of the Delaware*, pp. 7-8; discussions of the various alternatives proposed through the years can be found in *ibid.*, pp. 24-25, 75-76; Board of Consulting Engineers, *Preliminary Report: A New Water Supply from Upland Sources* (November, 1945); *idem, Report to the Philadelphia Water Commission: Development of an Upland Source of Water Supply and Suitability of Existing Sources of Supply with Augmented Facilities* (April, 1946); Bureau of Municipal Research, *Philadelphia's Water Supply* (June, 1946); and *Philadelphia Inquirer*, May 29, 1946, p. 21; June 5, 1946, p. 3; June 6, 1946, p. 25; June 27, 1946, p. 21; July 11, 1946, pp. 1, 34; September 2, 1946, p. 15; September 16, 1946, p. 17; September 22, 1946, B, p. 1; October 6, 1946, B, p. 1; November 13, 1946, p. 29.

Allocation of Water Supply

No particular controversy did or could center on the benefits promised by the Incodel plan in the form of stream flow regulation. It might be disputed whether the benefits were worth the cost, but no one would reject per se the values inherent in the increased minimum flow. Argument centered rather on the allocation of the increases in water supply, particularly for use outside the Valley. It will be remembered that this was the rock on which the two compacts of the 1920's had foundered. Three principal objections were made to the Incodel plan on this basis. (1) The allocation to New York City was too large —larger than the Supreme Court had considered equitable. (2) Since future withdrawals were made contingent on unanimous approval by the compact commission, New York would have its water supply needs taken care of, while Philadelphia would be dependent upon New York's approval for its own future needs. (3) A compact was inferior to action by the Court in that it would freeze water allocations left flexible by the Court's decree.[41] The last argument was most strongly advanced by William Schnader, Pennsylvania's counsel in the litigation before the Supreme Court.

Distribution of Costs among the States

This problem Incodel attempted to bypass in the campaign for its compact proposal. Although the engineering report had proposed a formula for apportioning costs incurred for stream flow regulation among the four states, the draft compact ignored the question, authorizing the compact commission to receive grants. In its letter of transmittal Incodel proposed that financing be left to later negotiation. This strategy of postponing the controversy over costs did not prove successful, as most individuals interested wanted to know what the cost would be before buying. It was generally assumed that the recommendations of the engineers' report would be acted upon and this assumption was made also by Incodel.[42]

[41] In various forms these criticisms will be found in Pennsylvania Water Resources Committee, Report (Harrisburg, February, 1953); William A. Schnader and Samuel A. Greeley, "The Delaware River Water Problem: Discussion of a Difficult Allocation Decision," Engineering News-Record, CLIV (January 13, 1955), pp. 35 et seq.; Address of Judge Grover C. Ladner to Greater Philadelphia-South Jersey Council, March 14, 1950 (mimeographed).

[42] Incodel, Report Filed with the Governors, p. 4; see also the address of Francis Pitkin at the Third Annual Meeting of the Pennsylvania Section, American Water Works Association, Philadelphia, September 20, 1951 (mimeographed).

In substance the engineers proposed that the costs of water supply "and compensation releases" be assigned to the purchasers of water supplies; the cost of stream flow regulation benefits would be prorated among the states by a formula, which would vary with the structures to be built. The objections were twofold. First, downstream interests were accustomed—under the Supreme Court decree—to the notion that if New York City wanted water from the Delaware it should provide compensation by contributing to minimum flows in the River. The Incodel engineers spoke also of charging the water supply users for "compensation releases" but the distinction between these and "stream flow regulation releases," chargeable to the downstream states, was by no means clear. Second, the benefits resulting from stream flow regulation were not measured by the engineers, the formula for the allocation of costs was essentially arbitrary, and the advantages resulting from stream flow regulation were not indisputably clear.

DEFEAT OF THE PLAN

In view of the public resistance it encountered, it is hardly surprising that the Incodel compact proposal met with difficulties in its consideration by the four state legislatures. More remarkable perhaps was the generally favorable reception accorded it. Delaware was the first state to act, ratifying unanimously. New Jersey followed suit with only limited opposition, chiefly from Democratic legislators along the river. New York, which had often enough ratified compacts later rejected in the other states, held back for a year waiting for Pennsylvania's approval. In 1952 the legislature voted to ratify and, despite an attempt by the Citizens Budget Commission to persuade the Governor to reject the measure, the compact was accepted by New York.

As more than once before, it was in Pennsylvania that the proposed compact faced its most serious opposition. The criticisms enumerated above applied there with greatest force. Governor Fine's first reaction to the proposal was to create a Pennsylvania Water Resources Committee to study the plan and appraise the water-resource needs of the state. He asked and received a legislative appropriation of $350,000 for the study, which continued on into 1953. In the meantime all legislative action on the proposal was suspended. New York City, declining to wait for what experience taught would be an indefinite period, filed a petition with the Supreme Court April 1, 1952, for modification of the 1931 decree to permit a diversion of 800 mgd. New York State filed in support on April 28, New Jersey answered May 8, and Pennsylvania joined May 15.

The two processes, negotiation among the parties to the Supreme Court case and consideration of the compact by Pennsylvania, continued simultaneously. In February of 1953 the Pennsylvania Water Resources Committee at length reported, recommending rejection of the Incodel plan. The reasons given were various, but the one most forcefully expressed was preference for a Pocono water supply source for Philadelphia. An attempt was made by the legislative leaders allied with Incodel to push the compact through, and the House of Representatives gave its approval (though, in deference to Pike County protests, without Wallpack Bend). The bill, however, died in Senate Committee because, it was said, of the opposition of Governor Fine.

The major issues sought to be disposed of by the compact were settled instead in the Supreme Court. Following the reopening of the case by New York City, the Court appointed Kurt F. Pantzer as Special Master to conduct hearings among the litigants and make recommendations to the Court. In his conduct of negotiations Pantzer placed heavy stress on securing agreement among the parties. New York City's petition requested permission to increase its diversion from the Delaware to 800 mgd and sought modification of the low-flow release schedule contained in the 1931 decree in the interest of simplifying operations. Both New Jersey and Pennsylvania raised vigorous objections. Early in 1953 New Jersey and New York reached an agreement that (1) New Jersey would consent to the 800 mgd diversion; (2) New Jersey would agree to a new formula for compensation releases, the "Montague Formula"; and (3) New York would consent to a diversion of 250 mgd by New Jersey for use outside the Delaware watershed.

Pennsylvania refused to join in this agreement, objecting to so large a diversion by New Jersey. Eventually, however, Pennsylvania agreed to an arrangement under which (1) New York would be allowed 800 mgd; (2) the Montague Formula would be adopted, but would be enforced by a river master appointed by the Court; (3) New Jersey would be allowed to divert 100 mgd without compensating releases; (4) New Jersey agreed to the repeal of an interstate compact of 1783 prohibiting a dam on the main stem of the Delaware between Pennsylvania and New Jersey; (5) New Jersey also agreed to exercise the power of eminent domain on Pennsylvania's behalf should that state wish to build a dam (at Wallpack Bend); and (6) all parties agreed

that New York's diversion was not to be considered a prior appropriation, nor was it to prohibit Pennsylvania from later applying to the
Supreme Court to reduce the New York diversion, without regard to
the investment of the City in the Cannonsville Reservoir.[43]
A special session of the New Jersey Legislature late in the year
fulfilled the commitments made by the state in the Supreme Court
proceedings. On June 7, 1954, the Supreme Court, without opinion,
adopted the decree as agreed upon among the party states and recommended by the Master. With no further ado the Incodel compact
was abandoned. In a belated postscript the Philadelphia District
Office of the Corps of Engineers in the spring of 1955, more than a
year after the last active discussion of the compact, at last completed
the review of the "308 Report" as affected by the Incodel plan. The
report was unfavorable to any federal expenditure and was submitted
to the North Atlantic Division Engineer on May 27, 1955. It was this
adverse review report that was awaiting action in the office of the Division Engineer when Hurricanes Connie and Diane struck the Delaware Basin. The review report was thereupon returned to the District
Engineer for reconsideration, and the sequence of events that resulted
in the Delaware Basin survey was set under way.[44]

CONCLUSIONS

During the last four years there has been considerable ferment in
the Delaware Basin. The Corps of Engineers has launched its far-
reaching survey. The governors of the four Valley states and the
mayors of New York City and Philadelphia have organized the Delaware River Basin Advisory Committee. A group of leading citizens,
stimulated by the DRBAC, have established the Water Research
Foundation for the Delaware River Basin, which in turn has fostered
the creation of the citizen-supported Water Resources Association.
The Committee and the Foundation have sponsored the study which
led to this report. These give every appearance of being significant
events, but they are current developments and their true import cannot be assayed this early. Let us, therefore, return to the end of the
foregoing account for conclusions regarding the nature and importance of developments in the Delaware Basin. The perspective on

[43] See discussion in Hufschmidt, *Supreme Court*, pp. 54-65; *Philadelphia Inquirer*,
June 22, 1953.
[44] U.S. Army Engineer District, Philadelphia, *Data Book: Survey of the Delaware
River Basin Water Resources* (Philadelphia, April 1, 1957), p. 2-1.

1956 is much sounder than that on 1960. And let us, without intention to appraise the events of the last four years, nevertheless employ the present tense.

The history of the efforts to bring order to the water resources of the Delaware Basin supports five major conclusions. First, despite the high hopes originally held by its sponsors, the Interstate Commission on the Delaware River Basin has played only a narrowly defined role in the development of the River. In Chapter 4 seven major categories of programs were described as appropriate responsibilities of a Basin-wide agency. Of these Incodel has sought to perform only one in full, that of representation and information. It has conducted a limited research program, and has attempted to coordinate state quality control activities. But when a plan for river development was needed, it delegated the task to private engineering firms. Incodel has avoided all operating programs, and in its compact plan proposed to create a new interstate commission to carry out the construction and operation of river control works rather than seeking to broaden its own duties.

Second, there is no comprehensive plan for the use or management of the water resources of the Basin, or for the integration of water-related activities, or for the economic development of the Valley as it is dependent on or conditioned by water resources. There has, indeed, been only one effort at comprehensive planning for the Basin's water, and many would question the application of "comprehensive" to that attempt. In any event, it proved abortive when the Incodel plan failed to win approval.

Third, there is no single agency for the management of the Basin's water resources. As has been noted, the only Basin-wide agency concerned with water, Incodel, has never aspired to the role of operating entity. The interstate commission provided for by the Incodel plan might have evolved into such an agency, but it, too, went into limbo with the failure of the plan. Meanwhile the task of water-resources administration is great and growing, as the evidence on every hand discloses. Meanwhile also the gap between regional needs and regional capacity to administer grows ever wider.

Fourth, the history of the Basin richly illustrates the difficulties inherent in any effort to launch a significant action program through interstate consensus. For literally decades the cooperation of the states in a Basin-wide program has been sought through interstate compact, but to no avail. Among those who would like to see the states play a vital part in the further development of the Basin are some who feel that "the times have changed," that the states would "go along" on an interstate compact if given the chance in the early 1960's. This may or may not be true, though the thesis is about to be tested. The history of the Basin does not afford much ground for optimism that a meaningful new interstate compact proposal will find early favor.

Fifth, a review of Delaware Basin efforts to organize for water-resources administration may be summarized in the observation that regional leadership has not rallied to that standard. This is not to say that the required leadership is not present, but only that its sense of urgency has not been touched nor its imagination challenged. The problem obviously is to present the needs and the opportunities of Basin water-resources development in a way that will first engage the attention and then enlist the support of those in positions to influence the course of public action. Clearly this has not been done success-fully in times past.

To summarize, progress toward bringing the Delaware Basin's water resources under control has been considerably less than satisfactory. Specifically, progress has not been satisfactory since the first halting step toward interstate cooperation, taken almost twenty-five years ago. The Basin requires action a good deal more energetic than any it has seen thus far. The call to such action is the challenge of the 1960's for the people of the Delaware Valley.

CHAPTER 16

Operating a Basin Control System

WHEN a basin control system goes into operation, two types of direct limitations to operations already exist. The first is the physical design, some features of which have been mandated by authorizing legislation, the second the political and economic conditions that have been laid down by court decree, law, compact, or administrative agreements. Two categories of work comprise the administration of the system. On the one hand a body of operating procedures and rules must be developed. Some of these will be of a nature suited to publication and circulation among affected parties. Others will be of an internal character and thus adapted to codification or to practice as standing, unwritten procedures. In the aggregate they will cover all purposes of the system and all directly related subjects. Since they are subject to modification in the face of changing conditions, they must be given continuing attention. On the other hand the system must be managed in accordance with the practices and purposes agreed upon at any one time. These are the tasks of actual water control that a new Delaware Basin agency might have—the core function of water administration.

A complete system of water control would include management of reservoirs and dams, ground water recharging, quality standards or minima by areas, quality monitoring, conditions of withdrawals (by whom, where, when, how much), monitoring of withdrawals, and flood-warning measures. So closely intertwined are all these phases that a single decision-making center is by all odds best suited to dealing with them. Such a system of comprehensive controls would mirror the familiar principle of hydrologic unity.

"Total control," however, has never been achieved in the United States, because (among other reasons) water shortages have never been great enough to justify the enormous capital outlays, the surrender of some functions by various governmental agencies, and the close administrative supervision that would be entailed. As water uses multiply during the next half century and as problems become more complex, establishment of such centralized administration of water controls throughout a basin will come to be regarded as more and more sensible.

In the following pages the means employed in the Tennessee, Missouri, Columbia, and Ohio basins to control water in the channel are described. Then there is a general discussion of administration of control over withdrawals and diversions in certain western states. Finally, the situation in the Delaware Valley under the terms of the 1954 Supreme Court decree is outlined. In each of these cases a very general water control formula or set of priorities has been laid down by a basic legal authority, and an administrative agency to carry out the terms of the formula has been provided, implicitly or explicitly, by the same authority. The language of the formula helps to determine the latitude of discretion available to the administrative agent. Many other factors, including especially the attitudes of affected governmental agencies, also have influence. And there are physical determinants, such as the question of the portion of the watershed subject to control through existing structures.

CONTROL OF WATER IN THE CHANNEL

The Tennessee

There are more reservoirs under one agency on the Tennessee than on any other river. A high degree of multiple-purpose basin-wide control is exercised by the Tennessee Valley Authority. The River Control Branch in the Division of Water Control Planning, Office of Engineering, is the specific staff charged with the management of TVA dams. In its work it is guided by the priorities set up in TVA's organic act: navigation, flood control, and electric power generation.

In discharging its water control responsibilities, the TVA brings into play as an integrated system the thirty [now 31] major dams on the Tennessee River and its tributaries. The annual cyclical pattern of rainfall and runoff, established by exhaustive analysis over the history of a century, governs the operation of the system. Operating guides called "rule curves," one for each storage reservoir in the system, show in graphic form the limits of fill and drawdown which can be allowed for a particular reservoir throughout the year. These guides and their use in the whole system of multiple-purpose reservoirs are probably the most distinctive characteristic of TVA water control operations.[1]

The River Control Branch performs these functions: (1) collects rainfall and stream flow data; (2) analyzes these data; and (3) applies the data to the current conditions to determine where it is necessary to impound or release water to maintain desired river flows and to produce other planned effects.[2] The general character of the priorities under which the branch operates provides it with wide limits of discretion within which to decide specifically when to release water.

The Main Stem of the Missouri

Apart from the Missouri Basin Inter-Agency Committee, but made possible by the atmosphere of expedient cooperation fostered by that body, is the system by which the five main-stem reservoirs are operated. The Corps of Engineers has legal responsibility for these dams, and the Omaha Division Engineer (Corps) operates the dams for all purposes. He is, however, regularly advised by a coordinating committee of seven federal agency representatives and nine state water engineers (Minnesota has not found it necessary to join).

The Committee functions through general meetings, usually twice a year, and through interim contacts with and reports from the Reservoir Control Center. An annual meeting is held, usually in September, to review tentative Annual Operating Plan schedules which have been prepared during August by the Reservoir Control Center. At this meeting the views of all interests are given full consideration, and a specific set of advance operating plans is agreed upon and finalized by the Committee as a basis for actual operations. A second Committee meeting usually is held in April of each year to review actual operations subsequent to the preceding August meeting, to discuss operations during the remainder of the year based on April 1 forecasts and revise the operating plan if necessary, and to outline operational objectives to be considered by the Reservoir Control Center in setting up the tentative operating plans for consideration at the September meetings. In addition,

---

[1] Harry Wiersema, "The River Control System," in Roscoe C. Martin (ed.), *TVA: The First Twenty Years*, pp. 91-92. See also Tennessee Valley Authority, *TVA, 1958: Twenty-fifth Anniversary Year*, pp. 28 ff. During fiscal 1958 a small electronic digital computer was used by this staff for the first time.

[2] Harry Wiersema, *op. cit.*, p. 93. The Tennessee's river control system was appraised in Chapter 14, in connection with an evaluation of the Tennessee Valley Authority.

special meetings are held to consider possible modifications of previously adopted Annual Operating Plans if unforeseen conditions that might warrant important modifications should arise.[3]

The annual operating plans are based upon predicted demands and operational requirements for all purposes during the coming year. They conclude

> . . . with specific operating proposals which are 'tailor made' for optimum coordination of the available water supply with water demands and operational requirements. These proposals are summarized into detailed month-by-month schedules of storage contents, releases, and power generation rates for each main stem reservoir and the system. In other words, they outline just where the water will be kept in storage at any given time, just what power plants will meet what portions of the system loads at any time, and just how water will be released from each reservoir at various times throughout the year.[4]

Similar coordinating committees are planned for the tributary basins, and they will be represented on the main coordinating committee through state and federal representatives already sitting there. For example, there is such a coordinating group for the Republican River, with members from the Corps, the Bureau, the Public Health Service, the Fish and Wildlife Service, and three states. In 1958, similar agencies existed also for the Kansas and North Platte Rivers and for the Boysen and Canyon Ferry Dams.

Prosecution of the annual operating plan for the main-stem dams then is turned over to the Reservoir Regulating Section (usually called the Reservoir Control Center). This staff, which is part of the Omaha Division office of the Corps, has 11 employees; in addition, there are about 20 other part-time workers in the district offices. The staff

> . . . acts as the information gatherer and base of activities for the members of the Coordinating Committee. It prepares advance estimates of main stem water supply, consolidates advance estimates of water supply requirements, and drafts up advance Annual Operating Plans for consideration of the Coordinating Committee. Then, after the Operating Plans are finalized by the Coordinating Committee, the Reservoir Control Center directs actual execution of the details of operation, by preparing and issuing daily schedules of water releases and power gen-

[3] R. J. Pafford, Jr., "Operation of Missouri River Main Stem Reservoirs," *Journal of the Waterways and Harbors Division, Proceedings of the American Society of Civil Engineers,* LXXXIII (September, 1957), Proc. Paper 1370, pp. 7-8.

[4] *Ibid.,* p. 5.

eration rates for each of the reservoirs and power plants in the system. It is this latter activity which converts the broad monthly-average schedules of the Annual Operating Plan into the actual day-to-day fulfillment of the various water and power requirements which it has previously been agreed will be met.[5]

For power scheduling purposes, the Section is in daily and often hourly contact with the Bureau of Reclamation power grid headquarters at Watertown, South Dakota. The Section is equipped with teletype, radio-telephone, and electronic data-processing equipment. The chief of the Section recently stated that the following priorities are followed in the annual operating plans:[6] (1) flood control; (2) "irrigation and other upstream tributary water uses"; (3) "downstream urban water supply and stream sanitation requirements"; (4) navigation and generation of power; and (5) "recreation, fish and wildlife and other secondary purposes."

There appears to be consensus among officials in the Basin that the control system, as a mechanism for coordination, works very well. It has blurred or softened the traditional Corps-Bureau rivalry or at least minimized its influence in the operation of the main-stem system. There have been some conflicts over main-stem reservoir operations since the Section began its work, but these have been attributed largely to under-average precipitation in the early years of operation.

In evaluating the Missouri control system, it must be emphasized that the Corps is the responsible authority and that its jurisdiction consists mainly of the five big main-stem dams. The assignment of main-stem river control to the Corps, however, directly affects neither the authority of other agencies in other fields nor water management on the tributaries. In these circumstances, general priorities stated by law can hardly be expected to eliminate basin-wide conflicts of interest among regions, states, or agencies. And the same observation applies to centralized administration of reservoir operations. Such centralized operation permits a broad and intelligent view of all water needs and provides a means of reconciliation of those needs through storage and release decisions. Thus are avoided duplication of effort and openly conflicting operating policies among different agencies. Yet such an arrangement can hardly harmonize all conflicting views. *Dominant* views will be incorporated in such operations, else the mechanism will not survive in a democratic administrative environment. Dissatisfaction, however, on the part of a few interests is to be expected, and

[5] *Ibid.*, p. 8.
[6] *Ibid.*, pp. 6-7.

their appeal to higher authority is probably an inevitable consequence of the operation of such a control mechanism.[7]

The Main Stem of the Columbia

On the Columbia River, unlike either the Tennessee or the Missouri, main-stem reservoir control is not centralized in the hands of one agency. Instead, it is divided among the Corps of Engineers, the Bureau of Reclamation, and the Bonneville Power Administration. That serious difficulties were likely to emerge from such a division, particularly with the construction of additional reservoirs on the main stem and tributaries, was recognized by the Columbia Basin Inter-Agency Committee (CBIAC) in 1950 when it set up a task force to investigate the problem and recommend a solution. That body commented to this effect:

> Efficient management of the water resources of the Columbia Basin requires bringing together and reconciling the requirements of the several different purposes served by the rivers. The problem is complex for a number of reasons. In some cases these requirements are of a conflicting nature; in others, though conflict is not involved, the adjustment of water management to all purposes which can be served may greatly increase the sum total of benefits.
>
> The main purposes of multi-purpose projects in the Columbia Basin are navigation, flood control, irrigation, and power. Such interests as soil conservation, fish and wildlife, pollution abatement, recreation and others have a subsidiary, but often important, bearing on how the rivers are managed.
>
> Reconciliation of the various viewpoints involved in river management is relatively simple at the present time, with only two Federal multi-purpose projects in operation on the main stem of the Columbia. However, this becomes more difficult as new projects are added. The large increase in the number of plants comprising the Federal system in the next decade will greatly increase the complexity of river management operations and will make more difficult the achievement of maximum economies possible. . . .[8]

The task force further contended that agreements by the Corps of Engineers and the Bureau of Reclamation with the Bonneville Power

---

[7] See Arthur Maass, *Muddy Waters*, p. 256, for elaboration and criticism of this point.

[8] Quoted by A. F. Darland in "Flood Control Operation on the Columbia River," *Minutes for Joint Meeting of the Columbia Basin (97th) and Missouri Basin (101st) Inter-Agency Committees,* June 25-26, 1958, Appendix E.

Administration affecting the operation of power plants at Corps and Reclamation dams were inadequate, and that multi-lateral rather than bi-lateral coordination was required.

The present machinery for coordination of river operations is cumbersome and unwieldy. It is incomplete in that it takes no organizational cognizance of the requirements of interests other than those represented by the agencies primarily concerned. Failure to remedy these defects may jeopardize full realization of the benefits which may be derived from the large investment the Federal Government is making in the Pacific Northwest.[9]

The task force recommended establishment of a water management subcommittee to coordinate the needs of all concerned. Approved by the CBIAC in 1951, the subcommittee now consists of a chairman and one member each from the Bonneville Power Administration, Corps of Engineers, Federal Power Commission, and Public Health Service; the Departments of Commerce, Interior, and Agriculture; and the states of Idaho, Montana, Oregon, and Washington. It has a technical staff of about four engineers in Portland, but much of the work is done by the subcommittee itself. There was an average of more than nine meetings per year from 1951 to 1958.

The subcommittee's planning for flood control and other operations is supplemented by inter-agency operating agreements between the Corps and Bureau and, in one case, between these agencies and the Bonneville Power Administration. Thus operating procedures are aimed at maximizing benefits at reservoirs which are the legal responsibility of different federal agencies. The inter-agency operating agreements and the water management subcommittee device thus represent a counterpart to the reservoir control center and coordinating committee procedure used on the Missouri. Further, the arrangements fulfill similar functions; that is, they attempt to coordinate river control operations in the interests of the major beneficiaries.

The Corps of Engineers and the Bureau of Reclamation are wellestablished in the Columbia Basin, and it would be hard to displace either from reservoir control simply by a theoretical demonstration of advantages that centralized operations in the hands of a single agency would bring. Whether these two major agencies can operate their growing number of reservoirs in a way that will integrate operations so as to maximize benefits for all purposes is doubtful. That dual or multiple control of reservoirs can approach the efficiency possible

[9] *Ibid.*, p. 6.

under unitary control, even with the aid of new techniques, is highly unlikely.

The Ohio

In the Ohio River Basin the only control over the river is exercised by the Corps of Engineers. Primary statutory authority stems from the Flood Control Act of 1938, which authorized the first stages of planning for flood control and allied purposes in the Ohio Valley. Unlike the Tennessee, Missouri, or Columbia systems, there are no flood control or storage reservoirs on the main stem of the Ohio.[10] Storage and release of water for controlling floods and releases for low-flow augmentation in the interest of stream sanitation, water supply, navigation, and other purposes is achieved by means of nearly 40 reservoirs on major tributaries, such as the Allegheny, the Monongahela, the Beaver, and the Muskingum.

Moreover, operations are not centralized in one office, but are under the authority of the four district offices of the Ohio River Division of the Corps. Ordinarily, standing guides for each of the tributary reservoirs govern storage and release procedures. Where purposes and thus alternatives are limited, standing guides apparently work very satisfactorily. In exceptional circumstances, special instructions may issue from the District Office with jurisdiction over the area where the reservoirs are located. The Division Office at Cincinnati is not a control center, except in the general sense that the Division Engineer commands the district offices. There are, however, no other agencies with substantial power to manipulate river flows; so coordinating operations in time of flood is relatively easy.

On these four great rivers control of water in the channel is a dramatic function, chiefly because there are systems of large reservoirs which exert major influences on the regular flows of the rivers. Yet the need for exercise of the control function is not limited to such situations. On all American rivers, it may be safely surmised, the seasonal variation in flows and the occurrence of water demands at points not served by sources immediately available in sufficient quantities mean that exercise of controls something like those described here will always be desirable and sometimes necessary. The systems outlined were not chosen as models, but as examples of way stations along the road all river basins ultimately will be forced to travel.

[10] The Corps is replacing some of the low main-stem dams with somewhat higher ones at which power generation may be possible.

CONTROL OF WITHDRAWALS AND DIVERSIONS

The best examples of control of withdrawals and diversions come from the dry West. The typical western water master performs a function tightly restricted in scope, a fact traceable in part to the unique character of western water law. Basic authority for the water master's work is ordinarily *state* law and court and administrative interpretations. Through these channels rights to use water are created; it is the prime business of the water masters to distribute or oversee distribution of water in fixed quantities to irrigators and other users.

The mechanism for selecting water masters varies greatly from state to state. In Idaho water districts, they are usually elected by owners of water rights. In Oklahoma they are appointed by the State Engineer with the approval of the Governor. After streams are adjudicated the California Department of Water Resources appoints most of the water masters in that state, while boards of directors of water improvement districts appoint them in Texas. The courts appoint "water commissioners" in Montana. And there are other methods.[11]

The nature of the appointing authority and the character of the continuing supervision over the water master have great bearing on the job he performs. As an appointive administrative official in Oklahoma, he appears to have some discretion in distributing water. He has policing powers over users who violate state laws. In Montana, where a court appoints him, fixes his term and pay, and adjudicates rights to the water he measures and distributes, he might be termed a judicial administrator. His discretion there seems to be somewhat more limited than elsewhere.

Idaho's District No. 36 on the Snake River is a case where geographic jurisdiction is so great and authority of the water master so general that he exercises wide discretionary powers. This District covers 1,175,000 acres or about one-half the irrigated land of the State (an area one-eighth the size of the Delaware Basin). Users an-

[11] See Lynn Crandall (District Engineer, U.S. Geological Survey and Snake River Water Master), "River Operation on Snake River, Idaho" (unpublished manuscript, n.d.), p. 1; *Oklahoma Statutes Annotated, Title 82;* "Water Masters," *Water Code,* State of California (1955), Chap. 3, Sec. 4050, p. 82; *Vernon's Civil Statutes of Texas,* Art. 7652; and Howard W. Heman, "Water Rights under the Law of Montana," *Montana Law Review,* X (Spring, 1949), pp. 22, 32-34. There are perhaps exceptions to these generalizations in all states. For example, in California the "water superintendent" of the Modesto Irrigation District is a regular employee of this old (1887) agency.

nually elect as water master the District Engineer of the U.S. Geological Survey, who is permitted by the Secretary of the Interior to hold both federal and state positions. Among his duties are the measurement of stream flows, reservoir storage levels, and precipitation. The water master operates ". . . under the general jurisdiction of the State Reclamation Department but [he also has] certain individual powers and authority of his own." He is advised by a Committee of Nine, representing different sections of the Valley. "He has to deliver the water according to the court decrees and state law, . . . and if he does a reasonably satisfactory job his water-users continue to elect him year after year. . . ." [12]

In none of these cases is provision made for formal policy-making or determination of individual water rights by the water master. That officer may order reservoir releases, but these are defined in terms of small and precise allocations over which he has no control. His ministerial status is further emphasized by the fact that the larger dams related to his operations are frequently under direct control of the Bureau of Reclamation or some other similar administrative agency.

In the East there are a few instances where state administrators perform tasks similar to those of western water masters. Two cases directly in point are found in New Jersey and New York. The New Jersey Department of Conservation and Economic Development since 1941 has been able to designate areas where diversion of ground water ". . . exceeds or threatens to exceed, or otherwise threatens or impairs, the natural replenishment of such waters, . . ." [13] and by the use of licensing power to control diversions of over 100,000 gpd in those localities. The law stemmed from the threat of salt water intrusion under coastal lands, and apparently it has operated in the Camden, Atlantic City, and other areas to forestall that threat. The possibility of extending similar controls to cover surface water diversions has been discussed in New Jersey in the past year or so. There is a chance that such an extension may occur in connection with irrigation and other primarily consumptive uses. In New York the Water Power and Control Commission for more than 20 years has had authority over ground water withdrawals on Long Island similar to that exercised by New Jersey.[14] Exertion by the states of fuller authority

[12] Lynn Crandall, *op. cit.*

[13] Chap. 375, P.L. 1947, amended by Chap. 195, P.L. 1951.

[14] Conservation Department, State of New York, *28th Annual Report of the Water Power and Control Commission* (Albany, December 31, 1954), gives a good idea of the scope of this task in recent years.

over water use may have to await a thorough revision of their systems of water law. Vested rights in surface waters are a major block to early or drastic change in the present system of judicial control of water use, which rests chiefly on the doctrine of riparian rights.

THE DELAWARE RIVER MASTER

On the Delaware River the control function centers on the upper reaches of the river.[15] The Office of River Master of the Delaware River was established in 1954 by the U.S. Supreme Court to oversee its revised decree permitting New York City eventually to take up to 800 mgd from the Basin.[16] This diversion is conditioned upon the city's releasing from its two (soon to be increased to three) reservoirs sufficient water to maintain flows downstream that are defined in terms of the so-called "Montague release formula." The River Master, an officer of the Supreme Court, performs functions similar to those of many western water masters, although potentially his duties are somewhat broader in scope.

The lengthy list of duties specified for the River Master in the decree narrow in practice to three: (1) overseeing New York City diversions from the Basin out of Pepacton and Neversink reservoirs (and, when completed, the new Cannonsville reservoir); (2) checking a New Jersey extra-Basin diversion through the Delaware and Raritan Canal; and (3) ordering and checking on releases from the New York dams to maintain a minimum flow of 1525 cfs (1750 cfs with Cannonsville completed) at the Montague gauge of the U.S. Geological Survey.[17] The first of these tasks consists of receiving daily reports from the outlet gauges on the New York City reservoirs. The second concerns the decree provision that New Jersey may take a monthly average of 100 mgd, but that no day's diversion may exceed 120 mg. It is performed by means of a gauge at Kingston, New Jersey. The third task involves daily study of readings from about six Geological

[15] There are 2585 square miles of basin above the Montague gauge from which flow is completely uncontrolled by the River Master, out of a total of 3480 square miles.

[16] 347 U.S. 995.

[17] From June 15 each year for a period of 120 days excess releases are computed at 83 per cent of the amount by which New York City's estimated demand in that year is less than its estimated continuous safe yield from all sources obtainable without pumping. This computation yields a flow rate in cubic feet per second which, multiplied by time, results in the total volume of water (cubic feet) available for excess release.

Survey gauges and the Montague gauge, occasional readings from several other gauges, and data from private utilities operating reservoirs on upstream tributaries. With these data and with U.S. Weather Bureau forecasts three days in advance, daily determination is made as to the need for releases in order to secure the required minimum flows. Orders for releases may occur daily during the summer months, and they are made three days in advance because of the time required for water from the farthest reservoir, Pepacton, to arrive at Montague.

This office is directly under the Water Resources Division of the Geological Survey, and the present River Master is a retired Chief Hydraulic Engineer of the Survey. His is a part-time job, but he has two full-time engineers on duty in Milford, Pennsylvania, across from Montague, New Jersey. An estimated total annual budget of $40,000, which includes payments for the services of Survey district offices nearby, is divided equally by the Survey among New York City, Pennsylvania, New Jersey, and Delaware.

An advisory committee was established soon after his appointment by the present River Master. This committee meets once each year to review operations and to advise the River Master. Its members include the President of the New York City Board of Water Supply, the Secretary of Forests and Waters of Pennsylvania, the Chief of the Division of Water Power and Control of New York State's Conservation Department, the State Geologist of Delaware, and the Director of the Division of Water Policy and Supply of the New Jersey Department of Conservation and Economic Development. The meetings of the advisory committee are reportedly amiable and constructive.

The relationship between the Milford office and New York City officials is said to be a cordial and cooperative one, and indeed there is continuous contact between them, ordinarily by telephone. Relationships with operating officials elsewhere also seem to be generally satisfactory. The one instance thus far of overt disagreement may reflect more upon the general politics of water in the Basin than upon the specific operation of the office of the River Master. On July 18, 1957, Delaware's Attorney General and on November 14, 1957, New Jersey's Deputy Attorney General charged that New York City had not lived up to the terms of the 1954 decree, in that it had failed to make the mandatory releases from its reservoirs.[18]

The President of the New York City Board of Water Supply pointed

[18] *New York Times,* November 14, 1957.

out that the city had followed the River Master's directions as to the amount of releases and contended that the Master's control over reservoir releases was administrative and not ministerial in character.[19] The facts were well known by the advisory committee and by other officials in all four Basin states. In simple truth the downstream flow of the River was quite low. In explanation, the River Master characterized 1957 as a year of "severe drought." [20] It is important to note that the maximum release possible, with reservoirs full and all gates wide open, is 1114 cfs (Pepacton, 781 cfs; Neversink, 333 cfs). Thus it is impossible for New York City to meet the requirements of the 1954 decree in extremely dry weather (when little flow is added between the reservoirs and Montague) until the Cannonsville dam comes into operation, at which time total releases possible from the three dams will be somewhat greater than the minimum flow at Montague required by the decree.

The 1957 incident suggests that as needs for water increase, more serious conflicts may arise over the Master's powers. Furthermore, in the absence of more complete court definition of his powers, it is evident that his discretion might become very broad. Already by the 1954 decree he is empowered to

> Conserve the waters in the river, its tributaries and in any reservoirs maintained in the Delaware River watershed by the City of New York or any which may hereafter be developed by any of the other parties thereto, . . .[21]

Maynard M. Hufschmidt suggests:

> Although the primary function of the River Master is to control the water diversions and releases along the river in accordance with the Court decree, it is possible that he may serve a wider function—that of promoting understanding and agreement among the states and even encouraging the preparation of basin-wide plans by the states acting cooperatively. The potential utility of this river master device for pro-

[19] *New York Times*, November 14, 1957.

[20] *Report of the River Master of the Delaware River for the Period December 1, 1956-November 30, 1957* (Washington, D.C.: Office of the Delaware River Master, April 1958), pp. 13, *passim*.

[21] 347 U.S. 995 at 1003. An instance of the exercise of these powers is the salinity investigation program for the estuary in which the River Master's Office has cooperated with the Geological Survey, the State of Delaware, and Philadelphia since 1955. Work at Milford has consisted mainly of collating and preparing an annual report.

moting interstate agreement on river basin plans is extremely great and remains to be explored.[22]

One may, of course, voice a serious doubt as to whether this is technically the type of function a court or its officer can perform well, or indeed whether it is wise public policy for a court to attempt to perform it at all. The Supreme Court itself has expressed these doubts.[23] A modified role for the River Master may emerge from the studies currently under way in the Basin, and it is not impossible that the office will be abolished. In the event a new control system should derive from present interest in the Delaware or from the recommendations made in this report (see below, Chapter 18), it is entirely possible that the Supreme Court would vacate its 1954 decree which provided that "Any of the parties hereto . . . may apply at the foot of this decree for other or further action or relief. . . ."[24] The Court undoubtedly would be willing to withdraw from administrative activity if it could be certain that the four Basin states were in agreement on creating a new, comprehensive control system for the River. It will be remembered that agreement by the states was an important prior condition to the 1954 decree.[25]

The Delaware River Master differs in important respects from western water masters. The latter have little discretion, since water rights are determined elsewhere. They form a specialized class of officialdom, as necessary to the distribution of water as policemen are to traffic control. Court-appointed masters like the one on the Delaware are created because of circumstances which require judicial control in the absence of legislative or administrative action.

The Delaware River Master differs also from other control agencies that have been discussed here, in that he is responsible to the Supreme Court and has not yet ventured (or found it necessary) to exercise the discretion characteristic of the control agents on the Tennessee, Missouri, Columbia, or Ohio. Nevertheless there are strong likenesses

[22] *The Supreme Court*, p. 72.

[23] *New York* v. *New Jersey*, 256 U.S. 296, and *Colorado* v. *Kansas*, 320 U.S. 383, 392, quoted in Hufschmidt, *op. cit.*, pp. 72-3.

[24] 347 U.S. 995 at 1005.

[25] Maynard M. Hufschmidt, *op. cit.*, p. 64. State courts have, like the U.S. Supreme Court, occasionally appointed masters to investigate disputes over water distribution. In at least one case a river master has been appointed by a state court to perform functions not unlike those of his prototype on the Delaware. *Hidalgo County Water Improvement District, No. 2* v. *Cameron County Water Control and Improvement District, No. 5*, 250 S.W. 2d 941, Texas Civ. App., 1952.

between the Milford, Pennsylvania, office and, for example, the Reservoir Regulating Section in the Omaha office of the Corps of Engineers. Engineers at both locations are engaged in continuous examination of available amounts of water, prediction of future availability, and ordering of releases from structures to obtain river levels demanded by higher authorities.

SUMMARY

From the experiences examined in this chapter several conclusions useful to administrators of future basin control systems in the East may be drawn. An underlying assumption of fundamental importance is that a logical accompaniment to planning and building a multiple-purpose basin development is an arrangement for unified administration. In the cases reviewed here, important missing elements preclude characterization of the control systems as comprehensive or unified— geographic jurisdictions do not include entire basins, some important uses of water are not considered, major dams are not within the operating schemes. In the Tennessee Valley the tests of basin-wide jurisdiction and complete control structure coverage are met, but even there the Corps of Engineers' supernumerary flood control function and the absence of control over ground and surface water uses are important limitations. Knowledge of ground water characteristics everywhere is still too sketchy, while the peculiar nature of eastern water law blocks effective control of withdrawals so that truly comprehensive control is currently impossible to attain in the East. Nevertheless the trend is in the direction of vesting the unified management of a system of control structures in a single agent or agency as a means of exercising basin-wide control over water-in-the-channel. Where weaknesses exist, they point to the need for unified direction.

Second, the constant need for complete and accurate basic data has been re-emphasized. In every basin the services of the Weather Bureau, the Geological Survey, and other federal and state agencies are continuously used. Their advice about daily operating problems is vital. Communication with them must remain open. In addition, contacts with other local, state, and national agencies are part of the usual pattern. The advisory or coordinating committee is the standard medium for this purpose.

Most important of all, however, is the finding that there are American experiences concerning a number of aspects of the theoretical concept of comprehensive control. On the basis of these experiences, and perhaps others that may be discovered abroad, future administration of water resources in the East must be erected.

CHAPTER 17

Lessons from American Experience

AMERICA's experience in river basin administration, though uneven and inconclusive, has many lessons for those who would approach the problem of water-resource management from the point of view of regional action. The Colorado, the Missouri, the Columbia, the Ohio, the Miami, the Arkansas, the Tennessee—all these and others contribute to the reservoir of history from which useful generalizations about river valley organization may be drawn. This experience may be examined under the following headings: inhibitors of regional action, inducers of regional action, conclusions regarding river basin organization, and transferability of regional experience.

INHIBITORS OF REGIONAL ACTION

Among the many obstacles confronting those who have sought to approach basin-wide problems through a regional organization, the most persistent perhaps is found in the amorphous and undefined character of the river basin. The watershed (of whatever size) is a hydrologic concept, and as such has a sound scientific base; but it is not a base readily related to the experiences of most people. One result is the absence of a regional awareness on the part of the public. The residents of a given river city do not understand that what happens to them, with respect to such common aberrations as floods and impure water, is determined not by the relatively short reach of the stream familiar to them but by occurrences elsewhere in the basin, sometimes hundreds of miles away. A corollary of the absence of regional awareness is found in the lack of identification and consequently of clear definition of regional problems. And once a problem—the control of floods, for example—has been identified as one of regional

322

import, more often than not it lacks still the sense of urgency necessary to vigorous action. A hundred-year flood occurs on the average only once in a hundred years; that the hundred-year number may come up in August of 1955 (as it did) and again in July of 1960 (as it may) is hardly conceivable. The people of New York City came to understand the problem of water supply only when they were put on short rations; it may be foretold with some confidence that the people of northern Jersey will remain similarly complacent until their water supply dramatically fails to meet their needs. There is in truth no occasion for immediate alarm regarding the supply of water in the Delaware Basin; but when the need for action has grown urgent, the time for thoughtful action will have passed.

Not only does the river basin generally fail to impress the people residing there as an entity with important public problems; there are also contrary forces exerting strong influences against the emergence of a regional spirit. Among them may be mentioned a series of persistent and widely prevalent intra-regional conflicts. These are manifest in the urban-rural rivalries, the industrial-agricultural differences, the upstream-downstream controversies, all of which exist in varying degrees of sharpness in the Delaware as in many another river valley. It follows almost of necessity that a strong regional consensus on any particular issue is very difficult of achievement. The problem is further complicated by the fact that, in a given river basin, there are likely to be found hundreds of governmental units and agencies and additional hundreds of private enterprises, each pursuing its own course without effective reference to regional issues or regional needs. In the confusion of decision makers which prevails, it is not surprising that region-oriented leadership fails to materialize. The point is worthy of positive statement: the basin's effective leadership exerts its very great influence almost uniformly in favor of the status quo. There is no dramatic issue, no effective rallying point around which to build a vigorous program for regional action. In any river basin at a given time numerous local or special foci of support for regional action may be found to exist; but they are so diffuse and so fragmented that it is next to impossible to marshal them effectively in a united movement.

The inchoate and little understood character of the river basin as a potential area for common action thus virtually ensures that such action will be tentative, uncertain, and slow to take form. But there are other difficulties as well. Even with a reasonable degree of public understanding, dedicated leadership, and general goodwill, the region remains an extremely complex organism. It is complex, in the first place, in the problems it presents for attention. These problems are inherently difficult, but they are further complicated by the manifold interests required to be harmonized and constituencies required to be reconciled. It is commonplace that a measure of congruence, of centrality, of common concern, adds appreciably to the likelihood of a successful resolution of a weighty public issue. One looks in vain for this favorable omen with respect to the most pressing problems of the region, whose social, economic, and political composition is such as to promote dissonance rather than community of purpose. The organizational fragmentation, public and private, mentioned above adds a strong component of formal pluralism to the complexities inherent in the region.

Another category of obstacles is found in the legal difficulties which beset the course of regional action. These have been examined in detail elsewhere, hence it will be necessary at this point to mention only two or three of the most important among them. The first is found in the federal system, which does not give effective recognition to the possible need for a regional organization. The federal system allows of a regional organization, in the sense that the latter is not positively prohibited by the Constitution; but almost the whole of our experience has been with the familiar three levels of government. Any proposal to modify the federal system in recognition of emergent regional needs meets with the stone wall of a century and a half of government with limited regional experience, and of a system of law designed to maintain the traditional practice of federalism, at least in form. Contributory to the legal conservatism which rules in this area is the concept of sovereignty, which serves as the chief bulwark of states' rights in any proposed move away from accepted patterns of organization and practice. The devices thus far designed for the circumvention of these difficulties—the interstate compact, for example—have proved ineffectual as trailblazers toward a dynamic conception of federalism.

Last among the major inhibitors of regional action may be mentioned certain obstacles which reside in the mind of the people. Foremost among these is the grassroots tradition, which has been dominant in American thinking since colonial days. Essentially, the grassroots doctrine consists of the propositions that, since the welfare of the individual is the end of government, public action must be kept as close as possible to the people, that "little government" therefore has a substantial monopoly of virtue, and that "big government" as a natural consequence is to be viewed with suspicion if not outright alarm. A basin-wide organization clearly would not fall within even a liberal interpretation of an acceptable arrangement by grassroots standards. Viewed from another vantage point, the people's tenacious adherence to grassroots dogmas may be rephrased as an inherent resistance to change, as a natural inclination to cherish familiar things and to view any proposed innovation with disfavor. Coupled with the conservatism of the people is that which flows from vested interests. Businessmen cling passionately to the patterns of organization and behavior under which they achieved success; public officials react defensively against any proposal that would lead to important modification in established institutions. The hostility to significant change of those in positions of authority is not always stated, but it is always, or almost always, present. It is among the most powerful of all the inhibitors of regional action.

Inducers of Regional Action

There is a countervailing set of factors which, either singly or in combination, may produce an atmosphere that is favorable to change. Chief among these are crisis and catastrophe, economic circumstance, leadership, and windfall. Depending upon conditions, these factors will vary in their impact from contributing to a public state of mind which makes action possible to perpetrating panic or paralysis which makes it mandatory.

Foremost among the inducers of dramatic action, or of an atmosphere in which such action can occur, are crisis and catastrophe. Note has often been made of the role of crisis—war, natural disaster, economic depression, international threats to our peace and security—in shaping the course of our national history. Not least among these crisis situations, in the present context, are the forces of natural destruction represented by floods. Floods are not of much moment so long as they remain in the threat stage: the sheer prospect of a flood cannot produce near-panic, as can an unfavorable turn in our outer-space contest with the Russians. At the same time, a flood can come quite as suddenly and dramatically as can a war; and it can produce quite as great a shock, if over a much more limited area. The threat of flood is not especially effective in producing public action to avert flood damage; the experience of the devastation wrought by flood, on the contrary, results in an immediate and overwhelming demand for remedial public action.

Demonstration of the validity of this proposition presents no problem. The two great reform movements of this century in the structure of city government found their inception in disasters following floods. The commission plan and the city manager plan both had had scattered adherents earlier, but it remained for the Galveston flood of 1900 to prove the former and for the Miami River flood of 1913 to test the latter. The Miami flood, indeed, yielded two significant innovations in government; for it was the proximate cause for the establishment of the Miami Conservancy District, which represented the earliest American experience in planned (if single-purpose) river basin development. Recurrent floods on the Mississippi have provided both proving grounds for flood control techniques and occasion for the extension of federal activity in the flood control field. The disastrous floods of the mid-thirties on the Lower Colorado River were a powerful stimulant to the development of plans for the Lower Colorado River Authority. The Missouri River flood of 1943 resulted directly in the renewed interest in that stream which one year later led to the Pick-Sloan Plan for the Missouri. The Corps of Engineers of the U.S. Army in the spring of 1955 concluded that the Delaware River posed no substantial flood threat; but within three months hurricanes Connie and Diane came to claim 100 lives and cause damage estimated at over $100,000,000.[1] The floods which attended the hurricanes were principally responsible for the current high level of interest in the river and its problems.

Two general observations regarding natural disasters and governmental change are in order. First, and to make explicit a point suggested earlier, the catastrophe must actually occur: there must be the experience of immediate and overwhelming disaster. The threat of ruin is not enough, nor is the danger of recurrence of an earlier catastrophe. The Declaration of Independence asserts that "Mankind are . . . disposed to suffer, while evils are sufferable, . . ." It is when evils become insufferable, as through actual experience of a natural disaster, that action may be expected. Second, the memory of man is short, and nowhere is it shorter than when it dwells on a physical disaster. Allow a few weeks for the flowers to wither on the new graves, the washed-out roads and bridges to be re-built, and the mud to be hosed off the buildings, and the countryside is as good as new. So are its inhabitants, whose emotional scars fade as the physical

---

[1] Statistically the Corps could justify its position, for the floods of 1955 resulted from a combination of events which may be expected to occur only once in 100 years. The statistics that mattered, however, were not those which upheld the Corps but those which described the destruction wrought by the floods. The latter were devastating.

wounds are healed. To paraphrase, there is a tide in the affairs of men which, taken at its flood, leads on to fruitful experimentation in government. That tide follows naturally on the heels of war, fire, famine—and flood.

Regional action which seeks to bring about economic development will be powerfully influenced by economic circumstance. A water-resources program for a river basin will of necessity affect, and will be affected by, economic considerations in a variety of ways. First, it will require financial outlays, outlays which are likely to prove very heavy if the program aspires to meet basin needs. Second, it will demand large investments not only of money but also of men and materials, which means that willy-nilly it is closely related to the general economy. Third, there is a strong disposition to link construction for basin development with the reserve of public works projects which can be set aside against a future recession or depression need. Fourth, plans for river basin development are affected, almost unavoidably and in any event quite naturally, by the national state of mind at a particular moment, and more especially by the state of mind of the national administration. This last impinges on the subject of leadership, but leadership in turn is sharply influenced by economic considerations.

As evidence of the influence of economic factors on regional action, let it be noted that two of America's most successful experiences in regional development originated as stepchildren of the Great Depression. The makings for regional action in the Tennessee valley were present in abundance, but the economic cataclysm resulting from the depression was required to galvanize the latent forces into action. The combination of armies of men clamoring for employment, materials going unused and materials suppliers going bankrupt for want of construction activity, basin-wide economic stagnation, and regional and national leadership committed to remedial action—this was, in essence, the grand combine which resulted in the passage of the Tennessee Valley Authority Act in 1933. A similar set of circumstances a thousand miles away led to the establishment of the Lower Colorado River Authority a few years later. It is fair to say that both the TVA and the LCRA found their immediate inspiration in the economic collapse of the early thirties. It must be noted at the same time that economic conditions do not have to reach the stage of disaster to influence action for regional development. The recession of 1957-58, to illustrate, relaxed the currently restrictive thinking about river basin construction quite considerably. That the relaxation led to only modest action is to be explained by the lack of severity of the recession and by the relative ease with which the country effected at least partial recovery.

The role of leadership in regional action may be supposed to be well known and widely understood. Seldom does significant public action occur in a vacuum. River basin development of whatever description is peculiarly dependent upon vigorous leadership; for as we have seen, the forces which may be expected to rise to the defense of the status quo normally are better organized, more vocal, and withal stronger than those which favor significant change. A. E. Morgan has emphasized the part played by leadership in the history of the Miami Conservancy District, whose development he attributes in considerable measure to the tireless efforts and the organizing ability of John H. Patterson, President of the National Cash Register Company of Dayton. The story of Senator George Norris and his long-time struggle in behalf of the development of the Tennessee Valley is known to all, though it is worth noting that his leadership was exerted to block as well as to foster action during that struggle: the properties of the United States Government at Muscle Shoals, which formed the basis for the government's interest in the basin and so, ultimately, for the Tennessee Valley Authority Act, might have been alienated to private interests but for his interposition. Less well known, perhaps, is the role of leadership in the development of the Lower Colorado River Authority. Not every river valley is blessed by the happy circumstance of having among its representatives in Congress the Chairman of the House Committee on Appropriations and the Chairman of the House Committee on Rivers and Harbors at one and the same time. It is altogether appropriate that the first dam constructed by the Tennessee Valley Authority should have been named for Senator Norris, and it is equally appropriate that the two major dams of the LCRA bear the names of Congressmen Buchanan and Mansfield. The part played by President Roosevelt with respect to these among countless similar enterprises, whether as work relief or as conservation measures, is too well known to require elaboration here. It is, however, worthy of note in passing that many such developments flowered under the vigorous presidential leadership which characterized the depression years.

This brings us to mention of a fourth and final inducer of regional action. It is to be found in the fact that few of the major water-control structures which dot the American landscape would have been built except for the element of a very considerable windfall. As employed here, a "windfall" may be defined as a fortuitous and usually determining financial (or equivalent) contribution, made almost always by the national government. Among the river basin developments which trace their origin to heavy federal contributions are, to cite familiar examples once more, the Tennessee Valley Authority and the Lower Colorado River Authority. These windfalls resulted from a national policy designed to combat the depression, and so were justified as counter-depression rather than as river valley development measures. Whatever their rationale, however, they left behind them, in these two instances, the seeds of vigorous basin development programs. The Missouri Valley is now in process of development under a similar system of federal contributions. Throughout the country literally hundreds of individual projects have been constructed under a system of federal contributions which demands minimal financial participation by non-federal (state and local) interests. New York State has erected a fairly elaborate flood control program under an arrangement by which the lion's share of financing is provided by the federal government. It would be interesting (if fruitless) to speculate on how many water-resource projects would have been conceived and carried through in the absence of federal sponsorship, including specifically heavy financial contributions. The conclusion seems inescapable that the element of windfall has been determining with respect to most major developments.

Conclusions Regarding River Basin Organization

The nation's experience in river basin organization might be appraised from a number of points of view. The legal base on which an organization rests suggests itself as a fruitful point of departure for evaluation, as does the kind of organization established (whether corporation, commission, informal committee, and so on). A third launching platform is provided by the government or governments inaugurating or sponsoring the organization. From the evidence at hand, neither legal foundation nor form seems as important in determining the success or failure of a basin organization as the level of government taking action. Let us, therefore, evaluate our national experience in river basin administration in terms of the origins and sponsorships of development programs.

The pages of the history of river basin organization are not bright with state success stories. Perhaps the most successful state agency with basin-wide responsibility for a water program is the Lower

Colorado River Authority, which as we have noted is an agency of the State of Texas. It is no denial of credit due Texas to observe that the LCRA in all probability would not have gotten off the ground but for a substantial federal investment. The same may be said of the Muskingum Conservancy District, which, established under Ohio law, drew heavily on the federal treasury for construction costs. New York has had some experience with so-called river regulating districts, which, authorized by state law, may engage in limited-purpose construction with local (beneficiary) support. Such districts have not, however, been outstandingly successful; after 45 years only two districts have been organized, and one of these has had an unsatisfactory history.

Two currently unfolding state developments will be watched with very great interest. First, California offers an example of a state possessed of (1) a long-standing water problem which promises to yield to an energetic and imaginative approach, (2) physiographic characteristics which make this problem largely intrastate in nature, (3) an administration committed to action, and (4) a vigorous, integrated Department of Water Resources to lead the attack. What will emerge from this favorable combination of factors cannot be foretold, but it is not too much to view the developing California experience as an important field on which the efficacy of state action will be tested. There is mounting evidence that the state at last means to meet its water problems with forthright action. Meanwhile, its ambitious Feather River Project calls for a large federal contribution, which again leads to the question whether a state is capable of financing an important water resources development from its own resources. Further, the two best-known water undertakings in California are not state enterprises at all: the Central Valley Project was conceived and constructed and is managed by the U.S. Bureau of Reclamation, the spectacular water distribution system to the south by the Metropolitan Water District of Southern California.

The second prospective development worthy of close attention is the Round Valley Project of the State of New Jersey. Here the state proposes by its own resources to construct two large reservoirs for the storage of water for municipal and industrial supply. Since the Round Valley Project is just now taking form, it will be years before meaningful conclusions can be drawn regarding it.

Summarizing, the record of the states in meeting their water problems with effective action through use of their own resources is far from outstanding. Some significant developments have occurred, of course, but they have been few and far between. Of the several limitations on the states, four may be mentioned here. The first concerns leadership, a commodity in short supply much of the time. The second has to do with structure; it finds reflection in the fact that very few states are organized to conceive, plan, or manage a meaningful water program or, more broadly, a natural resources program. The third arises from the fact that the states either are not willing to allocate the means they have to the support of a broad water program or are restrained by institutional limitations from effective action to that end. It may well be that in the approaching days of water scarcity the states will conclude that, given the conditions under which they operate, they simply cannot raise or do not wish to spend the money to pay for the necessary river basin development projects.

The fourth limitation on state action to be noted here arises from the fact that the most important streams are interstate, and so transcend both the powers and geographical limits of individual state action. The answer to this riddle, from the point of view of the states, is a fairly simple one, on paper at least: let the states join together, either by ad hoc negotiated agreements or by interstate compact, and attack the problem of the interstate stream by common action. The Interstate Commission on the Delaware River Basin represents an effort at interstate cooperation at the informal agreement level. Incodel's achievements have not been inconsiderable, but it has not been able to plan and carry into effect a water program for the Delaware. The Interstate Sanitation Commission has achieved some little success in cleaning up the waters of New York harbor, as has the Ohio River Sanitation Commission for that river. Other compact experience might be cited; but when all is said and done, the conclusion seems inescapable that the interstate compact has not lived up to its promise in respect either of water programs or of administrative structures for interstate streams. The compact has proved useful for arriving at interstate agreements requiring compromise and patience in negotiation; it has not proved equal to the task of establishing ongoing administrative structures capable of dealing positively with new problems. The record contains no case of a broad water program either planned or managed by an interstate compact agency. Partisans of the interstate compact maintain that the device's potential has not been realized, that the full range of its possibilities has not been probed. Those who would like to see the states play a more active part in river basin development would like to agree, but find it difficult to explain away the record. Meanwhile, the devotees of states rights can draw small comfort from the fact that a proposed interstate compact for the Missouri River Basin was dropped after some years in limbo because of sheer lack of interest on the part of those who might have been expected to be its most vigorous supporters, namely the governors of the basin states.

When the inventory of American experience is finished, it is impossible to escape the conclusion that the federal government has been the moving force in most significant basin developments. Its activities have extended often to the provision of a legal base for action, frequently to the establishment of the agency for action, and almost always to the contribution of a large part (oftentimes all) of the funds required for the development. The evidence for this conclusion is to be found on every hand. The reasons reside in jurisdictional and legal competence; in the ability to take a broad (or at any rate, a broader) view where such a view is required—as it is in the case of the interstate river basin; and, always and most importantly, financial strength adequate to the task to be done. From the solid base provided by navigation, the interest of the national government in the proper utilization of the country's water resources has expanded steadily and, particularly in the last three decades, rapidly. That this expansion will continue there is no reason to doubt.

And yet, even those who view the federal government with confidence contemplate this trend with a certain reserve. Granted that participation by the national government is a sine qua non, if only from financial considerations, the vesting of complete responsibility in Washington is accompanied by certain risks. First, a federal river basin organization may well encounter difficulties with respect to state and local cooperation in regional development. This result does not necessarily follow, although the tendency for state and local agencies to view a federal regional organization with suspicion is undeniable. Second, a federal basin organization is likely to find its relations with existing federal programs in the valley something less than smooth. Inter-agency cooperation does not flow readily from decree, nor is it procurable on order. Third, the prevailing federal pattern does not incorporate a regional agency, which, with no recognized geographical base, finds it difficult to build regional political or administrative strength. State legislators, governors, city councilmen, mayors, and congressmen all owe loyalty to geographical districts, but nowhere is any such district conterminous with a river basin. Fourth, and as a corollary, national support for a federal regional undertaking is slow to form and quick to dissolve, while state-local support, even if it could be fashioned, is not alone sufficient as a political base for a federal regional agency. Such a base must be constructed first in the Congress, and state and local officials are not up to that responsibility.

American experience yields inadequate data on the possibilities of federal-state-local collaboration in establishing and operating river basin organizations. The Commission on Intergovernmental Relations did not coin the phrase "cooperative federalism," but it did provide the term with a setting which it had theretofore lacked. The promise of cooperative federalism in the field of river basin administration would seem to be worthy of thorough and systematic exploration. That, however, is a record which, since it remains to be written, is not now available for analysis.

The national experience in river basin organization provides certain conclusions, finally, with respect to the implementation of regional organization plans. The first such conclusion is that the forces normally arrayed in opposition to regional action are very strong. The bureaucracy, federal, state, and local, may be expected to line up almost solidly in opposition, as may most of the units of government in the region. The result, which may be predicted with a high degree of assurance, is an almost solid phalanx of official opposition, or at the least indifference, to any significant proposal looking toward a basin administrative organization. Second, it is difficult to institutionalize reorganization (or reform) strength. Reformers, being human, grow weary or die. The resistance to reform has a built-in organizational base; being institutional, the opposition never tires and never dies. The nature of the drive for and the resistance to administrative reorganization emphasizes anew the importance of leadership for a river basin water program. Finally, the significance of time and tide for regional action is worthy of emphasis. The role of recession and public spending on the one hand and of prosperity and retrenchment on the other is not one to be minimized. A water program for a major river basin entails very large expenditures. A few unfavorable reports by the Bureau of Labor Statistics and the Office of Business Economics and a few bad days or weeks on the stock exchange may completely alter the nation's attitude toward public construction. If economic adversity is not a thing to be desired, neither is it a thing to be ignored when it does occur; for it is (or can be turned into) a powerful propellant toward positive action. Even a recession may prove not an unmixed evil.

In view of the growing recognition of the need to attack many water problems on a drainage area basis, it is important to inquire what part of America's experience in river basin development is transferable. What does the Columbia have to teach the residents of the Missouri Valley? How much of what has been found useful on the Ohio might prove adaptable to the needs of the Delaware? It is common knowledge that the country's best-known basin development agency, the Tennessee Valley Authority, has found no emulators in this country, though not without considerable progeny abroad. During the latter forties, as many as a dozen valley authority bills came before the Congress in one form or another. Not one passed. Why should this be so? Is there something about a particular river basin which, setting it apart from other regions, also decrees that its administrative experience, however successful, shall be of limited (or even of no) use elsewhere? It might be supposed that, in the abstract at least, certain general principles of river basin organization might have been uncovered along the way. At the same time, it is a truism that "No two river basins are the same." In the past the dissimilarities have outweighed the likenesses in drawing lessons of general application. It will be useful to begin, then, with an examination of the important differences which prevail among river basins.

First of all, such differences may be found in the physical characteristics of a given stream and its drainage area. Among the hydrologic and geographic factors which set a particular basin apart from any and all others are channel cross-section and gradient, length, amount and character of flow of water, mineral and biological content of water, angle of junction of tributaries, area and shape of the basin, slope, soil type, condition of tributary land surface, and nature of contributing aquifers. These features are significant with respect both to the main-stem and to the tributary streams. They indicate why no two watersheds are alike, and they give weight to the view that administrative action must be tailored explicitly to the needs of the river basin at hand.

River valleys differ from one to another further with reference to their nature and stage of development. Criteria which suggests themselves for consideration here concern the nature and degree of industrial development, the maturity and complexity of the basin's economy, the extent and nature of urbanization, urban/rural relationships, development potential, and kind and amount of water needs. No great erudition is required to discover that, judged by these standards, the Tennessee Valley of the early thirties and the Delaware Valley of 1960 are two markedly different regions. A quarter of a century ago the Tennessee Valley was possessed of a colonial, agricultural, extractive economy; its cities were small and scattered, for it was overwhelmingly rural; its development potential was high, though observers were not in uniform agreement on that point; and there was a considerable hydroelectric potential latent in the river. The Delaware Basin of 1960 stands in sharp contrast to the Tennessee Valley weighed by these criteria. In nature and stage of economic and social development the two basins are dramatically different.

In yet another area a particular river basin is likely to stand alone, for the tradition and practice of government which prevail there may well set it apart from all others. Features which come to mind are the strength of the state and local governments of the region, the attitude of the people toward government activity, the pattern of political behavior, the quality of political leadership, and the demonstrated capacity of the governments for administrative performance. By these criteria, too, the Tennessee Valley of 1933 stood in sharp contrast to the Delaware Basin of 1960. The Tennessee Valley states twenty-five years ago had given almost no attention to water problems, and only a little more to the less specialized problems of natural resources generally defined—there was no department of conservation or natural resources worthy of the name in any of the Valley states in 1933. Government generally, local as well as state, was ill-developed, and had been rendered even more flaccid through the ravages of the depression. The tradition of one-party government made for factional strife rather than for party contests based on significant public issues. The art and science of administration were but little advanced among the governments of the Valley states. By contrast on most points, the governments of the Delaware Basin of 1960 are comparatively well organized, efficient, and ably led, both politically and administratively. By the same token, they are also strong and firmly entrenched.

The contrast between the two regions is not fair to the Tennessee Valley, since it does not take into account a time difference of twenty-five years in favor of the Delaware; but it does serve to make the point that the Tennessee Valley of 1933 and the Delaware Valley of 1960 differ in many fundamental ways. From this it is but a short step to the further conclusion that what was good organizationally for the Tennessee Valley in 1933 is not necessarily good for the Delaware Basin—or for any other, for that matter—in 1960. The Valley of the Tennessee in the early thirties was unique, and its ills and the prescription necessary for their cure are not to be equated with those of another basin of another kind and character at a different point in time.

Notwithstanding the diversities which confer upon each region its own special character and its own particular set of problems, all river basins share certain experiences and certain prospects in common. It is well that these latter be noted, lest they be lost to view in contemplation of the obvious dissimilarities. In the first place, all drainage basins share both the limitations and the opportunities of the federal system. Second, all have equal access to the national experience in organizational structures and legal forms. Third, for the solution of regional organizational problems there is equal, if in terms of experience limited, choice with respect to administrative machinery. Fourth, watershed regions throughout the country face comparable problems with regard to the rapidly developing issue of water-resources administration. These problems can be approached ad hoc as individual phenomena, of course, as for the most part they have been in the past; but they can be dealt with much more intelligently, in terms of scientific considerations, if the proposed solutions are harmonized in a basin plan and couched in regional terms. The need to take a regional (basin-wide) view of the problem of water-resources administration is increasingly urgent throughout the country, though of course the urgency is not uniform in its pressure. The river basins therefore share an unlimited challenge to initiative, resourcefulness, inventiveness, and imagination—in other words, to vigorous and constructive leadership. The need to meet this challenge with courage is universal; it contributes a common element to all the country's major river basins. The necessity for positive action is clear and present.

There can be no serious doubt that American experience in river basin administration contains suggestions of viable solutions to the major identified regional water problems. What, specifically, does the experience of one river basin have to offer another? Put differently, what parts of America's generalized experience can be put to work in a particular river basin? A basin program in its essence may be said to consist first of a plan and second of a system for its administration. It is clear enough that a plan for the physical and economic development of one river basin cannot be transferred to another basin in toto and without change; that is, a developmental plan cannot be standardized in substance. On the other hand, river basin planning procedures and methods can be standardized within quite generous limits, hence the techniques of basin planning may be considered transferable. This is to say, perhaps, that the problems requiring solution tend to be universal, the solutions individual and particular. Cast in these terms, there is a considerable experience in river basin planning which any region can examine with profit. The only proviso with respect to such examination is that there shall be no effort to transfer the substance of a plan from one basin to another.[2]

The same general observations hold with reference to experience in regional administration. In this area, too, the issues are recurrent; they include representation on the regional agency, responsibility, public support, financing, relations with established agencies and units of government, executive authority, and the place of the basin agency in the federal system. These and like problems will require attention in every region where serious thought is given to a basin-wide administrative organization. It is wholly unlikely that workable solutions will turn out to be identical from region to region, though certain fundamental principles of river basin organization have emerged, as others will emerge with broadening experience, which are generally applicable and so are transferable. But if it is clear that there is a body of organizational principle which is transplantable, it is equally clear that a rigorously delineated structure probably would not find a new environment congenial. As in the case of the basin plan, the distinction is that between technique, which contains lessons that are subject to transfer, and substance, whose lessons are less likely to have general validity.

[2] The Corps of Engineers recognizes this distinction in its basin survey activities. Its procedures tend toward uniformity, but its findings and recommendations are tailored to the individual basin.

Part V: Conclusion

CHAPTER 18

An Administrative Structure
for the Delaware Basin

THE evidence examined to this point leads inescapably to the conclusions that, with respect to the Delaware Valley, (1) there are significant water-resource functions which presently are being poorly administered or, in some instances, ignored altogether; (2) the existing machinery of government is not adequate to important emerging needs in this field; and (3) an administrative agency with jurisdiction throughout the River Basin promises the most logical solution to the regional aspects of the water-resources problem. It remains to analyze the third proposition in terms of specifics. What would be the physical appearance, the powers, the metes and bounds of a structure for administering the water resources of the Delaware Basin?

A Two-Phase Organizational Plan

The new governmental arrangement for Delaware River water-resources administration proposed here is conceived in two phases. The first phase of basin organization will be marked by passage of a congressional statute to create a new Delaware River Agency for Water (DRAW). The states will be represented on this transitional agency along with the federal government. The second phase will begin when the four basin states have created, by compact among themselves and with the national government, a soundly-conceived and adequately-empowered organization to replace the first-phase federal agency. There are three reasons for this phasing of the new structural proposals.

The first reason has to do with timing. Even if it were considered wise to begin this new effort with a federal-interstate compact, several years would pass before such an instrument could be prepared and ratified. In that time federal agencies would surely increase their activities in the Basin, thus unnecessarily limiting the nascent agency. Furthermore, the federal-interstate compact outlined below as desirable for the Delaware is more complex in its provisions and comprehensive in its coverage than any compact now in effect. A less inclusive compact failed of adoption in 1953. The issues to be hammered out, if a new Delaware compact is to be equal to the tasks awaiting it, will be most intricate. The prudence and patience and inventiveness of the negotiators will be taxed to the utmost.

Granted that passage of a federal statute could also be protracted, it appears that a satisfactory statute might be passed by Congress fairly promptly and Delaware Basin water development begun. There is considerable support for federal action in the Basin, which in turn has strong representation not unfavorably inclined in Congress. The statute and the agency it establishes will remove pressure from state and federal governments to complete a compact rapidly, thereby enabling negotiations to proceed in an atmosphere of relative calm. This in turn will allow for much-needed adjustments in the compact device.

The second reason is financial in nature. No attempt will be made here to discuss fiscal considerations in detail; these have been treated in earlier chapters. It is apparent, however, that the main financial source for Delaware development in its early years will be the federal government. During this period the greater part of the funds for flood control—an extremely expensive purpose with a long history of federal interest and support—will be spent. A considerable part of the original investment in other phases of Delaware development for which substantial aid will come from Washington likewise will fall into the initial period. Without question Congress will require that a close watch be kept on all federally-financed operations. The first-phase arrangement would be conducive to the fiscal well-being of the new agency, on the logical assumption that Congress would be more willing to vote money for a federal than for a non-federal instrumentality. As development progresses and the need for large capital outlays diminishes, it should be possible for DRAW, the states, and the beneficiaries to assume an increasing share of the costs. And as this share becomes larger, it will become appropriate to alter the legal basis and the character of the new agency.

The third reason pertains to the functions to be performed by the agency. On the one hand, there are precedents for broad federal action in the water-resources field, and it would be quite impossible to avoid a considerable measure of activity by the national government in any comprehensive Basin water development program. Apart from that, it would also be highly undesirable. The first part of the proposed two-phase plan takes cognizance of the interest of the nation both in water resources and in every part of the country. But on the other hand some of the basic functions of water-resources administration reside by tradition in the states. This is true, for example, of quality control and control over withdrawals and diversions, both of which, though important from the beginning, will increase in significance to the Delaware Basin with the passing of time. The second phase of the organizational plan recognizes the long-standing interest of the states in these and other water management areas by proposing a procedure under which each of the Basin states by compact may join with the other three and with the federal government in creating a regional agency. The approval of a federal-interstate compact by the several parties would signalize the transfer of the responsibilities for administering the Basin water program from a federal agency to a compact agency. The transfer in turn would shift the center of gravity of regional action from a federal to a federal-interstate agency. It would also recognize the importance of state law and experience in the administration of water resources.

PHASE 1: AN AGENCY ESTABLISHED BY FEDERAL LAW

A Delaware River Agency for Water (DRAW) should be established by federal law as soon as possible, and to that end senators and representatives from the Delaware Basin states should draft a bill and introduce it in Congress. If organized under federal authority but with representation on the governing board by the states, DRAW can fulfill the criteria laid down in Chapter 5 and elsewhere in this study. The policy-making arm of DRAW should be a commission drawing one member from the national government and one from each of the four states. Its precise composition is a matter of debate which will not be settled and indeed cannot be settled in these pages. It seems beyond discussion, nonetheless, that it should have federal representation appointed by the President and state representation from Delaware, New Jersey, New York, and Pennsylvania, nominated by the respective governors and appointed by the President. It would be inappropriate to require approval by the several state legislatures since the governors' nominations will be for federal offices. DRAW should come into existence as soon as a majority of members is appointed. The prospect of taking part in Basin-wide policy-making and in administration of DRAW's functions will probably be adequate incentive to the states to join.

An argument might be made for representation on DRAW of the Philadelphia and the New York-northeastern New Jersey metropolitan areas, but it has been concluded that such an arrangement is impractical. Legal sovereignty of the states over cities is a strong rationale for this conclusion and would be a telling argument in any legislative debate over the matter. Furthermore, these metropolitan areas have no formal or legal being—they are physical, economic, and social aggregates that spread willy-nilly across the boundaries of established governments. Board members for DRAW could not appropriately represent any single component of a metropolitan area, for example the central city, and sit with equal powers beside state and federal members. Moreover, the apparent conflict of interest between fringe areas and central cities forestalls hope of suburban acceptance of such an arrangement. One day the New York Metropolitan Regional Council [1] may provide a base for representation for that great area, but it is in no position to represent the whole region today.

It might be argued that other devices could be created to offset this absence of formal entity in the face of the very real existence of these metropolitan areas and their common, water-related interests. The mayors of New York and Philadelphia or other officials might, for example, nominate candidates for DRAW's commission to represent thereon the whole of each metropolitan area. In turn, the President might appoint the representatives. New York and Pennsylvania officials and people might accept such an arrangement, but New Jersey would hardly do so. Of course, a New Jersey metropolitan representative could be nominated by, say, the Mayor of Newark and then appointed by the President. These complex kinds of arrangements, however, would confuse the citizen and would remove DRAW farther from the popular control now exercised through channels relatively familiar and available. There is also the practical necessity of keeping DRAW's

---

[1] This body, which was convened by Mayor Robert Wagner of New York City in 1956, has representatives from the various local governments in the area. Its duties are purely consultative.

commission small and manageable. All things considered, then, it seems wise to avoid any representation of less-than-state interests or populations, and therefore to recommend representation on DRAW of only the four Basin states and the national government.

Within the foregoing limits, arrangements for the commission may be arrived at which will best facilitate acceptance of the plan, because criteria are not at hand for refinement in detail. For example, the question may be argued among reasonable men whether the federal government should have a majority or less than a majority of members on the commission. For a federal majority, it may be argued that the basis of the whole first-phase organization is to be a federal statute, that federal appropriations will undoubtedly be the prime source of early funds, that Congressmen (among others) will be deeply concerned that adequate federal controls over DRAW be maintained, that the national interest should be kept uppermost in the new organization, and that the states may not display a degree of interest in the new organization that would warrant the expectation of prompt and vigorous action.

For a state majority, it may be argued that the state is the proper level at which to lodge responsibility for dealing with less-than-national issues, that a DRAW based on a federal law and supported mainly by federal funds will be held responsible to a sufficient degree by the President and Congress regardless of the composition of the commission, that many of the contemplated powers of DRAW may eventually have to rest on state constitutional and legal authority, and that a formal state majority on the commission may be a crucial lever in persuading the states to join in this enterprise. It needs no demonstration that water management is a policy area in which adjacent states do not always agree with each other, and there is thus no compelling reason to think that a formal vote on DRAW's commission would always find the four states in agreement and so able as a majority to force an issue.

One resolution of these issues would be found in a commission comprising one federal representative and four state representatives, with the requirements that the federal representative must vote for any decision taken and must be a part of the quorum for any meeting. It is of the utmost importance that the commission be kept of manageable size.

All members, whether five, seven, or nine in total, should be appointed for terms of four years. Initial appointments, however, should be staggered so that in subsequent years the President will appoint at least one new member annually.[2] In successive years the respective governors should make their new nominations to DRAW. That the President should name the federal member (or one of the federal members) as Chairman probably will cause little dispute.

The members of DRAW's commission should be paid actual expenses incurred in connection with official business. Whether or not they should be compensated for their service is a moot question. Three familiar alternatives are available: full compensation through payment of annual salaries, per diem payment for days served, and no compensation. The first is rejected outright in view of the fact that the commission will not be a full-time body, and in view of the further fact that its duties will not be primarily administrative in character. A better case can be made for the second alternative, which places the commission with respect to pay in the role of a board of directors whose members are compensated for attendance at meetings. Nevertheless the second option, along with the first, is rejected in favor of the third. Excellent results have been obtained through use of uncompensated, part-time boards, which command the services of citizens who would not be able or willing to accept appointment to full-time positions, frankly recognizing the duty of a citizen to render occasional public service without the expectation of compensation.

The commission is conceived as a policy body which will formulate the principal goals and courses of action for the new agency. Thus decisions may be taken by majority vote (including one or a majority of federal members) when a working consensus on a given problem cannot be reached. A majority of members, including at least one federal member, should constitute a quorum for the transaction of business. DRAW hopefully will meet no more than perhaps three days per month, once its staff is assembled and basic policies are agreed upon. Meetings should of course be matters of public record, and should occasionally be held in public as a means of keeping in touch with public opinion.

Since the President appoints the members, he will have the power to discharge them; and this may be the principal formal means of ensuring DRAW's responsiveness to the voters. It is also possible for individual governors to be given a provisional veto over commission actions that would cause DRAW to delay, say, three months before putting decisions into force. The interim would allow for discussions

---

[2] If there is only one federal representative, he should be appointed in the first year of successive Presidential terms of office.

and for DRAW's reconsideration of the contested action. Other means of ensuring the responsibility of federal agencies would of course apply to DRAW.

The commission should be able to organize its staff along the unitary lines which have proved so successful in private enterprise and in many public agencies. The commission should appoint a general manager with full administrative powers, and the manager in turn should be empowered to appoint such other officers and employees as are necessary for the transaction of business. All appointments should be made without term on the basis of merit alone, and salaries should be high enough to attract talented personnel regardless of residence.[3] An annual audit of DRAW's accounts should be mandatory.

The geographic area within which DRAW and its successor will operate may be roughly depicted as a series of overlaying uni-functional areas, centering on the Delaware River's topographic watershed. The specific area best suited to each function is noted below.

The organization proposed here will supply the Delaware Basin with a viable and responsible central agency, fully able to exercise the necessary powers and to personify the Basin interest in unified administration of its water programs. It is necessary now to examine the powers to be vested in the new agency. For present purposes those powers are discussed under two major headings: substantive powers— those concerning the major purposes for which the agency was established (with control over withdrawals and diversions separated for special attention)—and financial powers.

SUBSTANTIVE POWERS FOR A BASIN AGENCY

By its organic law, the Delaware River Agency for Water should be given power to:

1. Correlate, report on, and as necessary collect data relating to present and potential uses of water within the Delaware Basin and within any areas to which Delaware water is now or may be diverted, data relating to available sources of water for use in the Basin or any portion thereof, and data pertaining to its operating programs. Pri-

[3] There are ample precedents for these details. See *Compact between the States of New York and New Jersey for the Creation . . . and . . . Establishment of the Port of New York Authority*, 1921, Article XIV; *Tri-State Compact for Pollution Abatement*, 1936, Art. V; *Upper Colorado River Basin Compact*, 1949, Art. VIII; Council of State Governments, *Revised Draft, Missouri River Basin Compact*, 1953, Art. V.

marily this should consist of the power to contract for special studies by and to work with, advise, and consult data-collecting agencies already in existence, to the end that the best and most complete scientific information may be available at all times in the course of Delaware development. This power would extend to all of DRAW's other functions including, for example, data relevant to state, local, and private planning and operating of measures for adjusting to floods. DRAW's own data collection programs need not duplicate those of other governmental agencies unless it can be shown that data from those agencies are incorrect, derived by outmoded procedures, or otherwise insufficient to fulfill DRAW's operating and planning needs.[4]

2. Prepare, and in the interest of currency, accuracy, and completeness, continuously revise and supplement a comprehensive plan for the development of water and water-related resources of the Basin. The plan should be one which in the judgment of the commission will best serve the beneficial purposes of flood control and damage prevention, supply of municipal and industrial water, control of pollution and saline water intrusion, development and distribution of power, preservation and development of recreation and fish and wildlife resources, watershed management, soil conservation and forestry, irrigation, drainage, improvement of navigation, stabilization of streambanks, and related development of land and water resources. In connection both with its planning function and with the foregoing data collection function, DRAW should be empowered to conduct investigations and surveys to determine the extent and nature of water and related resources, to study current and emerging problems of management, and to recommend or undertake courses of action in connection therewith.

The commission should review and evaluate existing and future plans, projects, and programs of national, state, local, and private agencies both before prosecution and after completion, with special attention to actual costs and benefits.[5] To the extent that such projects

[4] Cf. Missouri Basin Survey Commission, *Missouri: Land and Water*, p. 265; Council of State Governments, *Revised Draft, Missouri River Basin Compact*, Art. VII.

[5] Evaluation of costs and benefits *after* project completion has rarely been carried out on a systematic basis, but it could be a valuable means of continuous improvement of reservoir operation. See Ohio River Valley Water Sanitation Commission, "Multiple-Purpose Reservoirs and Pollution Control Benefits" (Cincinnati, January, 1953), compiled by Edgar W. Landenberger; and Bruce R. Gilcrest, E. P. Schuleen, and E. W. Landenberger, "Flood Control Plan for the Ohio River Basin," *Journal of the Waterways and Harbors Division, Proceedings of the American Society of Civil Engineers*, LXXXIII (1957), Proc. Paper 1209.

and programs are compatible with the full development of the Basin's water resources DRAW should incorporate them into the Basin plan. All governmental agencies and private persons proposing projects with a substantial effect[6] on waters of the main stem or the main tributaries should be required to submit operating plans for the consideration of the commission. In any instance where DRAW's commission finds that the plan for operating a proposed project, or that the operation of an existing project, has or will have a substantial effect on water of the Delaware River system and conflicts with the comprehensive plan or with the policies or procedures adopted by it, it should make such recommendations as it deems necessary to the appropriate government or governments (except in cases where 3, below, applies).[7]

Each year the commission should prepare (1) a water-use budget and (2) a financial budget. These documents should of course be consistent with the comprehensive plan, and should show clearly the relationship between activities to be undertaken in the forthcoming year and activities proposed for a subsequent period of five or more years.

The annual water-use budget should comprise analyses of rainfall, ground, and surface water data, along with analyses of information on the quantity and quality of water use, current and prospective, in specific areas within the Basin and in adjacent areas where water use is integrally related to the Basin. As the coverage and quality of these types of information improve, in part as the result of DRAW's work, it is reasonable to expect that the water-use budget will become a more and more realistic and useful operating plan. It should then be possible to estimate the values of alternative water uses with such accuracy that the economic effects of possible changes could be anticipated and the River's maximum potential could be brought closer to realization. This annual process should be conducted in an atmosphere of close cooperation with the principal classes of water users through the medium of the Intergovernmental Advisory Com-

---

[6] For suggestions as to the reasoning DRAW might follow in defining "substantial effect," see Luna B. Leopold and Thomas Maddock, Jr., *op. cit.*, chaps. 4, 5, and pp. 223-6.

[7] Cf., Council of State Governments, *Revised Draft, Missouri River Basin Compact*, Art. VII; Missouri Basin Survey Commission, *op. cit.*; Frederick L. Zimmermann, "Draft of Delaware River Compact" (unpublished manuscript, September 24, 1956), Art. V; S. 1107, 85th Cong., 1st sess., Sec. 7. An excellent model, on which DRAW, however, may improve, is Department of Water Resources, State of California, *The California Water Plan.*

mittee (described below) or a subcommittee set up for this purpose. The annual water-use budget should be viewed as a balance sheet for all the Basin's water, a specific operating plan for the structures within DRAW's immediate jurisdiction, and a persuasive argument for wiser operation or use of structures, diversions, or processes not directly controlled by DRAW.[8]

The annual financial budget should be divided into capital and current sections. The capital section would show the relationship between building proposed for the next year and long-range construction plans. The current section should be classified to show outlays for DRAW staff activities, such as data gathering, planning, and operation and maintenance of structures, and outlays as well for parallel activities of other governmental agencies in the Basin. Sources of finance, current or capital, should be shown where possible in relation to the specific project purposes supported.[9]

Adoption of two budgetary procedures would strengthen the financial planning and management aspects of DRAW's program. The first would place DRAW in an advisory position with respect to the budgets of all national, state, and local agencies engaged in any aspect of water-resources development in the Basin. This function, primarily informational in character, could be discharged by and through the Intergovernmental Advisory Committee. Detailed information about budget proposals and programs of other agencies would provide an important data base for realistic budgeting by DRAW. Second, budgetary processes for DRAW, and indeed for all Basin water-resources programs, could be strengthened by modifying existing federal budget procedures in such a fashion that the U. S. Bureau of the Budget would bring together for information purposes the relevant portions of the budgets of federal agencies operating in the Delaware Basin.

[8] The procedures in the Missouri Basin are similar to the ones contemplated here, although the coverage in the Missouri is largely confined to the main stem. See the discussion of Missouri Basin procedures in Chapter 14 of this study. Two documents from Omaha, Missouri Basin Inter-Agency Committee, "Report on Adequacy of Flows in the Missouri River" (April 1951), and Corps of Engineers, Missouri River Division, Reservoir Control Center, "Missouri River Main Stem Reservoirs Summary of Actual 1955-56 Operations and Annual Operating Plan for 1956-57" (August 1956), may to some extent serve the new DRAW as models in the early stages of its operation.

[9] There is a brief discussion of a budget somewhat like that contemplated here in Missouri Basin Survey Commission, *op. cit.*, p. 265. The procedures laid down for the Upper Colorado River are much more limited in concept. See P.L. 485, 84th Cong., April 11, 1956.

This information could then be reviewed by appropriate subcommittees of the House and Senate appropriations committees. This would assure at least a minimum of budgetary integration in federal activities affecting the Delaware Valley. If these two budgetary procedures could be realized, DRAW would then be in a position to prepare annually a comprehensive financial summary of all water-resources programs, national, state, and local, in the Basin. Such a summary would prove highly useful both in program elaboration and in financial planning.

3. Design, build, make integrated operating plans for, maintain, operate, and dispose of the products of all water control structures and related structures and land areas on the main stem and main tributaries of the Delaware River. This power in reality expresses a goal at which drafters of DRAW's organic law should aim and toward which DRAW's actions should be directed early. Eventually DRAW should operate or regulate operation of all such river control structures, in behalf of every purpose their integrated operation may serve —flood control, water supply, hydroelectric power generation, recreation, fish and wildlife measures, salinity intrusion control, and related uses. One of the key techniques will be the maintenance of minimum flows at specific points on the River.

If the commission finds that the operation of an existing project by any governmental agency or private person, or any plan for a proposed project, has or will have a substantial adverse effect on its water control structures or their operation, it should notify the agency or person. The plans, policies, and procedures of DRAW should be controlling in such instances. In the event of non-compliance, DRAW should exhaust all possible means of accommodation, employing in particular the instrumentality of the Intergovernmental Advisory Committee. Failing agreement by negotiation, DRAW should then be able to seek enforcement of its ruling in the courts.

It is not recommended that an all-out effort be made to have DRAW early in its life gain authority to build the dams that may be recommended in the forthcoming survey by the Corps of Engineers. It is proposed that DRAW assume that responsibility when its staff and facilities have been developed to the point where assumption may be feasible. To that end the power to construct should be given to DRAW in its organic law. This power should include authority to acquire or otherwise assume responsibility for water control structures now in existence. Once it is a going concern, DRAW may proceed to negotiate with New York City, New Jersey, the Corps, and other owners or operators of major water control structures along the Delaware and its tributaries leading to eventual purchase of or other assumption by DRAW of operating responsibility for those structures. If this step proves politically or otherwise impracticable, at the very least DRAW or its successor should gain full control over releases from such structures as an essential part of integrated system control. Such integrated system control may not become mandatory for some years, hence assumption by the Basin agency of authority over structures now in existence may develop into a pressing need only after the second phase has commenced. In this event the new compact may be the means for vesting *full* control over all structures in one agency for the entire Basin.

Incident to this general power and to other related powers, DRAW should be authorized to acquire property by purchase and by eminent domain. This should include power to buy and reserve for a period of years land at reservoir sites and adjacent thereto, and to employ such land for recreation, fish and wildlife, and watershed management purposes until funds are available for building dams and related recreation or other facilities. DRAW must retain full responsibility for planning the use of such reservoir areas, including activities around new reservoirs. It should, however, negotiate agreements with states and local bodies for administration of these functions. Some reserved lands might subsequently be made available at cost to state and local governments for water-related purposes.

4. Protect and improve the quality of the waters of the Delaware Basin by collecting, studying, and disseminating information respecting water quality; establishing and enforcing reasonable physical, chemical, and bacteriological standards satisfactory for various classifications of use; grouping waters of the Basin into various classes in accordance with current or intended uses; and cooperating with state agencies or other entities and with the Public Health Service and other agencies of the United States for the purpose of promoting effective laws and regulations for quality control of Delaware waters.[10] When DRAW finds alleged water quality violations, it should immediately transmit its findings, together with all pertinent records and

[10] Cf. *Tri-State Compact for Pollution Abatement, op. cit.,* Arts. X-XII; *Ohio River Valley Water Sanitation Compact,* 1948, Arts. VIII, IX; *Klamath River Basin Compact* (1956), Art. VII; *New England Interstate Water Pollution Control Compact* (1951), Art. V; Columbia Interstate Compact Commission, Draft of "Columbia Interstate Compact and Proposed Federal Consent Legislation" (Spokane, 1956), Art. VIII.

data, to the United States Public Health Service with a request that action be instituted under the terms of Section 8 of the Federal Water Pollution Control Act of 1956.[11] If, after 90 days, the PHS has not instituted action, or alternatively made a finding adverse to DRAW's original finding, DRAW itself should be authorized to call a hearing in accordance with its own rules and regulations concerning the alleged water quality violations, make a finding, and issue an order or orders for the correction of such violations to the persons or agencies causing them. Further, it should be empowered to seek a court injunction to enforce such an order.

These powers to study, confer and make recommendations about, and enforce standards with regard to quality control will enable DRAW and DRC to cope with one of the major problems involved in the administration of Delaware water resources. The results that such powers can produce have been demonstrated in New York's harbor by the Interstate Sanitation Commission and on the Ohio River by the Ohio River Valley Water Sanitation Commission, and the compact for the second-stage DRC may be negotiated by the Delaware Basin states with those two models in mind. By compact agreement quality control could be exercised without a base in federal statute and apart from the nation-wide powers of the Public Health Service.

In the early stages of Delaware development, however, DRAW will be able to rely upon an anti-pollution enforcement power that the Public Health Service may exercise uniformly throughout the United States. DRAW may still, in final analysis, exercise its own authority to stop violations when the PHS is reluctant to take action. DRAW will be in an even more favorable position to maintain high quality because it will combine the enforcement power with the function of low-flow augmentation, itself an important aid to the maintenance of water quality.

DRAW must gain the fullest cooperation from the Public Health

---

[11] 70 Stat. L. 498. Section 8 provides a careful procedure for (1) calling a conference with state and interstate agencies; (2) holding a public hearing before a board appointed by the Secretary of Health, Education, and Welfare; and (3) if necessary, instituting federal court action. By 1958, step (1) had been employed 10 times, step (2) only once, and step (3) not at all. See "The Water Pollution Control Program of the U.S. Public Health Service, 1957–1958," Public Health Service Publication No. 631 (Washington, 1958), p. 19. In the Spring of 1959 step (2) was used again, and the Secretary of Health, Education and Welfare directed Sioux City, Iowa, and 10 meat processors there to stop discharging untreated wastes into the Missouri River. DRAW's rules and regulations might be modeled after these procedures used by the PHS.

Service, state and local governments, and private industry if quality control is to be carried out successfully. It will be to the interest of every individual near the River that the Delaware not become an open sewer as its banks become lined with people and industry. Giving DRAW the power outlined above will result in its superseding the Interstate Commission on the Delaware River Basin, an agency that for more than two decades has been active in this field. Incodel, however, depends purely upon cooperation among officials of the four states—it has no "teeth" with which to prevent or abate serious cases of pollution. Its program has been limited to collecting data, conferring, publicizing, and urging parallel action. A stricter watch over the quality of water in the Basin will be an essential to successful river management during the coming decades. The creation of DRAW offers the best chance of obtaining such a sentinel.

5. Represent the interests of the Delaware Basin before governmental agencies and private groups or persons, and generally in the public forum. This should include the responsibility to report annually to the President and the four governors; to issue other reports, studies, and informational bulletins from time to time; and to promote water conservation measures. DRAW should be able to intervene before federal and state tribunals in any dispute involving Delaware water, either in the Basin or elsewhere.

6. Promote the coordination of the activities of public and private water and other related natural resource or conservation agencies, and advise, consult, make payments to, or otherwise cooperate with any and all such agencies in the development and management of the water and related resources of the Delaware Basin.[12] These cooperative activities should extend to projects and programs covering all aspects of water use and control.

7. Exercise such other powers as may be conferred on it by state or federal laws.[13]

8. Conduct public hearings and issue rules and regulations for the submission to it of budgets, project plans, and operating plans, for control of withdrawals and diversions and for such other purposes

[12] Cf. Council of State Governments, *Revised Draft, Missouri River Basin Compact,* Art. VII, Sec. 2.

[13] Cf. *Compact between the States of New York and New Jersey,* 1921, Arts. III and VII; similar authority exists in the *Missouri-Illinois Bi-State Agency Compact, Ohio River Valley Water Sanitation Compact, Tri-State Compact for Pollution Abatement.* See also Zimmermann and Wendell, *op. cit.,* pp. 60-1.

as in its judgment may be appropriate to carry out its powers.[14] The commission should publish its rules and regulations in convenient form.

9. Study, negotiate regarding, and arrange for the transfer of all its staff, finances, other facilities and appurtenances, and functions to the Delaware River Commission when that agency shall have been created.

CONTROL OVER WITHDRAWALS AND DIVERSIONS AS A SPECIAL CASE

By its organic law, DRAW should also be given power to approve, license, or otherwise control withdrawals or diversions of over (amount to be determined) per day by governmental agencies or private persons from the ground, surface, or other waters of the Delaware Basin.[15] A Water Apportionment Appeals Board of three members should be appointed by DRAW to hear and decide on appeals from apportionments of water made by DRAW's administrative staff among public and private water users. Further appeals could be provided to DRAW's commission and thence to the courts. DRAW's basic statute should specify the status of existing riparian and prescriptive rights and judicially allocated diversions, although in all likelihood a Basin agency would respect them all without such a guarantee.

This power may be termed "contingent," in view of several facts and considered estimates of what the future holds in store in the Basin. First, problems of withdrawals and diversions have not yet become sufficiently serious and widespread to warrant vesting immediate, total control in a Basin agency. But second, the swiftly increasing demands for water are day by day bringing closer the time when strict control of use will be mandatory. Third, the present piecemeal and largely inadequate systems of control of withdrawals and diversions rest on the 1954 Supreme Court decree, on the discrete systems of riparian and prescriptive rights as interpreted by the courts of the four states, and on a few statutes. In all likelihood these partial measures will be found progressively more deficient in meeting the mounting needs of the highly urbanized and industrialized Delaware Basin. Ideally, a system of administrative controls should replace

[14] Cf. Council of State Governments, *Revised Draft, Missouri River Basin Compact*, Art. VII, Sec. 7; *Klamath River Basin Compact*, Art. IX C.

[15] Cf. N. J. P.L. 1947, Chap. 375, amended by N. J. P.L. 1951, Chap. 195; and State of California, *Water Code*, Divisions 1 and 2.

today's haphazard control of water withdrawals by the myriad courts in the Valley.

It is well to remember that DRAW will have the authority to study water use and quality continuously, to report thereon, and in fact to affect withdrawals directly by its operation of structures on the mainstem and main tributaries and by its augmentation of minimum flows. At the same time these structures could never be fully controlled and low flows could never be efficiently augmented without DRAW's having powers to regulate withdrawals.

In the early years of its existence the Basin agency will in all probability limit its control to the very largest users—those taking millions of gallons each day. As time goes on and its techniques of control are perfected, however, the size of use controlled could be reduced. DRAW must employ its research facilities to broaden knowledge of the techniques of such controls and of ground water and its relationship to the Basin's visible water resources.

Admittedly, this is a strong power for an eastern agency to exercise, although in the western states it is exercised on many streams. Merely to suggest it will be to arouse the opposition of strong interests. Its importance to the increasing domestic and industrial users in the Delaware Basin is obvious, however, and there will be strong political forces that will favor bestowing it on DRAW. If these forces prevail, the Basin may provide a pattern for the other parts of the East. It should be recalled that DRAW's performance of this withdrawal and diversion control function might conceivably be arranged through the instrumentalities of improved state administrative agencies and state laws and courts.

If the situation is such that it is impracticable to give this power to DRAW for immediate exercise, the best alternative will be to assert the power in DRAW's organic law but defer its effective date until the time when it shall have been determined that its exercise is imperative and that the water use situation has deteriorated to the point where no other course is tenable. The power thus reserved might be held in escrow for a decade. Adoption of this alternative would be much preferable to depending upon passage of a special law at some indefinite future date.

To be sure, proponents of DRAW may be able to obtain neither of these alternatives when they face the conflicting pressures revolving around withdrawals and diversions in Congress and in the public forum. A third alternative will be that of holding the power for employment by the federal-interstate compact agency, the Delaware

River Commission. If a compact comes quickly, this alternative will be as good as the first. To judge from experience in compact negotiation in other basins, however, one may predict that strong forces will favor the allocation of measured quantities of Delaware waters among the four states in such a compact. That eventuality is one to be avoided at almost all costs, for freezing the water allocation in a compact would be a solution divorced completely from the realities of urbanization and industrialization in the Basin and its service area. The key to successful management of water uses lies in vesting that process in an administrative agency where it can be held flexible and responsive to changing needs and demands.

The struggle to establish a structure for the rational management of Delaware water resources may well center on this power for DRAW. That would be an appropriate turn of events, for the exercise of a substantial measure of control over withdrawals and diversions at some future date will become crucial to the success of the Basin agency. The skill of the negotiators of the new law will be demonstrated by their ability to gain as much of this power as is possible for exercise by DRAW within a reasonable time.

FINANCIAL POWERS

DRAW, by its organic law, should be further empowered to:

1. Receive and expend funds appropriated to it by the Basin states which should contribute regularly to the support of both DRAW and DRC.

2. Receive and expend funds appropriated to it by the national government, in the forms of both capital and operating funds for navigation, water supply, and flood control, to continue data-gathering activities, and possibly to provide annual sums for plans and surveys. This source, together with state appropriations, will be especially important in the first decade of operations.

3. Measure, assess, and collect levies from beneficiaries of federally-financed low-flow augmentation that is subject to reimbursement. The national government seems to be moving toward assumption of expanded responsibility for low-flow augmentation, with part of the benefits to be financed on a non-reimbursable basis. Meanwhile DRAW can assume the role of investigator and negotiator in this important activity.

4. Undertake negotiations with water distribution agencies, public and private, to encourage water supply storage construction where

needed and to assure that capital investments by the national government will be reimbursed. It is reasonable to anticipate that, by the
turn of the century, revenue from water will be substantial, investment in water supply storage will be on a self-liquidating basis, and
this program may provide some net revenue for the support of other
water-resource programs.

5. Sell hydroelectric power generated at its dams. In the first years
of development, revenue from the sale of power could be the most
significant source of income for DRAW. The organic law should be
drafted so as to permit the agency to establish wholesale power
rates at levels above minimum assignable cost.

6. Investigate the possibilities of a differentiated-price policy with
respect to recreation facilities and programs carried on by DRAW
or other public or private agencies in the Delaware Basin.

7. Establish a permit system for all water users, including the
charge of fees therefor, but with an exemption for users of small
amounts. Subsequently DRAW should be authorized to introduce
user charges when further data and experience are available. The legal
and economic bases for general charges on water use are reasonably
firm, but there are many technical details to be explored in drawing
up a schedule.

PHASE 2: AN AGENCY ESTABLISHED BY FEDERAL-INTERSTATE COMPACT

Delaware, Pennsylvania, New Jersey, and New York, in concert with
the federal government, should establish a commission forthwith to
study the problems of, draft, and submit for approval a federal-interstate compact creating a Delaware River Commission (DRC) to
replace the first-phase Delaware River Agency for Water. Among the
first problems to be examined should be these: (1) the desirable limits
to federal participation in the DRC; (2) methods of making parallel
or reconciling the differences of water law in the four states; (3)
creation of a system of withdrawal and diversion controls based on
state laws or compact; (4) sources of finance for DRC; and (5)
means of assuring the responsibility of that agency.

The study and drafting commission might depend upon DRAW
for collecting and collating data, for research studies, and for advice
and other assistance. The commission should, of course, have a small
staff and budget of its own and should be able to employ the best
consultants. While its work is going on (a process that may well
occupy several years), the development of the Delaware Basin will

be going forward under the leadership of DRAW. Creation of DRC, therefore, can occur in an atmosphere of deliberate and thorough study, consultation, and cooperation on the part of the states and the federal government. The result should be a thoughtful, careful analysis of common interests and goals—and common conflicts. Too often the price of hurried negotiations has been a compact based upon the lowest common denominator of terms acceptable to the parties.

The completion of a joint compact and establishment of DRC will shift the basic legal authority for integrated and comprehensive development of water resources. The burden of responsibility will be transferred to the states, while at the same time the vital role of the federal government will continue to be recognized. This change in authority and emphasis will not necessarily affect the financial arrangements for Valley development. At the same time, it will give responsibility for regional action to the governments physically closest to the Basin and thereby in a position to relate regional problems to local interests, while at the same time retaining a frame of reference attuned to national interests.

Such a plan for action should meet with a warm response on the part of the four Valley states. It would afford them opportunity to take the lead in managing the Basin's water resources. In terms of coordinated resources administration, at least three of those states rate high when compared with the other forty-seven. If any states are capable of striking out with significant action in the field of interstate water-resources management, these in all likelihood are among them.

The Council of State Governments for some years has been encouraging state governments to launch an experiment like the federal-interstate compact proposed here. There are ample precedents for placing national representatives on interstate compact commissions. The precedents should be used as bases for devising an instrument to promote the fullest federal-state cooperation in the field of water management. A regular procedure exists for federal participation in compact negotiation, while state laws will control the appointment of state representatives for negotiating purposes. It would be highly advisable for each of the four Delaware states to allow its governor to appoint its negotiator.

A few major points should be made with respect to the substance of the federal-interstate compact for the Delaware River Commission. Granted that its advent is rather farther in the future than is that of the first-phase DRAW and that the water problems of the Delaware may change a good deal in the meantime, there are still some considerations that can be indicated as basic.

It is fundamental that DRC should be able to replace DRAW completely. With this in mind, it would be prudent to make the composition and terms of the DRC commission, and the functions, rules and regulations, and working methods of the DRC organization the same as those for DRAW. Of course, if DRAW were originally created with a majority of federal members, their number would perhaps have to be decreased upon DRC's establishment in order that the states might then have a clear majority on the commission. A stipulation should be written into DRAW's organic law for the transfer of all its staff, finances, facilities and appurtenances, and functions to DRC when, in the judgment of both commissions (if they are not then identical), the proper time has arrived.

It is especially important to note this provision for transferring DRAW's functions to DRC. There appear to be no substantial constitutional, legal, or administrative reasons why such a transfer of functions from an organization based principally on national statute to one based principally on federal-interstate compact could not take place. The subject will of course require further examination, and will inevitably be a major topic for study by DRAW's staff, for discussion in Congress, and for consideration in the course of future compact negotiations.

The "contingent" function of withdrawal and diversion control deserves further comment in this connection. This will be the area in which study will be most necessary and the shift of responsibility from a federal to a federal-interstate agency most complex. If, by the time of DRC's creation, DRAW has encompassed the power, transfer to DRC will be simple. If responsibility for the power remains in the several state governments at that time, the compact instrument itself could effect the transfer. By that time there will be much greater knowledge of the extent and character of Delaware water problems (particularly ground-water problems) and of the water law of the four Basin states. Further, better engineering and other technical means will have been developed for bringing about fuller and fairer control of withdrawals, diversions, and quality, and for relating them to the integrated management of all the Basin's water resources.

The compact drafters should pay particular attention to devising formal means for making and keeping DRC a responsible agency. A number of such devices are implicit in the compact device itself—the right of participating governments to withdraw (a specific procedure should be arranged) and the liability of individual commissioners to prosecution for misdeeds, for examples. It may be found desirable, however, to give the President, and/or, say, two governors acting jointly, the power to veto DRC actions. The governors should be given the power to remove their appointees from the Commission. All such devices should aim at producing democratically responsible administration for the Basin.

A Postscript on Intergovernmental Relations

It has been found that nearly all of the ongoing, water-related programs in the Basin are contributing positively to better water use, and the total program for development described here envisions their continuation. Among these, for example, are the building of local flood control structures, water supply systems, sewage disposal plants and mains, and power distribution facilities; recreation and fish and wildlife projects; small watershed programs; other soil conservation and forestry measures; and so on. Thus, existing grant-in-aid programs in agriculture, forestry, fish and wildlife, and water pollution control would not be interrupted, but instead would be improved and broadened through enhanced communication and through the advice and assistance, financial and otherwise, provided by DRAW and DRC. Recreation and water supply programs, among others, would be reinvigorated by the new agencies, which must be able to assist in these activities through advice, loans, grants, and the provision of land and other facilities.

Certain federal, state, local, and private agencies have built and will build water control structures that should in the long run be made part of the integrated river control system. The cases of the Catskill dams of the New York City Board of Water Supply, the future Raritan Valley structures for New Jersey, and the proposed Brandywine dams for Pennsylvania have been mentioned. The new Basin agencies, through their comprehensive plan, annual budget, and other means, ought to be able to assert themselves forcefully in Congress and the state legislatures with respect to any proposed major structures on the River and its principal tributaries. And the agencies should be in a position to insist on carrying out such construction themselves. By the organic law in DRAW's case and by the joint compact in DRC's, the right of the Basin agencies to determine what control structures shall be built, and by whom, should be affirmed.

As a key device for consultation about the whole gamut of intergovernmental cooperation possible in the Delaware Service Area, DRAW, and in the second phase DRC, should establish early an Intergovernmental Advisory Committee. Both the federal statute and the compact should make provision for such an agency.[16] On it should sit representatives of the public; national, state, and local water-resources agencies; water-using industries; labor; and agriculture. Through IAC, both DRAW and DRC may enlist the participation of all interested organizations and persons. They will find the Committee highly useful as a means of maintaining contact with important elements in the Basin, and as a device both for conveying information to the people and for sounding out public opinion. They may also deem it advisable to employ IAC as a channel for extending their advice and aid to state and local agencies and to the public. The Intergovernmental Advisory Committee looms therefore as a quasi-public body capable of rendering important auxiliary services. As such it is worthy of considerable time and attention on the part of the Basin agency.

[16] Cf. S. 3114, 85th Cong., 2d sess., Sec. 9; Missouri Basin Survey Commission, *op. cit.*, pp. 266-7.

CHAPTER 19

The Problem of Implementation

A FEATURE of the research for this study has been the systematic attention given to the problems of implementing the report, that is, of securing approval of the recommendations. It may seem strange to some that the factor of political feasibility has been taken into account, particularly in a study by a private research group with no political limitations imposed upon its actions. Upon reflection, however, it will become apparent that any realistic administrative research must proceed within the limits imposed by the considerations of political practicality. The most obvious of these is the limit of the United States Constitution; the difficulty of amending it requires ordinarily that it be treated as a fixed factor in a given situation. Thus a study of a local or regional problem that culminated in a recommendation for a federal constitutional amendment might reasonably be considered to have missed its mark, since the solution proposed would be incapable of accomplishment and hence would stand no chance of solving anything.[1] This is only the most obvious of such limitations; many other values could also be identified which are widely held within the society and which must be respected by those who wish to gain consideration for their proposals for reform.

In the sense that political considerations have been taken into account, this report is not notably different from others; for virtually every set of recommendations growing from a similar study has involved political judgments. The difference in approach of this study is that *systematic* attention has been given to the politics of water-resources administration from the beginning. The opinions expressed were not casually formed on the basis of limited personal experiences

[1] See Thomas H. Eliot, "Dilemmas in Metropolitan Research," *Midwest Journal of Political Science*, II (February, 1958), pp. 26-39.

or observations; they were based upon as extensive research as time and money permitted. Nor are they simply incorporated into the findings and recommendations as unexpressed reasons for saying what is said; in so far as possible they have been made explicit and labeled for what they are, judgments concerning the political limits upon the range of possibilities and the alternatives at hand. The advantages of such an approach are twofold: the accuracy of the political judgments can thereby be appraised, and their impact upon the final conclusions can be separated out for independent consideration.

Both points deserve explication. Not even the most enthusiastic believer in a science of political behavior is convinced that laws are presently known which are capable of identifying what is politically possible and distinguishing it from what is not. The systematic analysis of political behavior deals with probabilities, not certainties; thus one event is judged to be more likely to occur than another, but cannot be predicted with assurance. Improvement in the knowledge of political behavior consists of refining the calculation of the probabilities involved. By setting apart the political judgments it is made more apparent that they cannot be treated as determinate boundaries within which are found the available and feasible alternatives for action, but outside of which nothing is possible. Estimates of political possibilities might more accurately be visualized as weights indicating possible outcomes, suggesting a set of political factors to be considered along with others.[2]

This interpretation is important in dealing with the second question, which concerns the proper relationship between political and other factors in reaching decisions as to what recommendations should be made. At one extreme every possible alternative could be examined in terms of its political feasibility and the solution politically most popular chosen in each case. Well done, such a procedure might succeed in producing a report recommending precisely what would have happened in the absence of a report. The opposite approach would be to ignore considerations of acceptability altogether and to come out boldly for the theoretically "best" solution. In this report a third alternative, midway between these two, has been employed. The criterion of political feasibility has been used, but only as one among others. Where it has produced a recommendation contrary to what might have seemed desirable on other grounds, that fact has been noted. The political judgments can therefore be separated from the recom-

---

[2] Cf. Carl J. Friedrich, "What Is Meant by 'Politically Impossible'?", *Political Research: Organization and Design*, I (May, 1958), pp. 3-6.

mendations proper. And if the risk appears worth it, a more attractive alternative less likely of success can be advanced by those who wish to fight for something more.

Where questions of political feasibility have concerned specific recommendations in the report, reference has been made to them along the way. One further problem remains for consideration in this chapter: given the recommendations made in Chapter 18, what can be done with them? What is the next step? In what way can they be most effectively advanced and supported?

The Situation

The problem is a singularly difficult one. In reality it comprehends not one but at least three important considerations. The end-product desired is the establishment of an organization empowered to do certain things toward the accomplishment of specified goals. Breaking down this objective into its component parts, a decision to create such an organization requires that the appropriate level of government decide, first, that it will assume general responsibility for the major tasks or functions involved; second, that the specific projects proposed are appropriate ways of performing those functions; and third, that the best way to construct the projects to perform the functions is to establish the recommended agency.

The decision need not be approached in this fashion, of course, nor the sequence suggested followed. The three aspects of the problem might be considered individually, without recognition of their essential interdependence. Thus it might be possible to establish the agency first and then later to face the questions of what it is to do and how it is to go about it. Historically, however, this has seldom occurred. Rarely has it proved possible to prevent objections to one aspect of a valley development plan from spreading into a frontal attack on the whole enterprise. In reality, then, the three parts of the problem are inextricable. Nevertheless it may facilitate consideration of the difficulties involved to consider each separately.

Functions

Of the traditional developmental functions in the field of water resources a number have today become accepted as the legitimate province of the federal government. This is true certainly of navigation and flood control and, with limited exceptions, of irrigation and drainage. In other fields federal responsibilities are growing, but have not yet eclipsed those of other governments and private enterprise. These include watershed management, hydroelectric power generation, water-based recreation, and pollution control.[3] Strong support has been evidenced for a similar expansion of federal authority with respect to industrial and municipal water supply and low-flow augmentation.

In the extension of governmental activity into new program areas a regularity of pattern may be discerned. The first uses of water in a given field have tended to be private: the keel boatman making his own way downstream, the farmer building a dirt barrier to protect his home against flood or a ditch to drain the water from his field, the irrigator piling brush in the stream to divert water into a flume that will water his lands. The requirements of substantial construction have next opened the way to cooperative action or to development by private enterprise, or both, and then to action by local governments, most often by special districts. The role of the states normally has been either permissive or regulatory, with comparatively little direct state action. Finally, for reasons either fiscal or geographic, the assistance of the federal government has been called for until ultimately, though sometimes with reservations, the entire burden has been assumed by the national government. Such has been the story of flood control through the great Mississippi levees to the Mississippi River Commission, and such has been the story of navigation through private and public canal companies to its present dependence upon the Corps of Engineers.[4]

It would be far-fetched to suggest that the pattern is an inevitable one which must be repeated time after time without exception or variation.[5] As an example of an aberration, the initial enthusiasm for

[3] The last-named is not, strictly speaking, a developmental but a regulatory function. Federal programs, however, have consisted largely of research and financial assistance in the disposal of wastes; the federal enforcement power has never actually been used and only rarely has it been even threatened.

[4] Two telling examples of this sequence of events in irrigation, concerning the Salt River and Lower Rio Grande projects respectively, will be found in Albert N. Williams, *The Water and the Power* (New York: Duell, Sloan, and Pearce, 1951), pp. 69-78, 189-198.

[5] It might, however, be considered that the extensions of Federal authority in each of these fields simply constitute special cases of the sequence of events described as the "Life History of an Issue" in Bernard Berelson, Paul F. Lazarsfeld, and William N. McPhee, *Voting* (Chicago: University of Chicago Press, 1954), pp. 207-212. A cursory examination of votes would suggest that, unlike the pattern described by Berelson, support and opposition for each function has not ordinarily

making power generation a federal responsibility clearly has waned. Nonetheless there are certain common elements in the developmental history of the principal water functions that may well contain lessons applicable to the future.

1. It is notable that the decision to assume responsibility for a new function has rarely been taken by the federal government as a matter of conscious policy. The tendency has been rather for Congress to drift into acceptance of a new task by the piecemeal approval of individual projects. This was true for example of flood control, where individual measures on the Mississippi grew larger and larger, project by project, and where other rivers were added until eventually Federal responsibility was complete. This process is now being repeated in the area of water supply. A general policy of aid to municipal water supply was incorporated into the Omnibus Rivers and Harbors Act of 1958, but individual projects earlier had included water supply features. Significantly, one of the reasons given by the President for his veto of the original bill was the inclusion of a statement of general policy to extend federal responsibility to low-flow augmentation in an omnibus bill detailing specific projects, but the protest was more symbolic than real. The veto message—along with the bill—fell in the category of shutting the barn door after the theft of the horse, since low-flow augmentation had already been included in some Ohio River federal projects.

2. A second fact worthy of note has been the tendency of the federal government to move most quickly into the least remunerative fields of development. With few exceptions, governmental water-resource programs have been based on the benefit concept and have been justified as additions to the national economy. Yet, although the beneficiaries in several areas, especially irrigation and power, are expected to repay the development costs, the government has tended to invest in the most rather than the least speculative developments. The underlying reasons are both obvious and significant. The most effective check on governmental willingness to meet the demands of segments of the public for development programs has been the force of private competition. While not negligible in their national impact (especially when reinforced by the Bureau of the Budget), taxpayers' groups seeking a generalized economy in government have less influence upon the national government than upon state or local govern-

come from the same groups. Cf., however, Daniel M. Ogden, Jr., "The Politics of Conservation in the West, 1953-1954," paper presented at the American Political Science Association annual meeting, 1954.

ments. Probably the most important reason for this is that no individual taxpayer carries a large enough share of the national tax load to justify significant efforts on his part to influence government to reduce expenditures, while the individuals and groups that stand to profit directly from the government's action—or to suffer from its competition—are sufficiently affected to justify a maximum effort at influence.[6] Hence the most important opposition to navigation improvements at federal expense has come from the railroads, the most effective opposition to federal hydro power development from private utilities, etc. With the decline of the private water companies it seems unlikely that any powerful counter-force will arise to block the extension of federal programs in the fields of water supply and low-flow augmentation.[7]

3. As has been noted, the usual sequence of events has seen a water problem pass from individual action to cooperative and/or corporate action to local government to federal government. Rarely have the states interested themselves directly in water resource enterprises except through such creatures as local governments and special districts.[8] The reasons are many and various. One of the more important is found in the fact that the most serious water problems historically have arisen in western states, which are the least able in finances and population to cope with them. It is not without significance that the few examples of important state action have occurred in the stronger eastern states—New York, New Jersey, Pennsylvania, and Massachusetts[9]—and the most populous and prosperous western state, Cali-

[6] Cf. Anthony Downs, *An Economic Theory of Democracy* (New York: Harper and Brothers, 1957).

[7] The force of these tendencies is enhanced in the water resources field by the separation into distinct legislative compartments of the three acts: (1) the legislative decision to authorize in general terms the expenditure of federal funds for a given developmental function; (2) the authorization by the Congress of expenditures for a specific project; (3) the appropriation of funds for actual construction. The decisions are even lodged in separate committees, since (1) and (2) are considered by the Committees on Public Works in each house of Congress, while (3) is dealt with by the Committees on Appropriation. The forces of economy tend to make their maximum efforts at the third stage, which affords a partial explanation of the fact that many more projects are authorized than are ever constructed. It is much easier to secure legislative approval of expenditures for a new governmental function in the area of water management than it is to obtain money to implement the authorization.

[8] See Council of State Governments, *State Administration of Water Resources*, p. 25.

[9] This involves the classification of the Metropolitan District Commission as a department of the state government, which in most respects it is.

fornia. Whether this history will reassert itself in a reversal of pattern in the treatment of problems such as water supply and low-flow augmentation, which are more typical of the East, is problematical.

4. Finally, the national programs in each of the functional fields of water-resource development have become important—in terms of large-scale appropriations as well as initial authorization—only after the creation of some national organization to mobilize the natural alliance of those who stand to profit from a particular federal program. It can be expected either that such an organization will be created for the emerging areas of water supply and low-flow augmentation or that these federal programs will be slow to develop. Alternatively an existing organization—the American Municipal Association, the United States Conference of Mayors, the American Water Works Association—might add support of federal action in these fields to its own program. Although the former has not yet occurred, it seems the more likely alternative in the long run.

Projects

One of the features of water-resource development politics is the fact that a decision by the government to assume responsibility for performance of a function is only the beginning rather than the end. Each specific project must be examined in turn to see whether it constitutes an appropriate occasion for the exercise of the general responsibility. In this respect water-resource development decisions are unlike legislative decisions in such fields as labor-management relations, civil rights, or foreign policy, though they find parallels in such areas as public roads and housing. In all these the general decision to spend federal money for construction must be implemented through specific decisions, as to finance an interstate highway from one place to another. In most cases, however, the specific decisions regarding individual projects have been turned over to administrative agencies; only with respect to water has Congress retained the formal prerogative of making particular choices.[10]

It is unnecessary to give more than cursory attention to the problems involved in securing approval for individual construction projects since—hopefully—such disputes can be avoided by separating the legislation to establish a Delaware River Agency for Water from the legislation authorizing specific projects. (An attempt was made to

[10] In other areas—for example the construction of military bases—Congress continues to exercise informal controls.

separate the creation of an interstate commission from the engineers' recommendations for physical development in the case of the proposed Incodel compact, but the circumstances did not permit a clear-cut division of the issues.) Undoubtedly, however, some objections to individual project proposals will find expression in the view that the Delaware ought not to be developed at all and hence no agency of any kind is needed.

In generalized terms, the principal arguments against specific projects have emphasized these points:

1. Economic infeasibility. This comes down to the assertion that, though the function to be performed is an acceptable one, the cost of the project is too high for the benefits received. Although it is not invariably followed, the cost-benefit ratio is ordinarily employed to resolve this issue without public controversy.

2. The reservoir site. This, the classic argument against a particular project, is raised more or less vociferously with regard to most projects. To the extent that the costs of reservoir site acquisition can be quantified in dollar terms, they can be incorporated into the cost-benefit ratio. Inevitably, however, those living on the land to be inundated, or those accustomed to using it (sportsmen's groups, for example) object that additional intangible values will be lost which are in the literal sense "priceless." These non-quantifiable costs include the disruption of families whose pattern of life has been built on residence on the land, the loss of community assets in buildings, the violation of cemeteries, and the like.

3. Conflicting purposes. In actuality such conflicts between reservoir site owners and the proponents of construction are a special manifestation of what can more generally be described as conflicts among accepted development functions. The property owner asserts that his claim is superior to that of the beneficiary of construction; similar conflicts may occur between the proponents of recreational use and those of water supply, between the advocates of power development and shippers, and so forth. If one purpose which commands wide, vocal, and organized support, for example wildlife preservation, will be better served by inaction, its advocates may block the project. If alternative projects are advanced and strongly urged by the conflicting groups, it is quite possible that none will be approved.

4. Economic competition. Again, a project may be halted by the opposition of others—public agencies as well as private—whose own programs might suffer from the competition. The most obvious examples are in the power field, but the opposition of the Port of New

York Authority to the St. Lawrence Seaway is substantially identical in character. The Port Authority does not object to federal expenditures for navigation improvements in principle; indeed it welcomes them for improvements to the port of New York. It did, however, object to an improvement that it felt would be injurious to its service area and particularly to its shippers.

5. Allocation. Some projects, unobjectionable on their face, have been rejected because of inability to reach agreement on the allocation either of costs or of benefits. Notable instances of the latter are found in the West in the conflicts over water rights: the Boulder Canyon project was long delayed by such a controversy. More recently disputes over what states are to get how much power have become common: the Niagara project of the New York State Power Authority was held up briefly by this question.

6. Agency rivalry. In the western states, projects on which there was wide agreement as to substance have frequently been blocked by controversies between the Corps of Engineers and the Bureau of Reclamation as to which agency was to do the construction. Fortunately this particular conflict, the most serious of its kind, does not affect the Delaware. A similar controversy between the Department of Agriculture and the Corps at times has threatened to erupt, but so far direct conflict has been avoided.

Organizations

Another of the unusual features of water-resource development is the variety of organizational types among which a choice can be made. Probably in no other policy area does Congress possess such a luxuriance of alternatives among which to select in delegating power. The structural species have been enumerated and discussed above. The problems involved in securing approval of the organization recommended in this report may be discussed best in specifics.

THE PROBLEMS

All these comments have been general in character and might have been made about almost any river. From the record of experience in the Delaware detailed above it is possible to secure some evidence of their relevance to the case at hand. The conclusions that emerge from that account are fundamental to the assumptions made here as to the best course of action for the future. They may be summarized thus:

1. Effective action has followed only upon demands dramatized by circumstances. As noted in Chapter 17, a physical catastrophe is a powerful stimulant to positive action. But when the only reason for action is simply that it makes sense, rationality gives way to any strong pressure against it. The principles of comprehensive, multiple-purpose development and effective utilization of available resources have no enemies; but when they stand in the way of a powerfully supported single-purpose demand, they have few friends.

2. The most serious single obstacle to comprehensive development of the river basin has been the issue of allocation of water among the states. It was this problem that prevented ratification by the Delaware Valley states of the proposed interstate compacts of the 1920's. Despite its successes in other fields, Incodel failed in its efforts to secure identical, reciprocal diversion laws during its first decade of operation. And it was on this rock that the Incodel plan of the 1950's foundered.

3. The basic reason why the problem of allocation has never been resolved by agreement among the four Basin states resides in the existence of an alternative and to some parties preferable forum for adjudication in the Supreme Court. It has been neither sheer malice nor stupidity nor backwardness that has blocked proposed interstate agreements allocating the waters of the Delaware; the fact is that jurisdiction by the Supreme Court provides results different from those obtainable by interstate negotiation, and that these results are more acceptable to influential partisans than those promised by a compact. Even the second compact of the 1920's allowed New York City a diversion of 600 mgd; the Supreme Court in its first decree permitted 440. The Incodel plan of 1951 implied an eventual diversion by that city of 1370 mgd, the Supreme Court decree specified 800 mgd. In addition, the Supreme Court judgments are flexible in that they are subject to later appeal by any of the party states. Recourse to the Supreme Court therefore has been regarded as advantageous by certain states and so has discouraged agreement by compact.

4. Though of less importance in preventing interstate action than the conflict over allocation of water, the Valley states have never reached mutual agreement on the issue of hydroelectric power. The existence of a considerable power potential has been testified to by the Corps of Engineers, the Federal Power Commission, Incodel, and

two private development companies, but nothing has yet been done to generate hydro power on the River. The conflicts between public and private power and between thermal (coal) and hydroelectric power have never been settled. The attempt by Incodel to ignore this issue in its plan for Delaware development contributed to the rejection of its proposed compact, though realistically an alternative course might not have fared any better.

5. Opposition to inundation of lands within a reservoir site has not been a serious barrier to resource development in the Delaware Basin. In deference to the opponents of Wallpack Bend, that project was struck out of the Incodel compact bill as it passed the Pennsylvania House of Representatives; but the move was apparently a tactical one to produce a maximum favorable vote in the face of opposition by Governor Fine. Both Cannonsville and the Lackawaxen flood control dams were strongly condemned by those who would lose their lands, but both projects were approved nonetheless. The only proposal to create real excitement on this score was that by New York City to flood out Beaver Kill and the Willowemoc, famous trout streams in the Catskills, a plan now replaced by Cannonsville. Nowhere does opposition on the ground of flooding reservoir lands appear great enough to endanger a Delaware development plan.

6. Recurrent and strong opposition to federal action in the Delaware Basin has been expressed in the four Valley states. Today this opposition is personified in the Interstate Commission on the Delaware River Basin, a national leader in the struggle against federal river development. Incodel did not begin its career holding this view—indeed it received early subsidies from federal funds—and quite possibly it is less strongly opposed to federal action today than in the period of Ellwood Turner's leadership. Nonetheless a strong anti-federal bias exists in the Basin, and its long-term effect undoubtedly has been to make comprehensive development of the River more than ordinarily difficult. A genuinely comprehensive basin development program requires very heavy investment. The states could, of course, find the necessary money if they had to, but they have been unwilling to do so. Partly this unwillingness to act is inherent in their own internal revenue problems and in institutional limitations; partly it results from reaction against federal expenditure policies in general. At the same time the northeastern states protest the siphoning off of their funds by the national government and their expenditure elsewhere, they refuse to seek congressional appropriations for local or regional projects for

fear of federal control. The paradox is that the states of the Delaware Valley are too strong to be willing to let the federal government in but not strong enough to live without it.

This is one conclusion the Incodel leadership drew from the failure of their compact plan. Testifying two and a half years later at the Mt. Pocono hearings of the House Committee on Government Operations, Incodel Chairman Francis Pitkin said:

> . . . if we are to make progress in the solution of such highly complex problems involving tremendous sums of money and complicated intergovernmental relationships *we must look to the Federal Government for leadership and financial assistance.* While our experience in the effort to solve this kind of problem by interstate cooperation is limited to the Delaware River Basin, we believe that exactly the same situation would be encountered in any other major drainage basin in Pennsylvania or elsewhere in the Nation. So far as we know, no large-scale basin development program involving more than one State has gone ahead without Federal leadership and participation.[11]

The problem of financing is further complicated by the conflict over public power development. The one dependable source of revenue from a river development project derives from the sale of power, and power revenues have been used to finance almost all of the few state development projects. In the Delaware Valley, however, this source of revenue has been cut off by the opposition within the Basin states to public power.

7. A fundamental problem encountered in the attempt to devise and gain acceptance for a comprehensive plan for the development of the Delaware has lain in the failure to secure cooperation among the various levels of government. This problem, which is common to almost all water-resource projects, is peculiarly complex when municipal water supply is involved. Public water supply traditionally has been the responsibility of the municipality. Water-based recreation and fish and wildlife have fallen within the province of the state. Programs in navigation and flood control are conducted primarily by the federal government. Hydroelectric power development has been divided between private enterprise and (primarily) the federal government. A comprehensive water-resources program therefore of necessity cuts across a multitude of public activities and interests, thereby

---

[11] U.S. House of Representatives, 84th Cong., 1st sess. "Commission on Organization of the Executive Branch of the Government (Water Resources and Power Report), Part I—Mount Pocono, Pa.," Hearings before a Special Subcommittee on Government Operations (Washington, 1956), p. 16. Italics supplied.

further complicating what is already an extraordinarily complex area of action.

FEDERAL ACTION

The organizational plan recommended in Chapter 18 of this report envisages action on two levels, federal and state. The report proposes that reliance be placed first on federal authority; hence the first step necessarily must be the enactment of a statute by Congress. Simultaneously, however, it is recommended that the states initiate action looking toward negotiation of a federal-interstate compact that will create a commission to replace that established by Federal law. Legislative authorization to begin negotiations for a compact would maximize the chance for later approval. In addition, the effectiveness of the Federal agency, DRAW, will be enhanced if the states also instruct their own resource agencies to cooperate with it. Provision for comprehensive state cooperation would probably require affirmative action by the state legislature. Consequently, the problem is to evoke favorable action by five legislative bodies and their respective executives. In the first stage, however, the greatest dependence will rest on federal action: the creation of a federal commission for the Delaware including both Federal and state representatives. The first question therefore is, how can such federal action be elicited?

Not all, perhaps, will grant this constitutes a problem. One state legislator interviewed expressed the view: "Why, with all the congressmen you have in these four states there are no limits to what you can get done. It might take a year or two, but if they stick together, they're bound to get their way eventually." The legislator's observation is persuasive and in a sense quite true. Numerically the four states of the Delaware Valley have the votes in Congress to write their own ticket on what should be done with the Delaware. Blocs of states with far smaller total congressional representation have often secured substantial advantages for their regions. What the statement overlooks is that the effective congressional blocs by definition are those which can afford to be single-minded in their pursuit of a particular goal. Congressmen from the northeastern states cannot allow themselves this luxury with respect to water. Reference has been made earlier and often to the limited—if essential—role that water plays in the regional development of the Delaware area. The corollary of that fact is another: Delaware Valley congressmen have many responsibilities not connected with water that are vastly more important to them.

The argument can be put bluntly in the form of a question: how many Delaware area Congressmen would be willing to trade a vote on civil rights, or on labor-management relations, or on aid to distressed areas for a vote on Delaware water?

More significant than the overt trading of votes in Congress is the more subtle consequence of specialization of interests. A western senator can afford to make himself an expert on water; his entire office staff indeed may be assigned to water-resource problems. In the office of an eastern senator, water-resource legislation is likely to be one among other higher priority responsibilities of a single individual. And in congressional action deference is likely to be given to the legislator who knows and watches closely the issues involved. The clearest illustration of this tendency is that institutional recognition of special interests and specialization known as the committee system. General legislation concerning water resources as well as the authorization of individual projects is referred in both houses of Congress to the Committees on Public Works. Appropriations for individual projects are handled in the respective Committees on Appropriations, more particularly in their subcommittees on public works.

In the House of Representatives where the Delaware Valley states are most fully represented (88 of the 437 congressmen are from New York, New Jersey, Pennsylvania, and Delaware), regional representation on these key committees is substantial, though composed disproportionately of Republicans. Of the 34 members of the Committee on Public Works, seven are from the Delaware states, including both the committee chairman, Charles A. Buckley of New York, and the ranking minority member, James C. Auchincloss of New Jersey; five of the seven are Republicans.[12] Of the 13 members of the Subcommittee on Public Works of the House Committee on Appropriations, three, all Republicans, are from the four states.[13]

[12] The numerical ratio probably overstates the importance of the Delaware Basin Congressmen on the committee, so far as water resources are concerned. The committee's jurisdiction includes such other matters as public roads, and the Delaware Congressmen have tended to devote more attention to these. Moreover, while Rep. Buckley's position is an important one, he is handicapped by his duties as Democratic leader of the Bronx.

[13] John Taber of New York, Ivor Fenton of Pennsylvania, and John Pillion of New York. All reports of committee assignments in the current session are taken from the *Congressional Quarterly*, supplement to weekly edition of March 27, 1959, and are accurate as of that date. The Republicanism of the Delaware states' representatives is not unrelated to their power, since it places them ordinarily in a minority in a body dominated by Democrats.

In the Senate the position of the Delaware Valley is far weaker. Only one of the fifteen members of the Committee on Public Works is from the four states—Hugh Scott of Pennsylvania—and not one member of the Subcommittee on Public Works of the Senate Committee on Appropriations represents the area. This in turn reflects the weakness of the Mid-Atlantic states in the Senate as a whole; the arithmetic is elementary, but there are only eight Senators out of one hundred from the four states.

It would perhaps not be unfair to say that the suggestion that the Delaware area congressmen can write their own ticket for a water program is the precise opposite of the truth. So far as water-resource policy is concerned, the northeastern states are notoriously weak. Moreover, this situation is not an aberration that will one day soon be set right. It is rather the result of fundamental causes, chief among them a greater concern for other issues, that still continue to be effective. Presumably the pattern of preoccupation will gradually change as water shortages focus increasing public attention on the water problem in the Northeast, but it is extremely unlikely the change will be abrupt.[14]

The significance of the congressional weakness of the Northeast in water-resource matters, simply put, is this: notwithstanding their numerical strength in Congress, the Delaware Valley states cannot expect to modify national water policy to suit themselves. The interests most influential in the field and most deeply concerned with federal programs regarding water are located farther west. Any attempt to change national policies in their application to the Delware will be viewed in the light of the effects the new policy would have or threaten to have in the western states.

The most serious problem raised in this context concerns hydroelectric power. The Delaware Valley is not public power country, and apart from a few labor union endorsements there has been little public outcry for federal hydro development. It is easy to underestimate the influence of public power customers, for though comparatively

---

[14] The recent formation of a New York State congressional bloc has brought discussion of something wider for the Northeast generally, despite evidences of dissension within the New York ranks already. It would be unwise, however, to expect any immediate or dramatic alteration of the situation. Even if the Congressmen from these states should coalesce more firmly and even if they should show greater interest in water generally, there are numerous aspects of the problem to atomize their attention: transfer of the New York State Barge Canal to federal management, beach erosion, a deeper Delaware channel, Passaic River flooding, the Meadowlands project, etc.

few in number they have wide geographic representation and are included in many congressional constituencies. There seems little question, however, that if the four state legislatures were allowed to decide the issue the hydroelectric potential of the Delaware would be left to private development.[15]

The four legislatures, however, will not be left to themselves to decide the issue. The preference clause is today established federal policy. The attempt to substitute a policy of partnership with private utilities has bogged down completely. Further, from the viewpoint of those who would prefer a change in existing policy the political situation has deteriorated steadily. Following the 1958 congressional elections, the *Public Utilities Fortnightly* noted: "The greatly increased Democratic majorities in both the House and Senate are almost certain to produce, at least for consideration, legislation of an antiutility nature." [16] A determined effort to substitute a private power policy for preference in the Delaware Basin is likely to stalemate action for an indefinite period, and to sacrifice substantial non-power benefits to a philosophic dispute involving power outputs that are minimal in relation to the total power generated in the area.[17]

Another lesson to be learned from the weakness of the Delaware states in Congress emphasizes the need for unity in action. Such influence as the area possesses on water-resource matters must be exerted in concert to be effective. If it is dissipated by internal divisions

[15] The outcome would be least certain in New York State, which has chosen to develop power both at Niagara and on the St. Lawrence under public authority.

[16] *Public Utilities Fortnightly*, LXII (December, 1958), pp. 958-960. The report on "The 86th Congress" explained: "Utilities will probably be unable to depend too much on the development of a Republican-southern Democratic coalition which for the last fifteen years has kept punitive legislation at a minimum. It is true that the important committees in Congress will still be controlled by Southerners for the most part. But it is equally true that many Southerners have not been particularly conservative with respect to legislation affecting public utilities. In the past, their willingness to cooperate with Republican minorities in Congress has been dictated by their desire to prevent civil rights legislation which they regard as dangerous to their interests. The November election, however, retired a number of conservative Republicans who sympathized with the South on this issue, replacing them either with liberal Democrats or liberal Republicans who have no use for the South's position on civil rights."

[17] The controversy over Niagara power is a case in point, although the absence of federal investment there provided a better justification for abandonment of the preference clause than would be found where federal funds are used in development. See the exchange between Rep. Jones of Alabama and then Mayor Clark over the preference clause, *Mt. Pocono Hearings*, p. 31.

within the Valley it will be impossible to secure congressional approval of any bold or unusual governmental solutions.

A companion proposition stresses the necessity for cooperation with other areas with similar problems. The Connecticut, the Hudson, the Susquehanna, the Potomac, and the Ohio all resemble in many respects the Delaware. While it is not the philosophy of this report that the solution here proposed is a panacea that can be imposed on any and every river, it remains obvious that a successful operation by DRAW on the Delaware will evoke sympathetic consideration of its principal features elsewhere. And all of these areas share a common interest in securing federal recognition of (1) the emerging water problems of the urbanized, industrialized Northeast, and (2) the importance of an active role for state governments in the management of the water resources of the area.

Negotiation of such an alliance is not a matter for public oratory, nor can the unity of the Delaware area be secured by a televised debate. Conciliation and persuasion are more important than sound and fury. A time comes, however, for a formal expression of views and for the recognition—and rebuttal—of such opposition as exists. The Columbia River Development Corporation proposal may serve as a precedent in this regard.[18] After the circulation of several successive drafts of a proposed federal statute among the interested parties, extensive hearings were conducted by a subcommittee of the Senate Committee on Public Works. Through the courtesy of the chairman, Senator Robert Kerr of Oklahoma, the hearings were conducted by a representative of the area affected, Senator Richard Neuberger of Oregon.[19] Similar hearings on a bill to create a Delaware River Agency for Water would provide a focus for public attention, a documentary record of the views of all affected interests, and—hopefully—an expression of a consensus within the Valley in support of the plan.

State Action

Two kinds of major state action are contemplated in the recommendations of this report. First in time would be the passage of parallel state laws (1) instructing all agencies of the state governments concerned with water resources to cooperate with DRAW, and

[18] But, preferably, not in others since the Corporation plan in its original broad form is now dead.

[19] Senate Committee on Public Works, *Bonneville Project Act Amendments of 1958, Hearings* (Washington, 1958).

(2) establishing an interstate study commission to lay the ground-work for a federal-interstate compact. The second and more significant step would lead ultimately to the establishment, with federal partici-pation, of a commission to replace DRAW.

One important reason for choosing a two-phase approach to the problem of water-resource management on the Delaware is the belief that an excessive time would be required to secure approval for an interstate compact, plus the conviction that the terms of a compact prepared in haste and under pressure might be unduly restrictive and might provide for an organization incapable of meeting the needs of the Basin.

Undoubtedly some will disagree with this judgment. A long period of disillusionment followed the failure of the compacts of the 1920's. Not until 1950 were those interested in joint action willing to try an interstate compact again. The defeat of the Incodel compact in-troduced a new period of frustration,[20] but with the passage of time some hope of success has returned. In one sense the hope is justified, for there is no reason to doubt that some kind of interstate compact could be agreed upon. More dubious is the question of the powers that might be delegated to an interstate commission. The metropolitan transit compact controversy in New York and New Jersey illustrates the problem. Both states agreed that an interstate solution to the transit problem was desirable; but their inability to reach agreement on specific issues finally produced an interstate commission for study purposes only, and each state pursues its own separate program as before.

Broadly speaking, there are two types of obstacles that block the ratification of interstate compacts: first, fiscal objections that the state (or states) cannot afford the cost; and second, policy considera-tions, that is, criticisms of or doubts about the probable programs and actions of the proposed agency. Both kinds of obstacles have barred past interstate compact proposals for the Delaware and both kinds still confront the negotiators of a compact today.

As a part of the research preparatory to this report, extensive inter-views were conducted with both administrative and legislative per-sonnel. In all some 38 members of the legislatures of the four Valley

---

[20] See, for example, the testimony of Incodel Chairman Francis Pitkin at the *Mt. Pocono Hearings*, pp. 106-107. Pitkin's statement, ". . . we hold no high hopes for a reactivation, through interstate cooperation, of the whole Incodel pro-gram . . ." can be interpreted variously, but the overall tone is one of disillusion with the strictly interstate approach.

states were interviewed. The recurrent theme in virtually all of these interviews was this: "If it's going to cost very much, the states can't afford it." From the legislative viewpoint all four states are experiencing recurrent financial crises. A New Jersey legislator, however, acknowledged: "Of course, the money's there if we wanted to go after it, but we don't."

For most the obvious solution was the federal treasury. This included men prominent in the interstate cooperation movement as well as those outside it. An influential Pennsylvania legislator, for example, indicated his interest in the possibility of federal funds to meet the costs of low-flow augmentation. Such sentiments were reinforced by the fact that large segments of each state are not concerned about the problems of the Delaware. In western Pennsylvania, southern Delaware, southern New Jersey, and most of New York, a Delaware River program appears to be only another unwelcome charge on an already overburdened state budget.

A few legislators were hopeful that federal financing might still permit state control, but the majority considered such a hope unrealistic. "If the federal government is going to pay, the federal government is going to want to run it," was a view recurrently voiced. The problem was to salvage as much state authority as possible, and not all were interested even in doing this. A Pennsylvania senator, regarded as a conservative spokesman in the state, asserted that what is needed is "a Delaware Valley Authority, but without public power." Others expressed similar views: "The states squabble too much." "Unless the federal government does it, it won't be done at all."

This is not to minimize the general sentiment in favor of state control. If at all possible state legislators, not surprisingly, would like to see their own governments control Delaware Basin development. Very few, however, are willing to think of paying for control by substantial state outlays. The danger in immediate development by interstate compact, accordingly, rests in the likelihood that the states would decline to make the investments necessary to accomplish the job.

The second major obstacle to approval of an interstate compact lies in disagreement over principles, and here the chief conflict is that over allocations of water. It is extremely unlikely that New York State would agree to a compact that did not guarantee the present allocation to New York City. In the past, however, Pennsylvania has repeatedly refused to accept this diversion as final and has insisted on

terms in the Supreme Court decree leaving New York City's allocation open to future reconsideration. There is no convincing evidence
of Pennsylvania's readiness today to waive that right to reconsideration. Negotiations for a federal-interstate compact could easily come to
grief on this point.

A first-phase federal agency offers a way out. Positive action by the
federal government on the one hand would ensure that something
would be done while the states were engaged in negotiation. On the
other hand, by inaugurating a program in which the states would wish
to participate more fully, it would provide an incentive for a reconciliation of state differences.

The most convincing argument for federal action first lies in the
requirement of unanimity for ratification of an interstate compact. It
has been asserted that without substantial unity of thought within the
Delaware Basin a federal statute of the character described could not
be obtained. This is true, but an interstate compact requires still more.
An interstate compact among four states, with federal participation,
places a veto in the hands of each of 15 different agents of government, 10 legislative bodies and 5 executives. In the process of satisfying all, essential powers are likely to be left out. By creating an
agency by federal statute and endowing it with all appropriate powers
that can be derived from federal law, the negative influence of opposition will be sharply reduced and the prospect for a strong and vigorous second-phase organization created by compact greatly increased.

One thing appears certain: some steps will be taken toward further
control of the Delaware River; some dams will be built. Whether the
construction of new works for physical control of the waters of the
Delaware will be attended by new steps toward rational administration or by perpetuation of the present formless pattern of management will depend, in the last analysis, upon a leadership within the
Delaware Valley able to comprehend and willing to grasp the opportunity offered.

Index